t
ıy

ıystems

Contents of other volumes

Fourth edition

Jones' Instrument Technology Volume 4

Instrumentation Systems

Edited by **B E Noltingk**

Butterworths
London · Boston · Durban · Singapore ·
Sydney · Toronto · Wellington

First published 1987

British Library Cataloguing in Publication Data

Jones, E.B. (Ernest Beachcroft)
Jones' instrument technology—4th ed.
Vol. 4 : Instrumentation systems
1. Measuring instruments
I. Title II. Noltingk, B.E. III. Jones, E.B. (Ernest Beachcroft). Instrument technology
620'.0044 QC100.5

ISBN 0-408-01234-X

Library of Congress Cataloging-in-Publication Data
(Revised for vol. 4)

Jones, E.B. (Ernest Beachcroft)
Jones' Instrument technology.

Includes bibliographies and index.
Contents: v. 1. Mechanical measurements—v. 4. Instrumentation systems.
1. Engineering instruments. I. Noltingk, B. E. II. Title. III. Title: Instrument technology.
TA165.J622 1985 620'.0028 84-4273
ISBN 0-408-01231-5 (pbk. : v. 1)

Phototypeset by Scribe Design, Gillingham, Kent
Printed and bound in England by Page Bros Ltd., Norwich, Norfolk

Contents

Contributors

A. Danielsson, FIMechE, FInstMC, is with Wimpey Engineering Ltd. He was a member of the BS working party developing the Code of Practice for Instrumentation in Process Control Systems: Installation–Design

C. I. Daykin, MA, is Director of Research and Development at Automatic Systems Laboratories Ltd

J. G. Giles, TEng, has been with Ludlam Sysco for a number of years

E. H. Higham, MA, CEng, FIEE, MIMechE, MIERE, MInstMC, is Visiting Fellow at the Department of Fluid Engineering and Instrumentation at Cranfield Institute of Technology after a long career with Foxboro Great Britain Ltd

B. E. Noltingk, BSc, PhD, CEng, FIEE, CPhys, FInstP, is now a Consultant after some time as Head of the Instrumentation Section at Central Electricity Research Laboratories

M. L. Sanderson, BSc, PhD, is Director of the Centre for Fluid Instrumentation at Cranfield Institute of Technology

L. C. Towle, BSc, CEng, MIMechE, MIEE, MInstMC, is a Director of the MTL Instruments Group Ltd

Preface

This book is rather different in nature from the first three volumes of *Instrument Technology*. Those described how particular measurements could be made, their twenty-three chapters dealing with one quantity after another. That, however, is not the whole story of instrumentation, and in this volume we touch on matters common to many or all instruments. The wider relevance justifies the word 'Systems' in the title.

As I remarked in the preface to Volume 1, E. B. Jones in his earlier editions put a tacit emphasis on instruments for process control. I have thought it right to widen the total coverage so that we include techniques that are seldom or never applied online. However, the importance of plant instrumentation must never be played down, and in this volume we have included some chapters—Installation, Sampling, and perhaps Reliability—that are of chief significance for those using plant instruments continuously online. Calibration is, of course, a vital matter for online systems, and at one stage I thought of dealing with that here. In fact, however, calibrating varies greatly with the property it is being done for, so it has been thought more appropriate to talk of calibration in the individual chapters. The online message common to them all is simply the urgent need to calibrate carefully—and often.

The chapters collected here vary markedly. They are very different in length and in practical or theoretical content. They include the terse comments on Installation—if some are thought simple, how often has the hindsightedly obvious proved the most vital and the most neglected action? They include, at the other extreme, the wideranging chapter on Signal Processing, which almost extends to giving a general, and valuable, introduction to electronic circuitry. So the chapters vary in their style—authors would lose their humanity if they lost their diversity—as well as in their comprehensiveness: for some subjects are at the heart of instrument technology, while others have a much smaller, but still real, relevance. I believe the chapters have come together to make a useful book, as the volumes have come together to make a useful series.

I have reflected sometimes that, while the writer of any technical contribution is under an obligation to see that everything he says is true, the writer (or editor) of a book (or review) is also under a more searching obligation: he must see that everything he does *not* say is unimportant. This is because a reader is entitled to come to a book expecting that he will find that the whole of the chosen subject is covered to an appropriate depth, and not that a few awkward or uninteresting aspects are arbitrarily omitted. It would be conceited to claim that we have perfectly discharged those obligations. However, the aim has been there, and I am sure that anyone who has absorbed all of *Instrument Technology* would be an instrument technologist with a good foundation on which to build, perhaps building with the further reading that has been listed throughout. Remember also that we have deliberately excluded some topics (see Volume 1): it would be greedy not to leave something for other people to cover!

This, then, completes the task of bringing the classic E. B. Jones books up to date. I hope his tradition has been worthily maintained, and that we have made a contribution to teaching some of those things on which the modern industrial world depends so heavily for its efficient functioning.

I thank my team of contributors for what, with or without bludgeoning on my part, they have produced; the firms who have gladly allowed their drawings to be reproduced; and the publishers and editorial staff for their contribution to smooth productions. In the first preface, I thanked my wife for engaging in activities that enabled her to put up with my concentration on editorial tasks. I should repeat my thanks for what has sometimes extended to suspending her conjugal rights in the telephone, the dining-room table and even the compilation of our hospitality list. Bless her for her tolerance.

B. E. N.
1987

1 Design and construction of instruments

C.I. DAYKIN

1.1 Introduction

The purpose of this chapter is to give an insight into the types of components and construction used in commercial instrumentation.

To the designer, the *technology* in Instrument Technology depends on the availability of components and processes appropriate to his task. Being aware of what is possible is an important function of the designer, especially with the rapidity with which techniques now change. New materials such as ceramics and polymers will become increasingly important, as will semi-custom and large-scale integrated circuits. The need for low-cost automatic manufacture is having the greatest impact on design techniques, demanding fewer components and suitable geometries. Low-volume instruments and one-offs will be constructed in software.

The distinction between computer and instrument is already blurred, with many instruments offering a wide range of facilities and great flexibility. Smart sensors, which interface directly to a computer, will also shift the emphasis to software and mechanical aspects.

Historical practice, convention and the emergence of standards also contribute significantly to the subject. Standards, especially, benefit the designer and the user, and have made the task of the author and the reader somewhat simpler.

Commercial instruments exist because there is a market, and so details of their design and construction can only be understood in terms of a combination of commercial as well as technical reasons. A short section describes these trade-offs as a backdrop to the more technical information.

1.2 Instrument design

1.2.1 The designer's viewpoint

Many of the design features found in instruments are not obviously of direct benefit to the user. These can best be understood by also considering the designer's viewpoint.

The instrument designer's remit is to find the best compromise between cost and benefit to the users, especially when competition is fierce. For a typical, medium-volume instrument, its cost as a percentage of selling price, is distributed as follows:

Purchase cost	Design cost	20%
	Manufacturing cost	30%
	Selling costs	20%
	Other overheads	20%
	Profit	10%
		100%

Operating/maintenance cost may amount to 10% per annum. Benefits to the user can come from many features; for example:

Accuracy
Speed
Multi-purpose
Flexibility
Reliability
Integrity
Maintainability
Convenience

Fashion, as well as function, is very important since a smart, pleasing and professional appearance is often essential when selling instruments on a commercial basis.

For a particular product the unit cost can be reduced with higher volume production, and greater sales can be achieved with a lower selling price. The latter is called its 'market elasticity'. Since the manufacturer's objective is to maximize his return on investment, the combination of selling price and volume which yields the greatest profit is chosen.

1.2.2 Marketing

The designer is generally subordinate to marketing considerations, and consequently these play a major role in determining the design of an instrument and the method of its manufacture. A project will only go ahead if the anticipated return on investment is sufficiently high, and commensurate with the perceived level of risk. It is interesting to note that design accounts for a significant proportion of the total costs and, by its nature, involves a high degree of risk.

With the rapid developments in technology, product lifetimes are being reduced to as little as three years, and market elasticity is difficult to judge. In this way design is becoming more of a process of evolution, continuously responding to changes in market conditions. Initially, therefore, the designer will tend to err on the cautious side, and make cost reductions as volumes increase.

The anticipated volume is a major consideration, and calls for widely differing techniques in manufacture, depending on whether it is a low-, medium- or high-volume product.

1.2.3 Special instruments

Most instrumentation users configure systems from low-cost standard components with simple interfaces. Occasionally the need arises for a special component or system. It is preferable to modify a standard component wherever possible, since complete redesigns often take longer than anticipated, with an uncertain outcome.

Special systems also have to be tested and understood in order to achieve the necessary level of confidence. Maintenance adds to the extra cost, with the need for documentation and test equipment, making specials very expensive. This principle extends to software as well as hardware.

Table 1.1 Electronic components

Component and symbol	*Main types*	*Appearance*	*Range*	*Character*
Resistors	Metal oxide		0.1Ω–100 MΩ	1% general purpose
	Metal film		0.1Ω–100 MΩ	0.001% low drift
	Wirewound		0.01Ω–1 MΩ	0.01% high power
Capacitors	Air dielectric		0.01 pF–100 pF	0.01% high stability
	Ceramics		1 pF–10 μF	5% small size
	Polymer		1 pF–10 μF	1% general purpose
	Electrolytic		0.1 μF–1 F	10% small size
Inductors	Cylindrical core		0.1 μH–10 mH	10% general purpose
	Pot core		1 μH–1 H	0.1% high stability
	Toroidal core		100 μH–100 H	20% high values
				10^{-7} high accuracy ratios
Transformers	Cylindrical core		RF, IF types	
	Pot core		0.1 μH–1 mH	0.1% mutual inductor
	Toroidal core		0.1 H–10 H	20% high inductance
Diodes	PN junction		1 pA (on)–10^3 A (off)	Wide range
Transistors	Bipolar		10^{-17}W(input)–10^3W output	high freq, low noise
				high power etc.
	FETs		10^{-23}W(input)–10^3W output	as above.
Integrated circuits 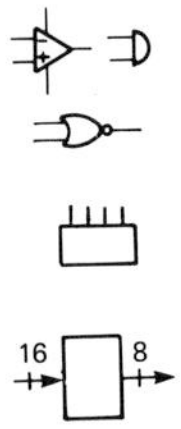	Analogue		operational amplifiers	wide range
			function blocks	multiply, divide
			amplifiers	high frequency
			switches	high accuracy
			semi custom	
	Digital		small scale integ. (SSI)	logic elements
			medium scale integ. (MSI)	function blocks
			large scale integ. (LSI)	major functions
			v. large scale integ. (VLSI)	complete systems
			semi custom	
	Monolithic hybrid		A/D D/A conversion	
			special functions	
			semi custom	
Others	Thyristors		1A–10^3A	high power switch
	Triacs		1A–10^3A	high power switch
	Opto-couplers		singles, duals, quads	
	Thermistors		+ or − temp. coefficient	
	Relays		0.01Ω(on)–10^{12}Ω (off)	

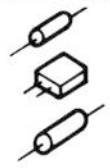

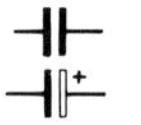

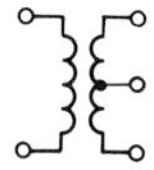

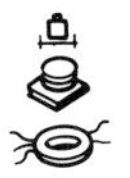

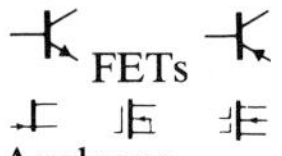

1.3 Elements of construction

1.3.1 Electronic components and printed circuits

Electronic circuitry now forms the basis of most modern measuring instruments. A wide range of electronic components are now available, from the simple resistor to complete data acquisition subsystems. Table 1.1 lists some of the more commonly used types.

Computer-aided design makes it possible to design complete systems on silicon using standard cells or by providing the interconnection pattern for a standard chip which has an array of basic components. This offers reductions in size and cost and improved design security.

The most common method of mounting and interconnecting electronic components is by double-sided through-hole plated, fibreglass printed circuit board (PCB) (Figure 1.1(a)). Component leads or pins are pushed through holes and soldered to tinned copper pads (Figure 1.1(b)). This secures the component and provides the connections. The solder joint is thus the most commonly used component and probably the most troublesome.

Tinning the copper pads with solder stops corrosion and makes soldering easier. Fluxes reduce oxidation and surface tension but a temperature-controlled soldering iron is indispensable. Large-

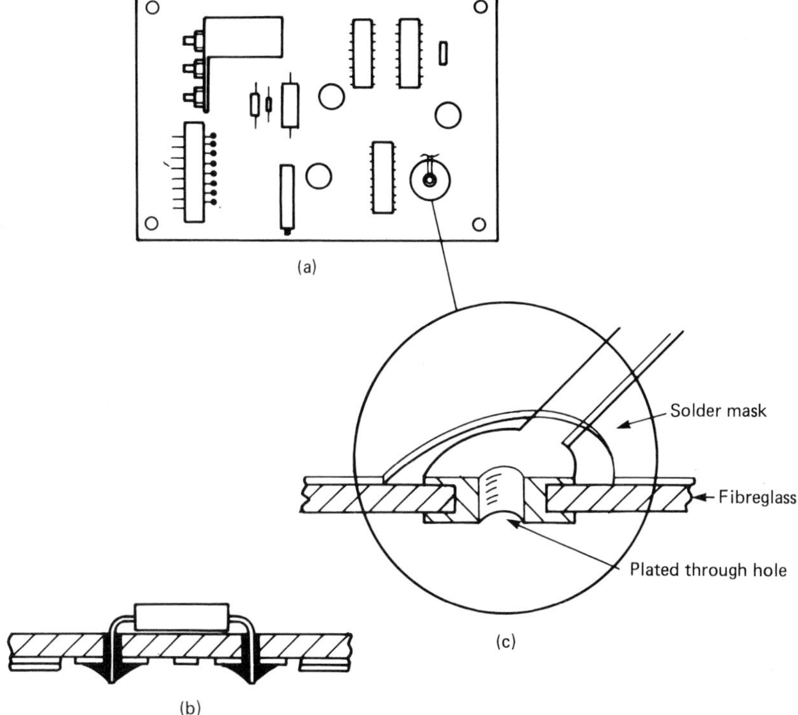

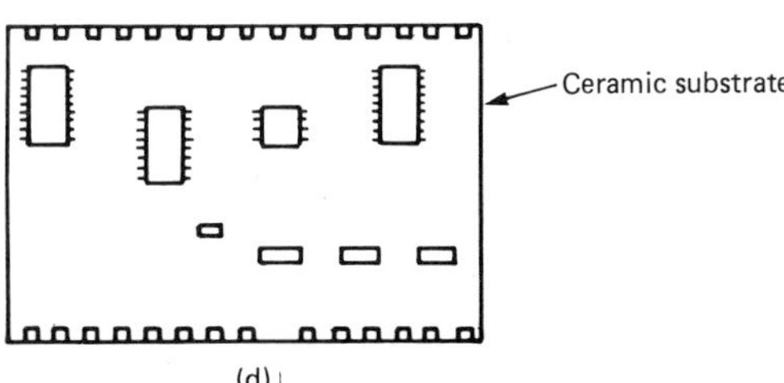

Figure 1.1 Printed electronic circuits. (a) Printed circuit board (PCB); (b) traditional axial component; (c) through-hole plating (close-up); (d) surface-mounted assemblies.

volume soldering can be done by a wave-soldering machine, where the circuit board is passed over a standing wave of molten solder. Components have to be on one side only, although this is also usually the case with manual soldering.

The often complicated routing of connections between components is made easier by having two layers of printed 'tracks', one on each surface, permitting cross-overs. Connections between the top and bottom conductor layers are provided by plated-through 'via' holes. It is generally considered bad practice to use the holes in which components are mounted as via holes, because of the possibility of damaging the connection when components are replaced. The through-hole plating (see Figure 1.1(c)) provides extra support for small pads, reducing the risk of them peeling off during soldering. They do, however, make component removal more difficult, often requiring the destruction of the component so that its leads can be removed individually. The more expensive components are therefore generally provided with sockets, which also makes testing and servicing much simpler.

The PCB is completed by the addition of a solder mask and a printed (silk-screened) component identification layer. The solder mask is to prevent solder bridges between adjacent tracks and pads, especially when using an automatic soldering technique such as wave soldering. The component identification layer helps assembly, test and servicing.

For very simple low-density circuits a single-sided PCB is often used, since manufacturing cost is lower. The pads and tracks must be larger, however, since without through-hole plating they tend to lift off more easily when soldering.

For very high-density circuits, especially digital, multilayer PCBs are used, as many as nine layers of printed circuits being laminated together with through-hole plating providing the interconnections.

Most electronic components have evolved to be suitable for this type of construction, along with machines for automatic handling and insertion. The humble resistor is an interesting example; this was originally designed for wiring between posts or tag-strips in valve circuits. Currently, they are supplied on long ribbons, and machines or hand tools are used for bending and cropping the leads, ready for insertion (see Figure 1.1(b)).

1.3.2 Surface-mounted assemblies (Figure 1.1(d))

The demand for greater complexity and higher density of circuits has resulted in important new developments which are predicted to overtake current methods by the year 1990. Semiconductors, chip resistors and chip capacitors are available in very small outline packages, and are easier to handle with automatic placement machines. Surface mounting eliminates the difficult problem of automatic insertion and, in most cases, the costly drilling process as well. Slightly higher densities can be achieved by using a ceramic substrate instead of fibreglass. Conductors of palladium silver, insulators and resistive inks are silk screened and baked onto the substrate to provide connections, cross-overs and some of the components. These techniques have been developed from the older 'chip and wire' hybrid thick film integrated circuit technique, used mainly in high-density military applications. In both cases, reflow soldering techniques are used due to the small size. Here, the solder is applied as a paste and silk screened onto the surface bonding pads. The component is then placed on its pads and the solder made to reflow by application of a short burst of heat which is not enough to damage the component. The heat can be applied by placing the substrate onto a hot vapour which then condenses at a precise temperature above the melting point of the solder. More simply, the substrate can be placed on a temperature-controlled hotplate or passed under a strip of hot air or radiant heat.

The technique is therefore very cost effective in high volumes, and with the increasing sophistication of silicon circuits results in 'smart sensors' where the circuitry may be printed onto any flat surface.

1.3.2.1 Circuit board replacement

When deciding servicing policy it should be realized that replacing a whole circuit board is often more cost effective than trying to trace a faulty component or connection. To this end, PCBs can be mounted for easy access and provided with a connector or connectors for rapid removal. The faulty circuit board can then be thrown away or returned to the supplier for repair.

1.3.3 Interconnections

There are many ways to provide the interconnection between circuit boards and the rest of the instrument, of which the most common are described below.

Connectors are used to facilitate rapid making and breaking of these connections, and simplify assembly test and servicing. Conventional wiring looms are still used because of their flexibility and because they can be designed for complicated routing and branching requirements. Termination of the wires can be by soldering, crimp or wire-wrap onto connector or circuit board pins. This, however, is a labour-intensive technique and is prone to wiring errors. Looms are given mechanical strength by lacing or sleeving wires as a tight bunch and anchoring to the chassis with cable ties.

Ribbon cable and insulation displacement connectors are now replacing conventional looms in many applications. As many as sixty connections can be made with one simple loom with very low labour costs. Wiring errors are eliminated since the routing is fixed at the design stage (see Figure 1.2).

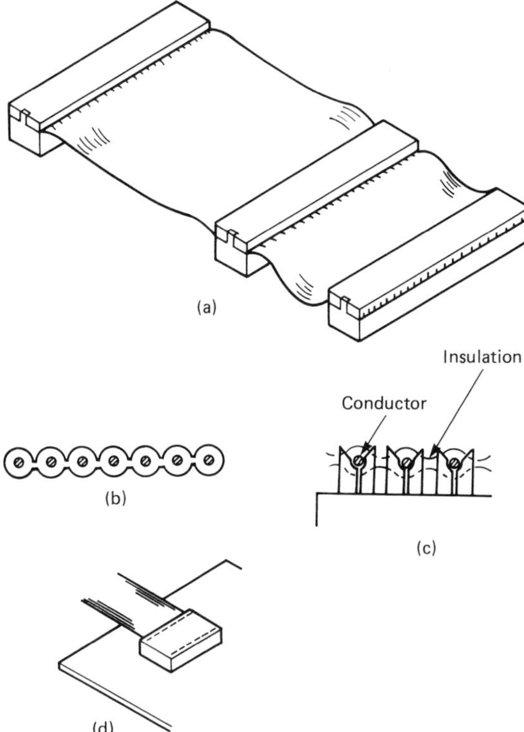

Figure 1.2 Ribbon cable interconnection. (a) Ribbon cable assembly; (b) ribbon cable cross-section; (c) insulation displacement terminator; (d) dual in-line header.

Connectors are very useful for isolating or removing a subassembly conveniently. They are, however, somewhat expensive and a common source of unreliability.

Another technique, which is used in demanding applications where space is at a premium, is the flexy circuit. Printed circuit boards are laminated with a thin, flexible sheet of Kapton which carries conductors. The connections are permanent, but the whole assembly can be folded up to fit into a limited space.

It is inappropriate to list here the many types of connectors. The connector manufacturers issue catalogues full of different types, and these are readily available.

1.3.4 Materials

A considerable variety of materials are available to the instrument designer, and new ones are being developed with special or improved characteristics, including polymers and superstrong ceramics. These materials can be bought in various forms, including sheet, block, rod and tube, and processed in a variety of ways.

1.3.4.1 Metals

Metals are usually used for strength and low cost as structural members. Aluminium for low weight and steel are the most common. Metals are also suitable for machining precise shapes to tight tolerances.

Stainless steels are used to resist corrosion and precious metal in thin layers helps to maintain clean electrical contacts. Metals are good conductors, and provide electrical screening as well as support. Mumetal and radiometal have high permeabilities and are used as very effective magnetic screens or in magnetic components. Some alloys—notably beryllium–copper—have very good spring characteristics, improved by annealing, and this is used to convert force into displacement in load cells and pressure transducers. Springs made of nimonic keep their properties at high temperatures, which is important in some transducer applications.

The precise thermal coefficient of the expansion of metals makes it possible to produce compensating designs, using different metals or alloys, and so maintaining critical distances independent of temperature. Invar has the lowest coefficient of expansion at less than 1 ppm per K over a useful range, but it is difficult to machine precisely.

Metals can be processed to change their characteristics as well as their shape; some can be hardened after machining and ground or honed to a very accurate and smooth finish, as found in bearings.

Metal components can be annealed, i.e. taken to a high temperature, in order to reduce internal stresses caused in the manufacture of the material and machining. Heat treatments can also improve stability, strength, spring quality, magnetic permeability or hardness.

1.3.4.2 Ceramics

For very high temperatures, ceramics are used as electrical and heat insulators or conductors (e.g. silicon carbide). The latest ceramics (e.g. zirconia, sialon, silicon nitride and silicon carbide) exhibit very high strength, hardness and stability even at temperatures over 1000°C. Processes for shaping them include slip casting, hot isostatic pressing

(HIP), green machining, flame spraying and grinding to finished size. Being hard, their grinding is best done by diamond or cubic boron nitride (CBN) tools. Alumina is widely used, despite being brittle, and many standard mechanical or electrical components are available.

Glass-loaded machinable ceramics are very convenient, having very similar properties to alumina, but are restricted to lower temperatures (less than 500°C). Special components can be made to accurate final size with conventional machining and tungsten tools.

Other compounds based on silicon include sapphires, quartz, glasses, artificial granite and the pure crystalline or amorphous substance. These have well-behaved and known properties (e.g. thermal expansion coefficient, conductivity and refractive index), which can be finely adjusted by adding different ingredients. The manufacture of electronic circuitry, with photolithography, chemical doping and milling, represents the ultimate in materials technology. Many of these techniques are applicable to instrument manufacture, and the gap between sensor and circuitry is narrowing—for example, in chemfets, in which a reversible chemical reaction produces a chemical potential that is coupled to one or more field-effect transistors. These transistors give amplification and possibly conversion to digital form before transmission to an indicator instrument with resulting higher integrity.

1.3.4.3 Plastics and polymers

Low-cost, lightweight and good insulating properties make plastics and polymers popular choices for standard mechanical components and enclosures. They can be moulded into elaborate shapes and given a pleasing appearance at very low cost in high volumes. PVC, PTFE, polyethylene, polypropylene, polycarbonates and nylon are widely used and available as a range of composites, strengthened with fibres or other ingredients to achieve the desired properties. More recently, carbon composites and Kevlar exhibit very high strength-to-weight ratio, useful for structural members. Carbon fibre is also very stable, making it suitable for dimensional calibration standards. Kapton and polyamides are used at higher temperatures and radiation levels.

A biodegradable plastic, (poly 3-hydroxybutyrate) or PHB is also available which can be controlled for operating life. Manufactured by cloned bacteria, this material represents one of many new materials emerging from advances in biotechnology.

More exotic materials are used for special applications, and a few examples are:

(1) Mumetal—very high magnetic permeability;
(2) PVDF—polyvinyledene fluoride, piezoelectric effect;
(3) Samarium/cobalt—very high magnetic remanence (fixed magnet);
(4) Sapphire—very high thermal conductivity;
(5) Ferrites—very stable magnetic permeability, wide range available.

1.3.4.4 Epoxy resins

Two-part epoxy resins can be used as adhesives, as potting material and paint. Parameters such as viscosity, setting time, set hardness and colour can be controlled. Most have good insulating properties, although conducting epoxies exist, and all are mechanically strong, some up to 300°C. The resin features in the important structure material: epoxy bonded fibreglass. Delicate assemblies can be ruggedized or passivated by a prophylactic layer of resin, which also improves design security.

Epoxy resin can be applied to a component and machined to size when cured. It can allow construction of an insulating joint with precisely controlled dimensions. Generally speaking, the thinner the glue layer, the stronger and more stable the join.

1.3.4.5 Paints and finishes

The appearance of an instrument is enhanced by the judicious use of texture and colour in combination with its controls and displays. A wide range of British Standard coordinated colours are available, allowing consistent results (BS 5252 and 4800).

Anodized or brushed aluminium panels have been popular for many years, although the trend is now back towards painted or plastic panels with more exotic colours. Nearly all materials, including plastic, can be spray painted by using suitable preparation and curing. Matt, gloss and a variety of textures are available.

Despite its age, silk-screen printing is used widely for lettering, diagrams and logos, especially on front panels.

Photosensitive plastic films, in one or a mixture of colours, are used for stick-on labels or as complete front panels with an LED display filter. The latter are often used in conjunction with laminated pressure pad-switches to provide a rugged, easy to clean splashproof control panel.

1.3.5 Mechanical manufacturing processes

Materials can be processed in many ways to produce the required component. The methods chosen depend on the type of material, the volume required and the type of shape and dimensional accuracy.

1.3.5.1 Bending and punching

Low-cost sheet metal or plastic can be bent or pressed into the required shape and holes punched with standard or special tools (Figure 1.3). Simple bending machines and a fly press cover most requirements, although hard tooling is more cost effective in large volumes. Most plastics are thermosetting and require heating, but metals are normally worked cold. Dimensional accuracy is typically not better than 0.5 mm.

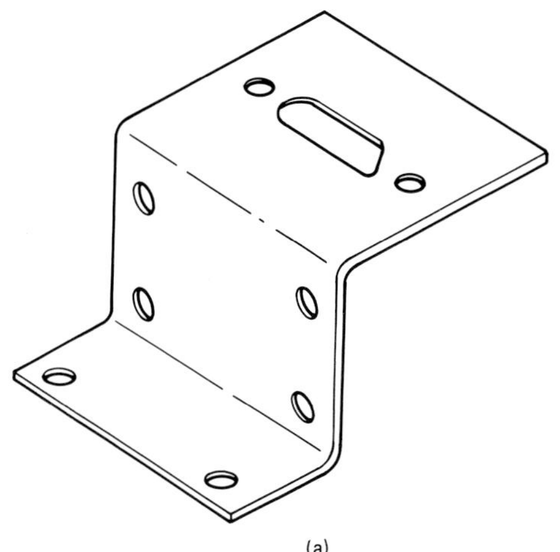

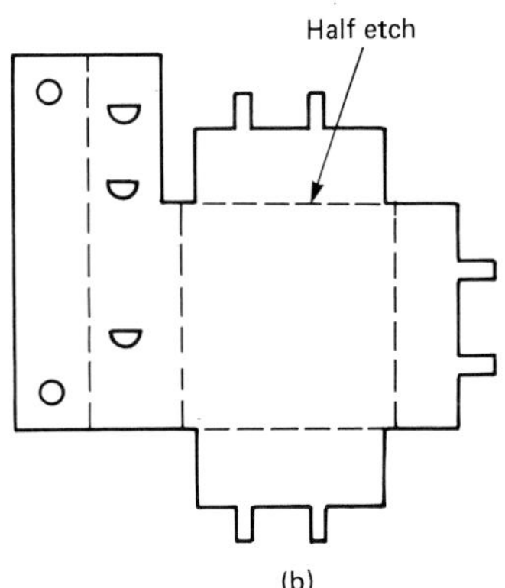

Figure 1.3 Sheet metal. (a) Bent and drilled or punched; (b) chemical milling.

1.3.5.2 Drilling and milling

Most materials can be machined, although glass (including fibreglass), ceramics and some metals require specially hardened tools. The hand or pillar drill is the simplest tool, and high accuracy can be achieved by using a jig to hold the workpiece and guide the rotating bit.

A milling machine is more complex, where the workpiece can be moved precisely relative to the rotating tool. Drills, reamers, cutters and slotting saws are used to create complex and accurate shapes. Tolerances of 1 μm can be achieved.

1.3.5.3 Turning

Rotating the workpiece against a tool is a method for turning long bars of material into large numbers of components at low unit cost. High accuracies can be achieved for internal and external diameters and length, typically 1 μm, making cylindrical components a popular choice in all branches of engineering.

A fully automatic machining centre and tool changer and component handler can produce vast numbers of precise components of many different types under computer control.

1.3.5.4 Grinding and honing

With grinding, a hard stone is used to remove a small but controlled amount of material. When grinding, both tool and component are moved to produce accurate geometries including relative concentricity and straightness (e.g. parallel) but with a poor surface finish. Precise flats, cylinders, cones and spherics are possible. The material must be fairly hard to get the best results and is usually metal or ceramic.

Honing requires a finer stone and produces a much better surface finish and potentially very high accuracy (0.1 μm). Relative accuracy (e.g. concentricity between outside and inside diameters) is not controllable, and so honing is usually preceded by grinding or precise turning.

1.3.5.5 Lapping

A fine sludge of abrasive is rubbed onto the workpiece surface to achieve ultra-high accuracy, better than 10 nm if the metal is very hard. In principle, any shape can be lapped, but optical surfaces such as flats and spherics are most common, since these can be checked by sensitive optical methods.

1.3.5.6 Chemical and electrochemical milling

Metal can be removed or deposited by chemical and electrochemical reactions. Surfaces can be selectively treated through masks. Complex shapes can be etched from sheet material of most kinds of metal using photolithographic techniques. Figure 1.3(b) shows an example where accuracies of 0.1 mm are achieved.

Gold, tin, copper and chromium can be deposited for printed circuit board manufacture or servicing of bearing components. Chemical etching of mechanical structures into silicon in combination with electronic circuitry is a process currently under development.

1.3.5.7 Extruding

In extruding, the material, in a plastic state and usually at a high temperature, is pushed through an orifice with the desired shape. Complex cross sections can be achieved and a wide range of standard items are available, cut to length. Extruded components are used for structural members, heat sinks and enclosures (Figure 1.4). Initial tooling is, however, expensive for non-standard sections.

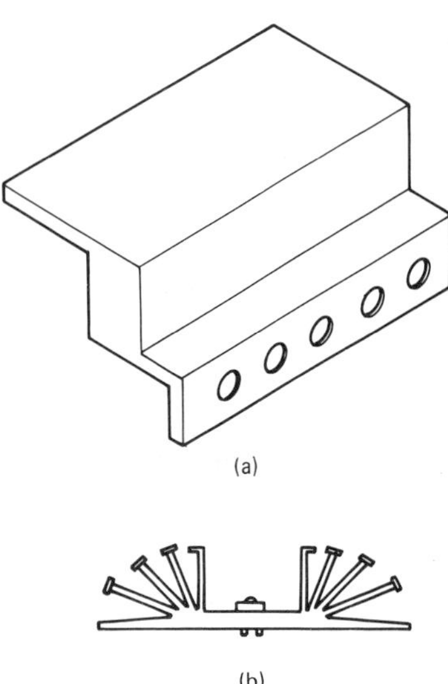

Figure 1.4 Extrusion. (a) Structural member; (b) heat sink.

1.3.5.8 Casting and moulding

Casting, like moulding, makes the component from the liquid or plastic phase but results in the destruction of the mould. It usually refers to components made of metals such as aluminium alloys and sand casts made from a pattern. Very elaborate forms can be made but further machining is required for accuracies better than 0.5 mm. Examples are shown in Figure 1.5. Plastics are moulded in a variety of ways and the mould can be used many times. Vacuum forming and injection moulding are used to achieve very low unit cost but tooling costs are high.

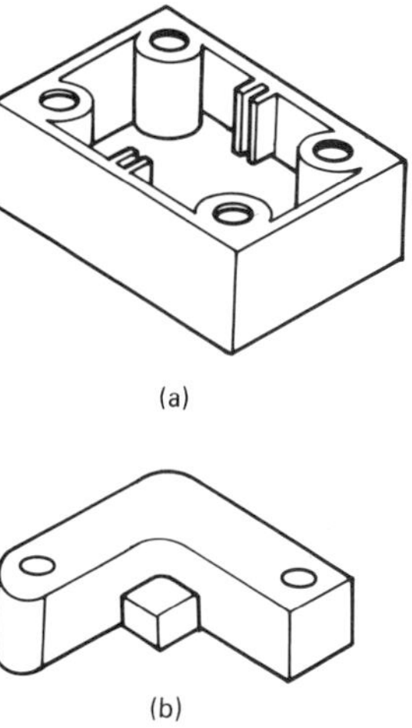

Figure 1.5 Examples of casting and moulding. (a) Moulded enclosure; (b) cast fixing.

1.3.5.9 Adhesives

Adhesive technology is advancing at a considerable rate, finding increasing use in instrument construction. Thin layers of adhesive can be stable and strong and provide electrical conduction or insulation. Almost any material can be glued, although high-temperature curing is still required for some applications. Metal components can be recovered by disintegration of the adhesive at high temperatures. Two-part adhesives are usually best for increased shelf life.

Jigs can be used for high dimensional accuracies, and automatic dispensing for high volume and low cost assembly.

1.3.6 Functional components

A wide range of devices are available, including bearings, couplings, gears and springs. Figure 1.6 shows the main types of components used and their principal characteristics.

1.3.6.1 Bearings

Bearings are used when a controlled movement either linear or rotary, is required. The simplest bearing consists of rubbing surfaces, prismatic for linear, cylindrical for rotation and spherical for universal movement. Soft materials such as copper and bronze and PTFE are used for reduced friction, and high precision can be achieved. Liquid or solid lubricants are sometimes used, including thin deposits of PTFE, graphite, organic and mineral oils. Friction can be further reduced by introducing a gap and rolling elements between the surfaces. The hardened steel balls or cylinders are held in cages or a recirculating mechanism. Roller bearings can be precise, low friction, relatively immune to contamination and capable of taking large loads.

The most precise bearing is the air bearing. A thin cushion of pressurized air is maintained between the bearing surfaces, considerably reducing the friction and giving a position governed by the average surface geometry. Accuracies of 0.01 μm are possible, but a source of clean, dry, pressurized air is required. Magnetic bearings maintain an air gap and have low friction but cannot tolerate side loads.

With bearings have evolved seals to eliminate contamination. For limited movement, elastic balloons of rubber or metal provide complete and possibly hermetic sealing. Seals made of low-friction polymer composites exclude larger particles and magnetic liquid lubricant can be trapped between magnets, providing an excellent low-friction seal for unlimited linear or rotary movement.

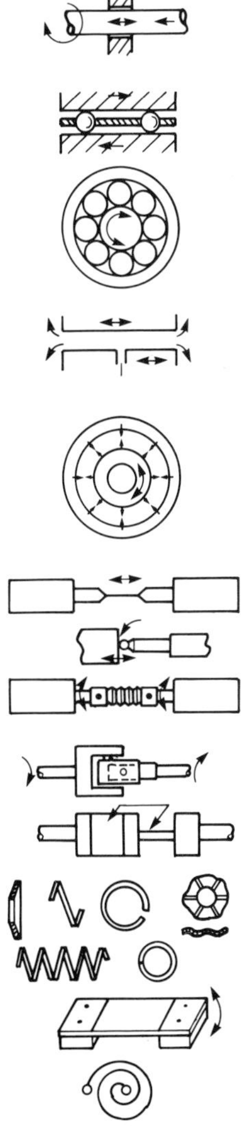

Figure 1.6 Mechanical components.

1.3.6.2 Couplings

It is occasionally necessary to couple the movement of two bearings, which creates problems of clashing. This can be overcome by using a flexible coupling which is stiff in the required direction and compliant to misalignment of the bearings. Couplings commonly used include:

(1) Spring wire or filaments;
(2) Bellows;
(3) Double hinges.

Each type is suitable for different combinations of side load, misalignment and torsional stiffness.

1.3.6.3 Springs

Springs are used to produce a controlled amount of force (e.g. for preloaded bearings, force/pressure transducers or fixings). They can take the form of a diaphragm, helix, crinkled washer or shaped flat sheet leaf spring. A thin circular disc with chemically milled Archimedes spinal slots is an increasingly used example of the latter. A pair of these can produce an accurate linear motion with good sideways stiffness and controllable spring constant.

1.4 Construction of electronic instruments

Electronic instruments can be categorized by the way they are intended to be used physically, resulting in certain types of construction:

(1) Site mounting;
(2) Panel mounting;
(3) Bench mounting;
(4) Rack mounting;
(5) Portable instruments.

Figure 1.7 Instrument for site mounting (courtesy Solarton Instruments).

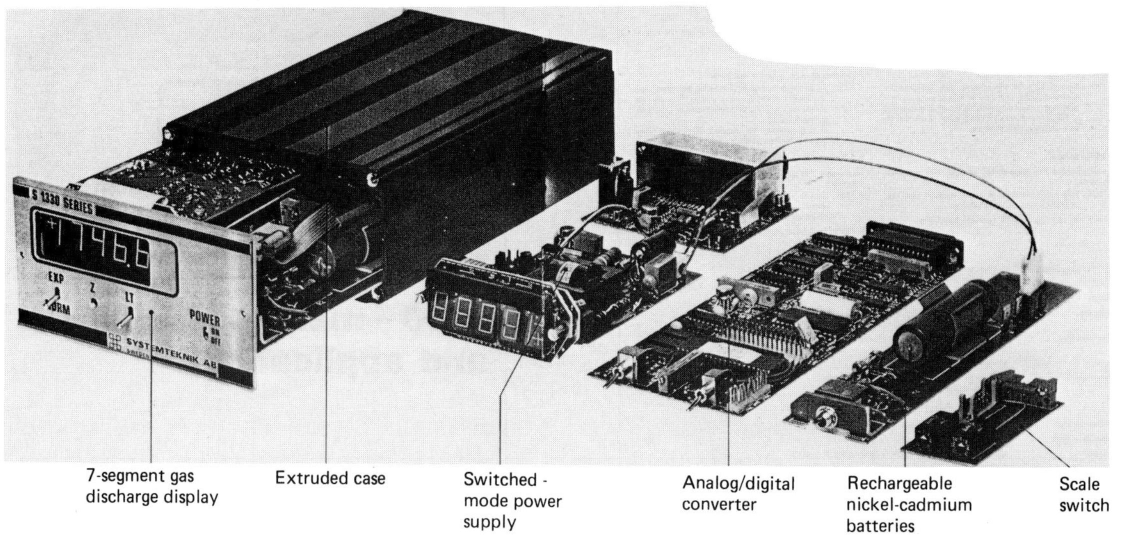

Figure 1.8 Panel-mounting instrument (courtesy Systemteknik AB).

1.4.1 Site mounting

The overriding consideration here is usually to get close to the physical process which is being measured or controlled. This usually results in the need to tolerate harsh environmental conditions such as extreme temperature, physical shock, muck and water. Signal conditioners and data-acquisition subsystems, which are connected to transducers and actuators, produce signals suitable for transmission over long distances, possibly to a central instrumentation and control system some miles away. Whole computerized systems are also available with ruggedized construction for use in less hostile environments.

The internal construction is usually very simple, since there are few, if any, controls or displays. Figure 1.7 shows an interesting example which tackles the common problem of wire terminations. The moulded plastic enclosure is sealed at the front with a rubber 'O' ring and is designed to pass the IPC 65 'hosepipe' test (see BS 5490). The main electronic circuit is on one printed circuit board mounted on pillars, connected to one of a variety of optional interface cards. The unit is easily bolted to a wall or the side of a machine.

1.4.2 Panel mounting

A convenient way for an instrument engineer to

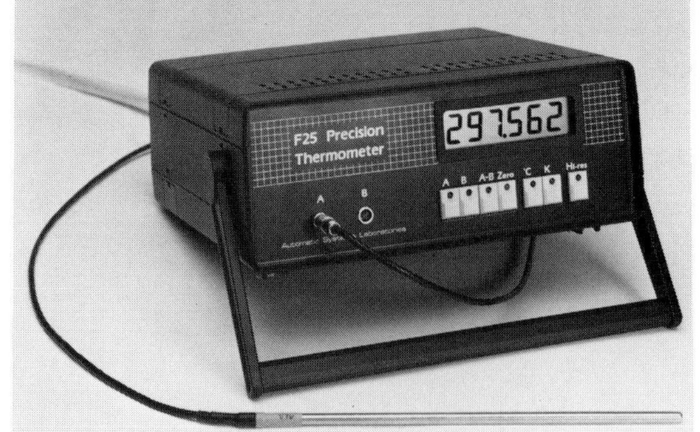

Figure 1.9(a) Bench-mounting instrument (courtesy Automatic Systems Laboratories Ltd).

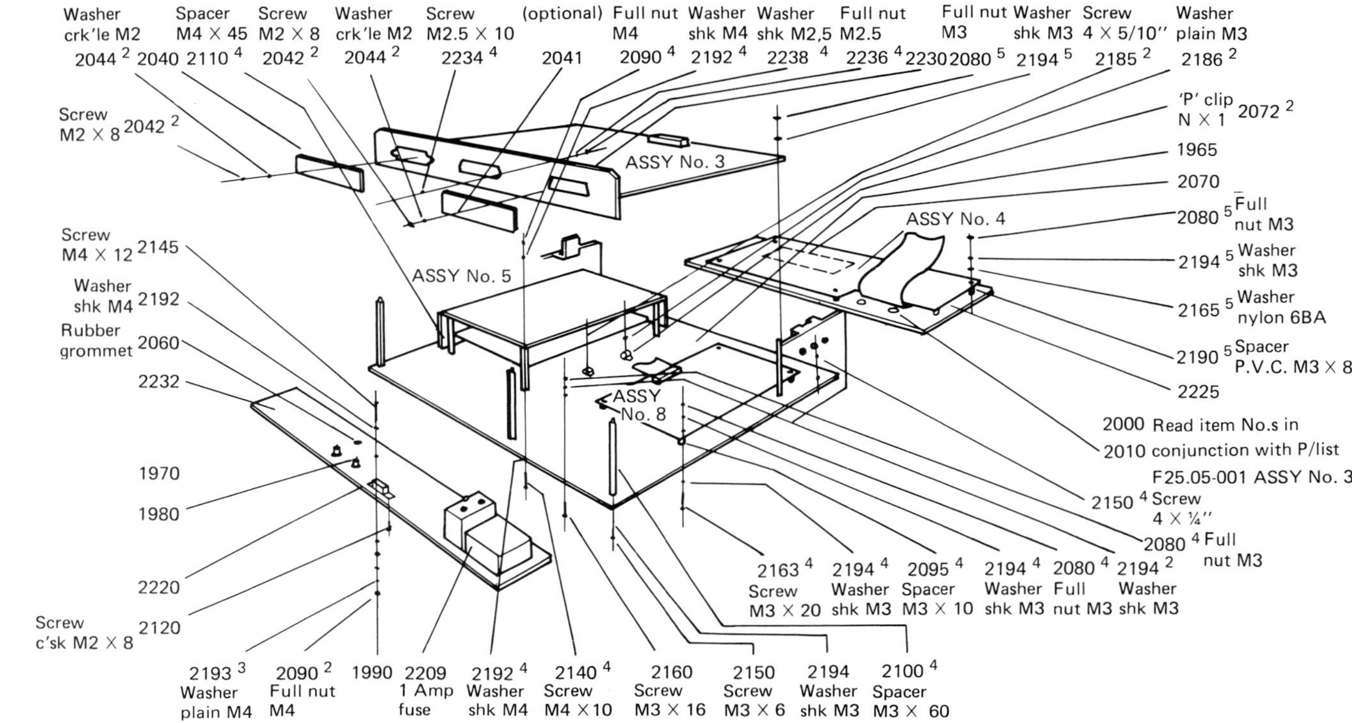

Figure 1.9(b) General assembly drawing of instrument shown in Figure 1.9(a).

construct a system is to mount the various instruments which require control or readout on a panel with the wiring and other system components protected inside a cabinet. Instruments designed for this purpose generally fit into one of a number of DIN standard cut-outs (see DIN 43 700). Figure 1.8 is an example illustrating the following features:

(1) The enclosure is an extruded aluminium tube;
(2) Internal construction is based around five printed circuit boards, onto which the electronic displays are soldered. The PCBs plug together and can be replaced easily for servicing;
(3) All user connections are at the rear, for permanent or semi-permanent installation.

1.4.3 Bench-mounting instruments

Instruments which require an external power source but a degree of portability are usually for benchtop operation. Size is important, since bench space is always in short supply.

Instruments in this category often have a wide range of controls and a display requiring careful attention to ergonomics. Figure 1.9(a) shows a typical instrument, where the following points are worth noting:

(1) The user inputs are at the front for easy access;
(2) There is a large clear display for comfortable viewing;
(3) The carrying handle doubles up as a tilt bar;
(4) It has modular internal construction with connectors for quick servicing.

The general assembly drawing for this instrument is included as Figure 1.9(b), to show how the parts fit together.

1.4.4 Rack-mounting instruments

Most large electronic instrumentation systems are constructed in 19-in wide metal cabinets of variable height (in units of 1.75 in = 1U). These can be for bench mounting, free standing or wall mounting. Large instruments are normally designed for bench operation or rack mounting for which optional brackets are supplied. Smaller modules plug into subracks which can then be bolted into a 19-in cabinet.

Figure 1.10 shows some of the elements of a modular instrumentation system with the following points:

(1) The modules are standard Eurocard sizes and widths (DIN 41914 or IEC 297);
(2) The connectors are to DIN standard (DIN 41612);
(3) The subrack uses standard mechanical components and can form part of a much larger instrumentation system.

The degree of modularity and standardization enables the user to mix a wide range of instruments and components from a large number of different suppliers worldwide.

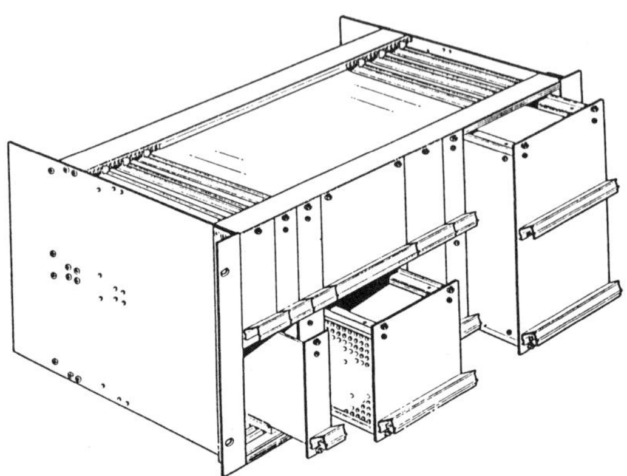

Figure 1.10 Rack-based modular instruments (courtesy Schroff (UK) Ltd and Automatic Systems Laboratories Ltd).

1.4.5 Portable instruments

Truly portable instruments are now common, due to the reduction in size and power consumption of electronic circuitry. Figure 1.11 shows good examples which incorporate the following features:

(1) Lightweight, low-cost moulded plastic case;
(2) Low-power CMOS circuitry and liquid crystal display (LCD);
(3) Battery power source gives long operating life.

Size reduction is mainly from circuit integration onto silicon and the use of small outline components.

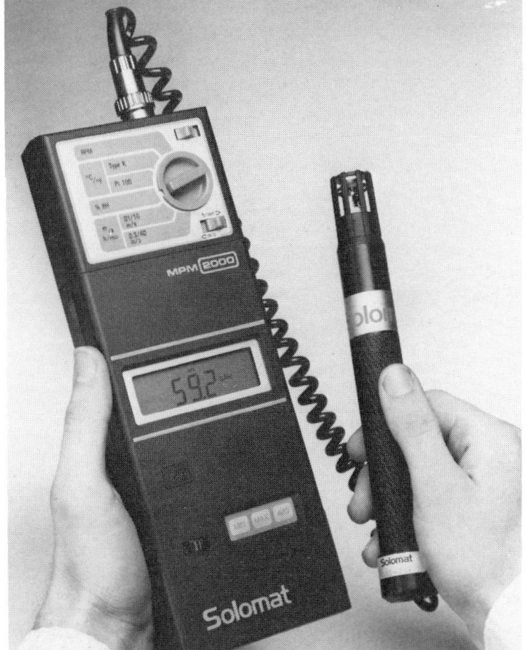

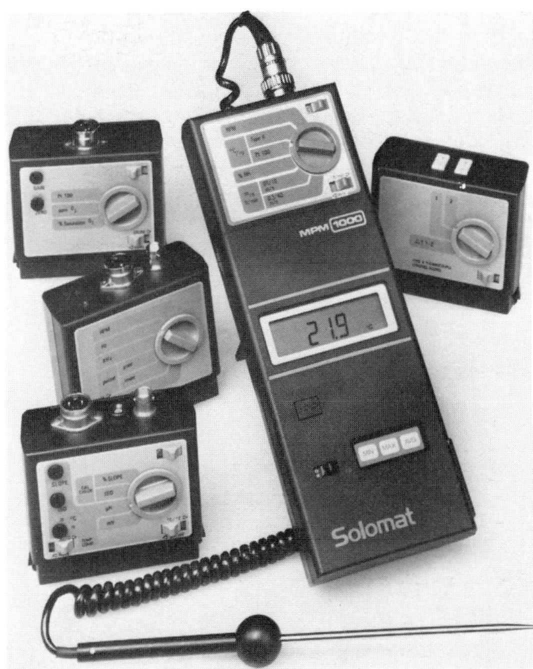

Figure 1.11 Portable instruments (courtesy Solomat SA).

1.4.6 Encapsulation

For particularly severe conditions, especially with regard to vibration, groups of electronic components are sometimes *encapsulated* (familiarly referred to as 'potting'). This involves casting them in a suitable material, commonly epoxy resin. This holds the components very securely in position and they are also protected from the atmosphere to which the instrument is exposed. To give further protection against stress (for instance, from differential thermal expansion) a complex procedure is occasionally used, with compliant silicone rubber introduced as well as the harder resin.

Some epoxies are strong up to 300°C. At higher temperatures (450°C) they are destroyed, allowing encapsulated components to be recovered if they are themselves heat resistant. Normally an encapsulated group would be thrown away if any fault developed inside it.

1.5 Mechanical instruments

Mechanical instruments are mainly used to interface between the physical world and electronic instrumentation. Examples are:

(1) Displacement transducers (linear and rotary);
(2) Force transducers (load cells);
(3) Accelerometers.

Such transducers often have to endure a wide temperature range, shock and vibration, requiring careful selection of materials and construction.

Many matters contribute to good mechanical design and construction, some of which are brought out in the devices described in other chapters of this book. We add to that here by showing details of one or two instruments where particular principles of design can be seen. Before that, however, we give a more general outline of kinematic design, a way of proceeding that can be of great value for designing instruments.

1.5.1 Kinematic design

A particular approach sometimes used for high-precision mechanical items is called kinematic design. When the relative location of two bodies must be constrained, so that there is either no movement or a closely controlled movement between them, it represents a way of overcoming the uncertainties that arise from the impossibility of achieving geometrical perfection in construction. A simple illustration is two flat surfaces in contact. If they can be regarded as ideal geometrical planes then the relative movement of the two bodies is accurately defined. However, it is expensive to approach geometrical perfection, and the imperfections of the surfaces mean that the relative position of the two parts will depend upon contact between high spots, and will vary slightly if the points of application of the forces holding them together are varied. The points of contact can be reduced, for instance, to four with a conventional chair, but it is notorious that a four-legged chair can rock unless the bottoms of the legs match the floor perfectly. *Kinematic design* calls for a three-legged chair, to avoid the *redundancy* of having its position decided by four points of contact.

More generally, a rigid solid body has 6 *degrees of freedom* which can be used to fix its position in space. These are often thought of as three Cartesian coordinates to give the position of one point of the body, and when that has been settled, rotation about three mutually perpendicular axes describes the body's attitude in space. The essence of kinematic design is that each degree of freedom should be constrained in an identifiable localized way.

Consider again the three-legged stool on a flat surface. The Z-coordinate of the tip of the leg has been constrained, as has rotation about two axes in the flat surface. There is still freedom of X and Y coordinates and for rotation about an axis perpendicular to the surface: 3 degrees of freedom removed by the three constraints between the leg-tips and the surface.

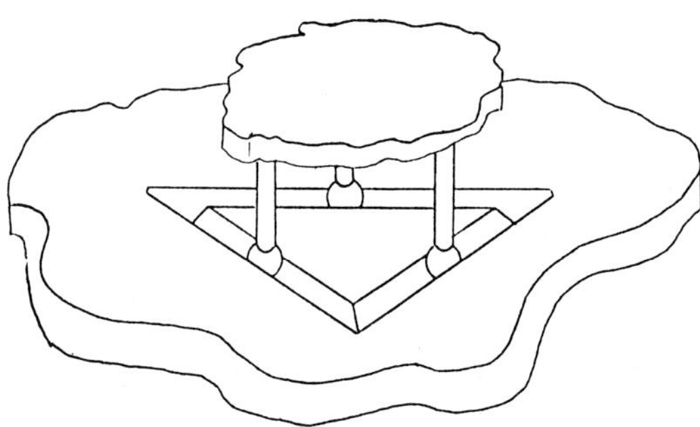

Figure 1.12 Kinematic design: six constraints locate a body.

A classical way of introducing six constraints and so locating one body relative to another is to have three V-grooves in one body and three hemispheres attached to the other body, as shown in Figure 1.12. When the hemispheres enter the grooves (which should be deep enough for contact to be made with their sides and not their edges) each has two constraints from touching two sides, making a total of six.

If one degree of freedom, say linear displacement, is required, five spheres can be used in a precise groove as in Figure 1.13. Each corresponds to a restricted movement.

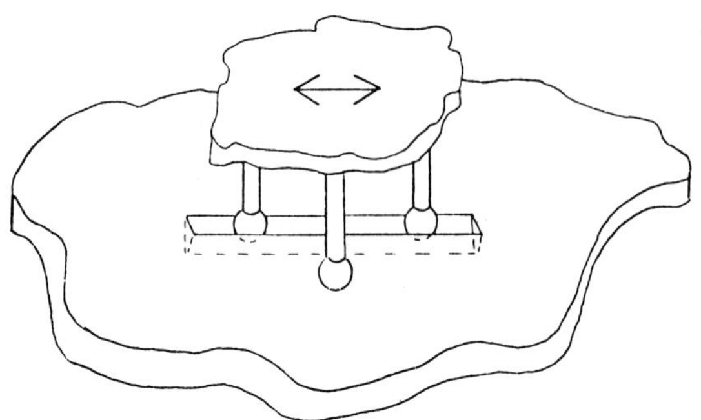

Figure 1.13 Kinematic design: five constraints allow linear movement.

For the required mating, it is important that contact should approximate to point contact and that the construction materials should be hard enough to allow very little deformation perpendicular to the surface under the loads normally encountered. The sphere-on-plane configuration described is one possible arrangement: crossed cylinders are similar in their behaviour and may be easier to construct.

Elastic hinges may be thought of as an extension of kinematic design. A conventional type of door hinge is expensive to produce if friction and play are to be greatly reduced, particularly for small devices. An alternative approach may be adopted when small, repeatable rotations must be catered for. Under this approach, some part is markedly weakened, as in Figure 1.14, so that the bending caused by a turning moment is concentrated in a small region. There is elastic resistance to deformation but very little friction and high repeatability.

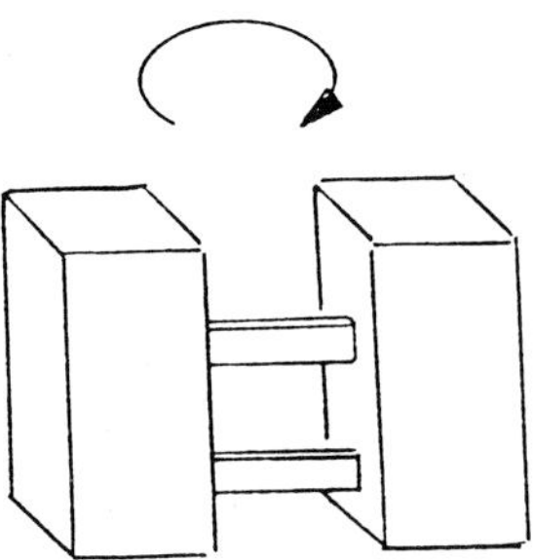

Figure 1.14 Principle of elastic hinge.

The advantages of kinematic design may be listed as:

(1) Commonly, only simple machining operations are needed at critical points.
(2) Wide tolerances on these operations should not affect repeatability, though they may downgrade absolute performance.
(3) Only small forces are needed. Often gravity is sufficient or a light spring if the direction relative to the vertical may change from time to time.
(4) Analysis and prediction of behaviour is simplified.

The main disadvantage arises if large forces have to be accommodated. Kinematically designed constraints normally work with small forces holding parts together and if these forces are overcome—even momentarily under the inertia forces of vibration—there can be serious malfunction. Indeed, the lack of symmetry in behaviour under kinematic design can prove a more general disadvantage (for instance, when considering the effects of wear).

Of course, the small additional complexity often means that it is not worth changing to kinematic design. Sometimes a compromise approach is adopted, such as localizing the points of contact between large structures without making them literal spheres on planes. In any case, when considering movements and locations in instruments it is helpful to bear the ideas of kinematic design in mind as a background to analysis.

1.5.2 Proximity transducer

This is a simple device which is used to detect the presence of an earthed surface which affects the capacitance between the two electrodes E1 and E2 in Figure 1.15. In a special application it is required to operate at a temperature cycling between 200°C and 400°C in a corrosive atmosphere and survive shocks of 1000 g. Design points to note are:

(1) The device is machined out of the solid to avoid a weak weld at position A.
(2) The temperature cycling causes thermal stresses which are taken up by the spring washer B (special nimonic spring material for high temperatures).
(3) The ceramic insulator blocks are under compression for increased strength.

1.5.3 Load cell

As discussed in Chapter 7 of Volume 1, a load cell converts force into movement against the reaction of a spring. The movement is then measured by a displacement transducer and converted into electrical form.

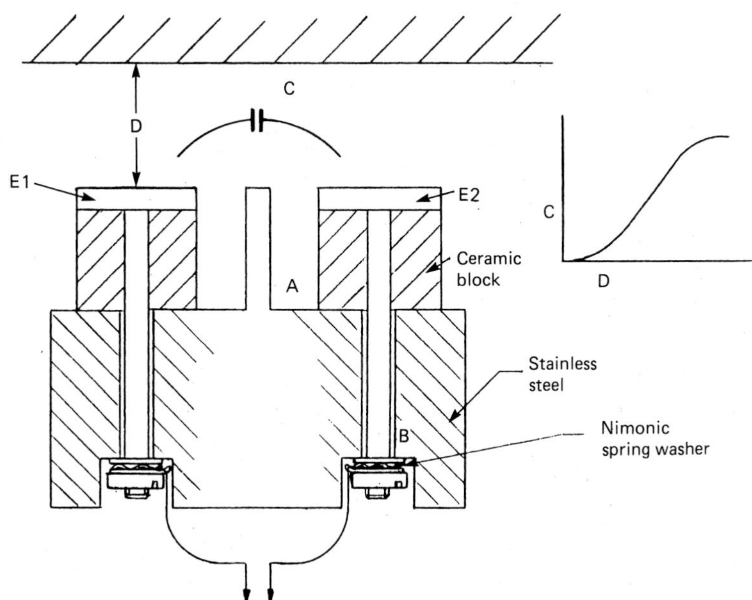

Figure 1.15 Rugged proximity transducer.

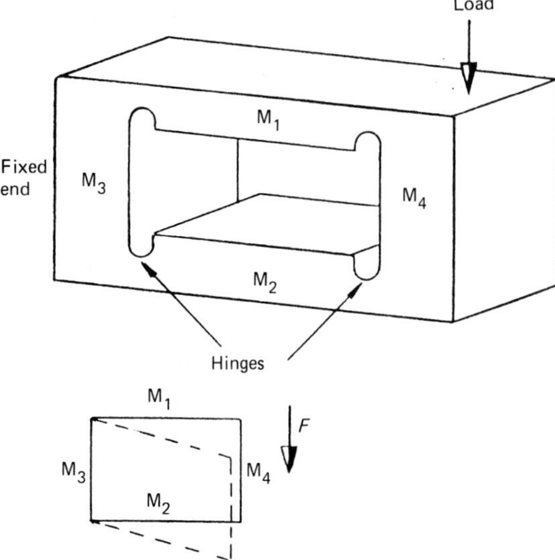

Figure 1.16 Load cell spring mechanism.

The load cell in Figure 1.16 consists of four stiff members and four flexures, machined out of a solid block of high-quality spring material in the shape of a parallelogram. The members M1, M2 and M3, M4 remain parallel as the force *F* bends the flexures at the thin sections (called hinges).

Any torque, caused by the load being offset from the vertical, will result in a small twisting of the load cell, but this is kept within the required limit by arranging the rotational stiffness to be much greater than the vertical stiffness. This is determined by the width.

The trapezoidal construction is far better in this respect than a normal cantilever, which would result in a non-linear response.

1.5.4 Combined actuator transducer

Figure 1.17 illustrates a more complex example, requiring a number of processing techniques to fabricate the complete item. The combined actuator

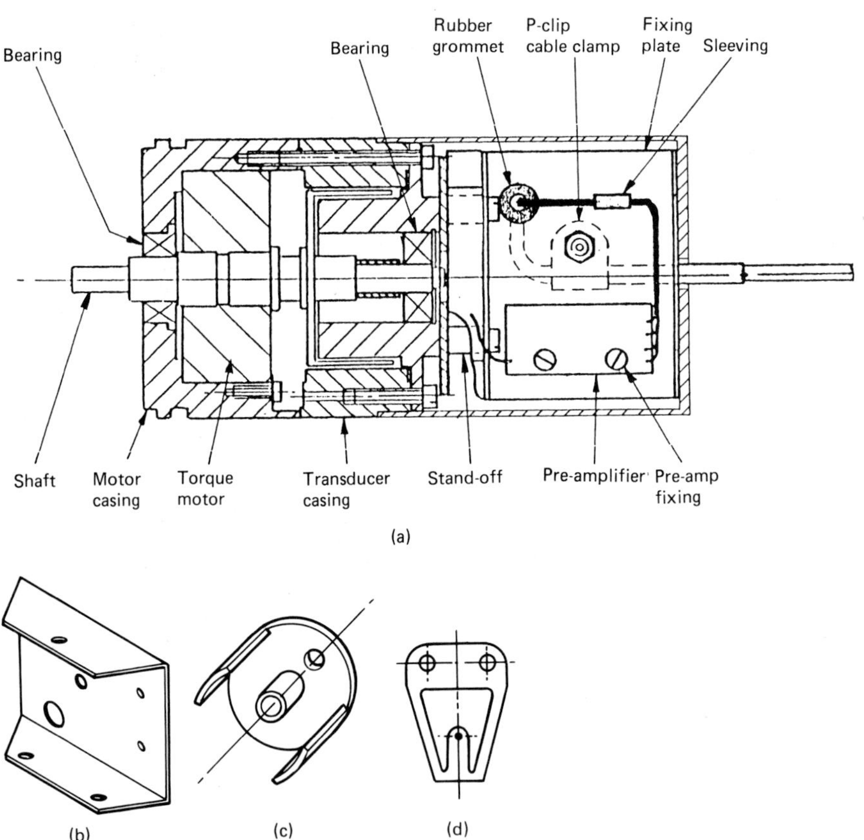

Figure 1.17 Combined actuator/transducer. (a) Whole assembly; (b) fixing plate; (c) transducer rotor; (d) spring contact.

transducer (CAT) is a low-volume product with applications in automatic optical instruments for mirror positioning. The major bought-in components are a torque motor and a miniature pre-amplifier produced by specialist suppliers. The motor incorporates the most advanced rare-earth magnetic materials for compactness and stability and the pre-amplifier uses small outline electronic components, surface mounted on a copper/fibreglass printed circuit board.

The assembled CAT is shown in Figure 1.17(a). It consists of three sections: the motor in its housing, a capacitive angular transducer in its housing and a rear-mounted plate (Figure 1.17(b)) for pre-amplifier fixing and cable clamping. The motor produces a torque which rotates the shaft in the bearings. Position information is provided by the transducer which produces an output via the pre-amplifier. The associated electronic servocontrol unit provides the power output stage, position feedback and loop-stabilization components to control the shaft angle to an arc second. This accuracy is attainable by the use of precise ballbearings which maintain radial and axial movement to within 10 μm.

The shaft, motor casing and transducer components are manufactured by precise turning of a non-magnetic stainless steel bar and finished by fine bead blasting. The motor and transducer electrodes (not shown) are glued in place with a thin layer of epoxy resin and in the latter case finished by turning to final size.

The two parts of the transducer stator are jigged concentric and held together by three screws in threaded holes A, leaving a precisely determined gap in which the transducer rotor (Figure 1.17(c)) rotates. The transducer rotor is also turned but the screens are precision ground to size, as this determines the transducer sensitivity and range.

The screens are earthed, via the shaft and a hardened gold rotating point contact held against vibration by a spring (Figure 1.17(d)). The spring is chemically milled from thin beryllium copper sheet.

The shaft with motor and transducer rotor glued in place, motor stator and casing, transducer stator and bearings are then assembled and held together with three screws as B. The fixing plate, assembled with cable, clamp and pre-amplifier separately, is added, mounted on standard standoffs, the wires made off, and then finally the cover put on.

In addition to the processes mentioned the manufacture of this unit requires drilling, reaming, bending, screen printing, soldering, heat treatment and anodizing. Materials include copper, PTFE, stainless steel, samarium cobalt, epoxy fibreglass, gold and aluminium, and machining tolerances are typically 25 μm for turning, 3 μm for grinding and 0.1 mm for bending.

The only external feature is the clamping ring at the shaft end for axial fixing (standard servo type size 20). This is provided because radial force could distort the thin wall section and cause transducer errors.

1.6 References

BIRKBECK, G. 'Mechanical Design', in *A Guide to Instrument Design*, SIMA and BSIRA, Taylor and Francis, London (1963)

CLAYTON, G. B. *Operational Amplifiers*, Butterworths, London (1979)

FURSE, J. E. 'Kinematic design of fine mechanisms in instruments', in *Instrument Science and Technology*, Volume 2, ed. E. B. Jones, Adam Hilger, Bristol (1983)

HOROWITZ, P. and HILL, W. *The Art of Electronics*, Cambridge University Press, Cambridge (1980)

KIBBLE, B. P. and RAYNER, G. H. *Co-axial AC Bridges*, Adam Hilger, Bristol (1984)

MORRELL, R. *Handbook of Properties of Technical and Engineering Ceramics*. Part 1, An introduction for the engineer and designer, HMSO, London (1985)

OBERG, E. and JONES, F. D. *Machinery's Handbook*, The Machinery Publishing Company, (1979)

SHIELDS, J. *Adhesives Handbook*, Butterworths, London (revised 3rd edn, 1985)

The standards referred to in the text are:

BS 5252 (1976) and 4800 (1981): Framework for colour co-ordination for building purposes

BS 5490 (1977 and 1985): Environmental protection provided by enclosures

DIN 43 700 (1982): Cutout dimensions for panel mounting instruments

DIN 41612: Standards for Eurocard connectors

DIN 41914 and IEC 297: Standards for Eurocards

2 Instrument installation and commissioning

A. DANIELSSON

2.1 Introduction

Plant safety and continuous effective plant operability are totally dependent upon correct installation and commissioning of the instrumentation systems. Process plants are increasingly becoming dependent upon automatic control systems owing to the advanced control functions and monitoring facilities that can be provided in order to improve plant efficiency, product throughput and product quality.

The instrumentation on a process plant represents a significant capital investment, and the importance of careful handling on site and the exactitude of the installation cannot be overstressed. Correct installation is also important in order to ensure long-term reliability and to obtain the best results from instruments which are capable of higher-order accuracies due to advances in technology. Quality control of the completed work is also an important function.

2.2 General requirements

Installation should be carried out using the best engineering practices by skilled personnel who are fully acquainted with the safety requirements and regulations governing a plant site. Prior to commencement of the work for a specific project, installation design details should be made available which define the scope of work and the extent of material supply and which give detailed installation information related to location, fixing, piping and wiring. Such design details should have already taken account of established installation recommendations and measuring technology requirements. The details contained in this chapter are intended to give general installation guidelines.

2.3 Storage and protection

When instruments are received on a job site it is of utmost importance that they are unpacked with care, examined for superficial damage and then placed in a secure store which should be free from dust and suitably heated. In order to minimize handling, large items of equipment such as control panels should be programmed to go directly into their intended location, but temporary anti-condensation heaters should be installed if the intended air-conditioning systems have not been commissioned.

Throughout construction, instruments and equipment installed in the field should be fitted with suitable coverings to protect them from mechanical abuse such as paint spraying, etc. Preferably, after an installation has been fabricated, the instrument should be removed from site and returned to the store for safe keeping until ready for precalibration and final loop checking. Again, when instruments are removed, care should be taken to seal the ends of piping, etc. to prevent ingress of foreign matter.

2.4 Mounting and accessibility

When instruments are mounted in their intended location, either on pipe stands, brackets or directly connected to vessels, etc., they should be vertically plumbed and firmly secured. Instrument mountings should be vibration free and should be located so that they do not obstruct access ways which may be required for maintenance to other items of equipment. They should also be clear of obvious hazards such as hot surfaces or drainage points from process equipment.

Locations should also be selected to ensure that the instruments are accessible for observation and maintenance. Where instruments are mounted at higher elevations, it must be ensured that they are accessible either by permanent or temporary means.

Instruments should be located as close as possible to their process tapping points in order to minimize the length of impulse lines, but consideration should be paid to the possibility of expansion of piping or vessels which could take place under operating conditions and which could result in damage if not properly catered for. All brackets and supports should be adequately protected against corrosion by priming and painting.

When installing final control elements such as control valves, again the requirement for maintenance access must be considered and clearance should be allowed above and below the valve to facilitate servicing of the valve actuator and the valve internals.

2.5 Piping systems

All instrument piping or tubing runs should be routed to meet the following requirements:

(1) They should be kept as short as possible;
(2) They should not cause any obstruction that would prohibit personnel or traffic access;
(3) They should not interfere with the accessibility for maintenance of other items of equipment;
(4) They should avoid hot environments or potential fire-risk areas;
(5) They should be located with sufficient clearance to permit lagging which may be required on adjacent pipework;
(6) The number of joints should be kept to a minimum consistent with good practice;
(7) All piping and tubing should be adequately supported along its entire length from supports attached to firm steelwork or structures (not handrails).

(*Note*: Tubing can be regarded as thin-walled seamless pipe that cannot be threaded and which is joined by compression fittings, as opposed to piping, which can be threaded or welded.)

2.5.1 Air supplies

Air supplies to instruments should be clean, dry and oil free. Air is normally distributed around a plant from a high-pressure header (e.g. 6–7 bar g), ideally forming a ring main. This header, usually of galvanized steel, should be sized to cope with the maximum demand of the instrument air users being serviced and an allowance should be made for possible future expansion or modifications to its duty.

Branch headers should be provided to supply individual instruments or groups of instruments. Again, adequate spare tappings should be allowed to cater for future expansion. Branch headers should be self draining and have adequate drainage/blow-off facilities. On small headers this may be achieved by the instrument air filter/regulators.

Each instrument air user should have an individual filter regulator. Piping and fittings installed after filter regulators should be non-ferrous.

2.5.2 Pneumatic signals

Pneumatic transmission signals are normally in the range of 0.2–1.0 bar g, and for these signals copper tubing is most commonly used, preferably with a PVC outer sheath. Other materials are sometimes used, depending on environmental considerations (e.g. alloy tubing or stainless steel). Although expensive, stainless steel tubing is the most durable and will withstand the most arduous service conditions.

Plastic tubing should preferably only be used within control panels. There are several problems to be considered when using plastic tubes on a plant site, as they are very vulnerable to damage unless adequately protected, they generally cannot be installed at subzero temperatures and they can be considerably weakened by exposure to hot surfaces. Also it should be remembered that they can be totally lost in the event of a fire.

Pneumatic tubing should be run on a cable tray or similar supporting steelwork for its entire length and securely clipped at regular intervals. Where a number of pneumatic signals are to be routed to a remote control room they should be marshalled in a remote junction box and the signals conveyed to the control room via multitube bundles. Such junction boxes should be carefully positioned in the plant in order to minimize the lengths of the individually run tubes. (See Figure 2.1 for typical termination of pneumatic multitubes.)

2.5.3 Impulse lines

These are the lines containing process fluid which run between the instrument impulse connection and the process tapping point, and are usually made up from piping and pipe fittings or tubing and compression fittings. Piping materials must be compatible with the process fluid.

Generally, tubing is easier to install and is capable of handling most service conditions provided that the correct fittings are used for terminating the tubing. Such fittings must be compatible with the tubing being run (i.e. of the same material).

Impulse lines should be designed to be as short as possible, and should be installed so that they are self draining for liquids and self venting for vapours or gases. If necessary, vent plugs or valves should be located at high points in liquid-filled lines and, similarly, drain plugs or valves should be fitted at low points in gas or vapour-filled lines. In any case, it should be ensured that there are provisions for isolation and depressurizing of instruments for maintenance purposes. Furthermore, filling plugs should be provided where lines are to be liquid sealed for chemical protection and, on services

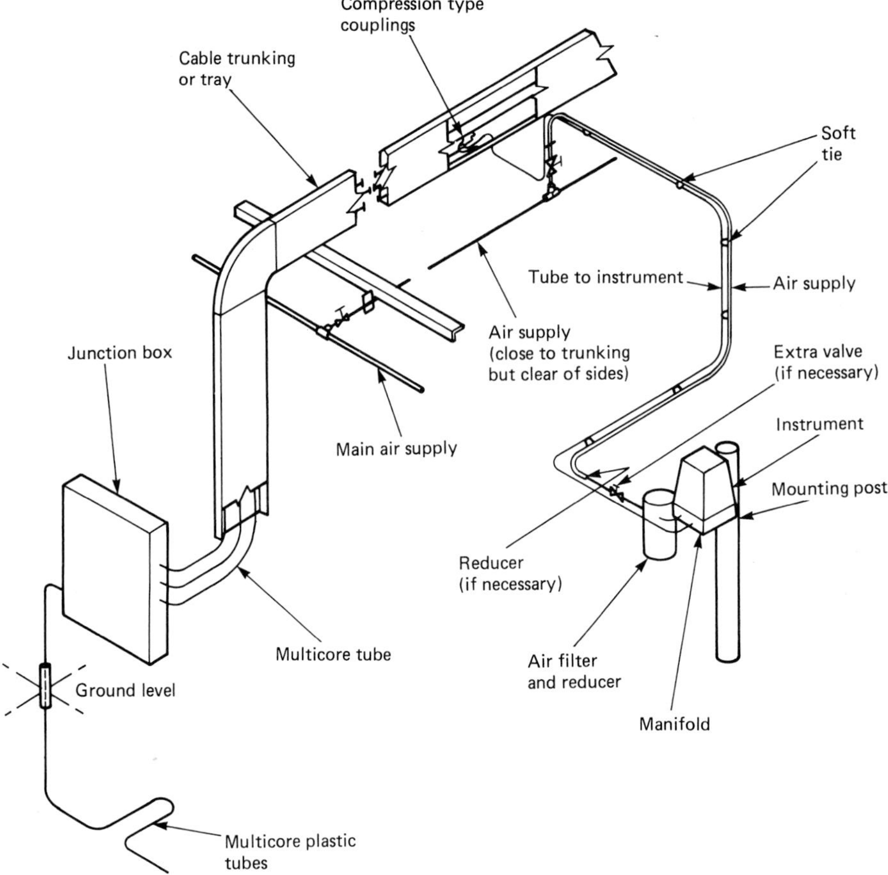

Figure 2.1 Typical field termination of pneumatic multitubes.

which are prone to plugging, rodding-out connections should be provided close to the tapping points.

2.6 Cabling

2.6.1 General requirements

Instrument cabling is generally run in multi-core cables from the control room to the plant area (either below or above ground) and then from field junction boxes in single pairs to the field measurement or actuating devices.

For distributed microprocessor systems the interconnection between the field and the control room is usually via duplicate data highways from remote located multiplexers or process interface units. Such duplicate highways would take totally independent routes from each other for plant security reasons.

Junction boxes must meet the hazardous area requirements applicable to their intended location and should be carefully positioned in order to minimize the lengths of individually run cables, always bearing in mind the potential hazards that could be created by fire.

Cable routes should be selected to meet the following requirements:

(1) They should be kept as short as possible.
(2) They should not cause any obstruction that would prohibit personnel or traffic access.
(3) They should not interfere with the accessibility for maintenance of other items of equipment.
(4) They should avoid hot environments or potential fire-risk areas.
(5) They should avoid areas where spillage is liable to occur or where escaping vapours or gases could present a hazard.

Cables should be supported for their whole run length by a cable tray or similar supporting steelwork. Cable trays should preferably be installed with their breadth in a vertical plane. The layout of cable trays on a plant should be carefully selected so that the minimum number of instruments in the immediate vicinity would be affected in the case of a local fire. Cable joints should be avoided other than in approved junction boxes or termination points. Cables entering junction boxes from below ground should be specially protected by fire-resistant ducting or something similar.

2.6.2 Cable types

There are three types of signal cabling generally under consideration, i.e.

(1) Instrument power supplies (above 50 V);
(2) High-level signals (between 6 and 50 V). This includes digital signals, alarm signals and high-level analogue signals (e.g. 4–20 mA).
(3) Low-level signals (below 5 V). This generally covers thermocouple compensating leads and resistance element leads.

Signal wiring should be made up in twisted pairs. Solid conductors are preferable so that there is no degradation of signal due to broken strands that may occur in stranded conductors. Where stranded conductors are used, crimped connectors should be fitted. Cable screens should be provided for instrument signals, particularly low-level analogue signals, unless the electronic system being used is deemed to have sufficient built-in 'noise' rejection. Further mechanical protection should be provided in the form of single-wire armour and PVC outer sheath, especially if the cables are installed in exposed areas, e.g. on open cable trays. Cables routed below ground in sand-filled trenches should also have an overall lead sheath if the area is prone to hydrocarbon or chemical spillage.

2.6.4 Cable segregation

Only signals of the same type should be contained within any one multicore cable. In addition, conductors forming part of intrinsically safe circuits should be contained in a multicore reserved solely for such circuits.

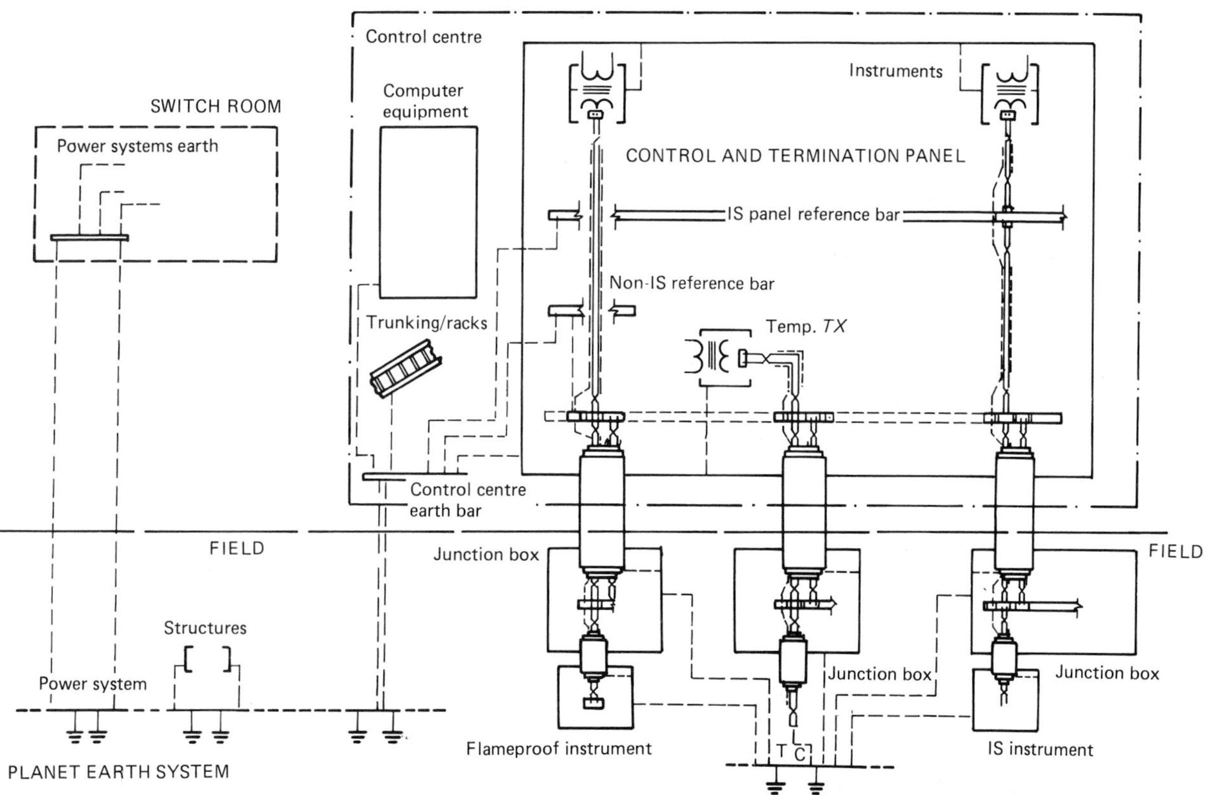

Figure 2.2 A typical control centre-earthing system.

When installing cables above or below ground they should be separated into groups according to the signal level and segregated with positive spacing between the cables. As a general rule, low-level signals should be installed furthest apart from instrument power supply cables with the high-level signal cables in between. Long parallel runs of dissimilar signals should be avoided as far as possible, as this is the situation where interference is most likely to occur.

Cables used for high-integrity systems such as emergency shutdown systems or data highways should take totally independent routes or should be positively segregated from other cables. Instrument cables should be run well clear of electrical power cables and should also, as far as possible, avoid noise-generating equipment such as motors. Cable crossings should always be made at right angles.

When cables are run in trenches, the routing of such trenches should be clearly marked with concrete cable markers on both sides of the trench, and the cables should be protected by earthenware or concrete covers.

2.7 Earthing

2.7.1 General requirements

Special attention must be paid to instrument earthing, particularly where field instruments are connected to a computer or microprocessor type control system. Where cable screens are used, earth continuity of screens must be maintained throughout the installation with the earthing at one point only, i.e. in the control room. At the field end the cable screen should be cut back and taped so that it is independent from earth. Intrinsically safe systems should be earthed through their own earth bar in the control room. Static earthing of instrument cases, panel frames, etc. should be connected to the electrical common plant earth. (See Figure 2.2 for a typical earthing system.)

Instrument earths should be wired to a common bus bar within the control centre and this should be connected to a remote earth electrode via an independent cable (preferably duplicated for security and test purposes). The resistance to earth, measured in the control room, should usually not exceed 1 Ω unless otherwise specified by a system manufacturer or by a certifying authority.

2.8 Testing and precommissioning

2.8.1 General

Before starting up a new installation the completed instrument installation must be fully tested to ensure that the equipment is in full working order. This testing normally falls into three phases, i.e. pre-installation testing; piping and cable testing; loop testing or precommissioning.

2.8.2 Pre-installation testing

This is the testing of each instrument for correct calibration and operation prior to its being installed in the field. Such testing is normally carried out in a workshop which is fully equipped for the purpose and should contain a means of generating the measured variable signals and also a method of accurately measuring the instrument input and output (where applicable). Test instruments should have a standard of accuracy better than the manufacturer's stated accuracy for the instruments being tested and should be regularly certified.

Instruments are normally calibration checked at five points (i.e. 0, 25, 50, 75 and 100 per cent) for both rising and falling signals, ensuring that the readings are within the manufacturer's stated tolerance.

After testing, instruments should be drained of any testing fluids that may have been used and, if necessary, blown through with dry air. Electronic instruments should be energized for a 24-h warm-up period prior to the calibration test being made. Control valves should be tested *in situ* after the pipework fabrication has been finished and flushing operations completed. Control valves should be checked for correct stroking at 0, 50 and 100 per cent open and at the same time the valves should be checked for correct closure action.

2.8.3 Piping and cable testing

This is an essential operation prior to loop testing.

2.8.3.1 Pneumatic lines

All air lines should be blown through with clean, dry air prior to final connection to instruments and they should also be pressure tested for a timed interval to ensure that they are leak free. This should be in the form of a continuity test from the field end to its destination (e.g. the control room).

2.8.3.2 Process piping

Impulse lines should also be flushed through and hydrostatically tested prior to connection of the instruments. All isolation valves or manifold valves should be checked for tight shutoff. On completion of hydrostatic tests, all piping should be drained and thoroughly dried out prior to reconnecting to any instruments.

2.8.3.3 Instrument cables

All instrument cables should be checked for continuity and insulation resistance before connection to any instrument or apparatus. The resistance should be checked core to core and core to earth. Cable screens must also be checked for continuity and insulation. Cable tests should comply with the requirements of Part 6 of the IEE Regulation for Electrical Installations (latest edition), or the rules and regulations with which the installation has to comply. Where cables are installed below ground, testing should be carried out before the trenches are back filled. Coaxial cables should be tested using sine-wave reflective testing techniques. As a prerequisite to cable testing it should be ensured that all cables and cable ends are properly identified.

2.8.4 Loop testing

The purpose of loop testing is to ensure that all instrumentation components in a loop are in full operational order when interconnected and are in a state ready for plant commissioning.

Prior to loop testing, inspection of the whole installation, including piping, wiring, mounting, etc., should be carried out to ensure that the installation is complete and that the work has been carried out in a professional manner. The control room panels or display stations must also be in a fully functional state.

Loop testing is generally a two-man operation, one in the field and one in the control room who should be equipped with some form of communication, e.g. field telephones or radio transceivers. Simulation signals should be injected at the field end equivalent to 0, 50 and 100 per cent of the instrument range and the loop function should be checked for correct operation in both rising and falling modes. All results should be properly documented on calibration or loop check sheets. All ancillary components in the loop should be checked at the same time.

Alarm and shutdown systems must also be systematically tested and all systems should be checked for 'fail-safe' operation including the checking of 'burn-out' features on thermocouple installations. At the loop-checking stage all ancillary work should be completed, such as setting zeros, filling liquid seals and fitting of accessories such as charts, ink, fuses, etc.

2.9 Plant commissioning

Commissioning is the bringing 'on-stream' of a process plant and the tuning of all instruments and controls to suit the process operational requirements. A plant, or section thereof is considered to be ready for commissioning when all instrument installations are mechanically complete and all testing, including loop testing, has been effected.

Before commissioning can be attempted it should be ensured that all air supplies are available and that all power supplies are fully functional, including any emergency standby supplies. It should also be ensured that all ancillary devices are operational, such as protective heating systems, air conditioning, etc. All control valve lubricators (when fitted) should be charged with the correct lubricant.

Commissioning is usually achieved by first commissioning the measuring system with any controller mode overridden. When a satisfactory measured variable is obtained, the responsiveness of a control system can be checked by varying the control valve position using the 'manual' control function. Once the system is seen to respond correctly and the required process variable reading is obtained it is then possible to switch to 'auto' in order to bring the controller function into action. The controller responses should then be adjusted to obtain optimum settings to suit the automatic operation of plant.

Alarm and shutdown systems should also be systematically brought into operation, but it is necessary to obtain the strict agreement of the plant operation supervisor before any overriding of trip systems is attempted or shutdown features are operated.

Finally, all instrumentation and control systems would need to be demonstrated to work satisfactorily before formal acceptance by the plant owner.

2.10 References

BS 6739, British Standard Code of Practice for Instrumentation in Process Control Systems: Installation Design and Practice (1986)

REGULATIONS FOR ELECTRICAL INSTILLATIONS 15TH ED. (1981) as issued by the Institution of Electrical Engineers

3 Sampling

J.G. GILES

3.1 Introduction

3.1.1 Importance of sampling

Any form of analysis instrument can only be as effective as its sampling system. Analysis instruments are out of commission more frequently due to troubles in the sampling system than to any other cause. Therefore time and care expended in designing and installing an efficient sampling system is well repaid in the saving of servicing time and dependability of instrument readings. The object of a sampling system is to obtain a truly representative sample of the solid, liquid or gas which is to be analysed, at an adequate and steady rate, and transport it without change to the analysis instrument, and all precautions necessary should be taken to ensure that this happens. Before the sample enters the instrument it may be necessary to process it to the required physical and chemical state, i.e. correct temperature, pressure, flow, purity, etc., without removing essential components. It is also essential to dispose of the sample and any reagent after analysis without introducing a toxic or explosive hazard. For this reason, the sample, after analysis, is continuously returned to the process at a suitable point or a sample-recovery and disposal system is provided.

3.1.2 Representative sample

It is essential that the sample taken should represent the mean composition of the process material. The methods used to overcome the problem of uneven sampling depend on the phase of the process sample, which may be in solid, liquid, gas or mixed-phase form.

3.1.2.1 Solids

When the process sample is solid in sheet form it is necessary to scan the whole sheet for a reliable measurement of the state of the sheet (e.g. thickness, density or moisture content). A measurement at one point is insufficient to give a representative value of the parameter being measured.

If the solid is in the form of granules or powder of uniform size a sample collected across a belt or chute and thoroughly mixed will give a reasonably representative sample. If measurement of density or moisture content of the solid can be made while it is in a vertical chute under a constant head, packing density problems may be avoided.

In some industries where the solids are transported as slurries it is possible to carry out the analysis directly on the slurry if a method is available to compensate for the carrier fluid and the velocities are high enough to ensure turbulent flow at the measurement point.

Variable-size solids are much more difficult to sample and specialist work on the subject should be consulted.

3.1.2.2 Liquids

When sampling liquid it is essential to ensure that either the liquid is turbulent in the process line or that there is at least 200 pipe diameters between the point of adding constituents and the sampling point. If neither is possible, a motorized or static mixer should be inserted into the process upstream of the sample point.

3.1.2.3 Gases

Gas samples must be thoroughly mixed and, as gas process lines are usually turbulent, the problem of finding a satisfactory sample point is reduced. The main exception is in large ducts such as furnace or boiler flues, where stratification can occur and the composition of the gas may vary from one point to another. In these cases special methods of sampling may be necessary such as multiple probes or long probes with multiple inlets in order to obtain a representative sample.

3.1.2.4 Mixed-phase sampling

Mixed phases such as liquid/gas mixtures or liquid/solids (i.e. slurries) are best avoided for any analytical method that involves taking a sample from the process. It is always preferable to use an in-line analysis method where this is possible.

3.1.3 Parts of analysis equipment

The analysis equipment consists of five main parts:

(1) Sample probe;
(2) Sample-transport system;
(3) Sample-conditioning equipment;
(4) The analysis instrument;
(5) Sample disposal.

3.1.3.1 Sample probe

This is the sampling tube that is used to withdraw the sample from the process.

3.1.3.2 Sample-transport system

This is the tube or pipe that transports the sample from the sample point to the sample-conditioning system.

3.1.3.3 Sample-conditioning system

This system ensures that the analyser receives the sample at the correct pressure and in the correct state to suit the analyser. This may require pressure increase (i.e. pumps) or reduction, filtration, cooling, drying and other equipment to protect the analyser from process upsets. Additionally, safety equipment and facilities for the introduction of calibration samples into the analyser may also be necessary.

3.1.3.4 The analysis instrument

This is the process analyser complete with the services such as power, air, steam, drain vents, carrier gases and signal conditioning that are required to make the instrument operational. (Analysis techniques are described in Volume 2 of *Instrument Technology*.)

3.1.3.5 Sample disposal

The sample flowing from the analyser and sample conditioning system must be disposed of safely. In many cases it is possible to vent gases to atmosphere or allow liquids to drain, but there are times when this is not satisfactory. Flammable or toxic gases must be vented in such a way that a hazard is not created. Liquids such as hydrocarbons can be collected in a suitable tank and pumped back into the process, whereas hazardous aqueous liquids may have to be treated before being allowed to flow into the drainage system.

3.1.4 Time lags

In any measuring instrument, particularly one which may be used with a controller, it is desirable that the time interval between occurrence of a change in the process fluid and its detection at the instrument should be as short as possible consistent with reliable measurement. In order to keep this time interval to a minimum the following points should be kept in mind.

3.1.4.1 Sample-transport line length

The distance between the sampling point and the analyser should be kept to the minimum. Where long sample transport lines are unavoidable a 'fast loop' may be used. The fast loop transports the sample at a flow rate higher than that required by the analyser, and the excess sample is either returned to the process, vented to atmosphere or allowed to flow to drain. The analyser is supplied with the required amount of sample from the fast loop through a short length of tubing.

3.1.4.2 Sampling components

Pipe, valves, filter and all sample-conditioning components should have the smallest volume consistent with a permissible pressure drop.

3.1.4.3 Pressure reduction

Gaseous samples should be filtered, and flow in the sample line at the lowest possible pressure, as the mass of gas in the system depends on the pressure of the gas as well as the volume in the system.

When sampling high-pressure gases the pressure-reducing valve must be situated at the sample point. This is necessary, because for a fixed mass flow rate of gas the response time will increase in proportion to the absolute pressure of the gas in the sample line (i.e. gas at 10 bar A will have a time lag five times that of gas at 2 bar A). This problem becomes more acute when the sample is a liquid which has to be vaporized for analysis (e.g. liquid butane or propane).

The ratio of volume of gas to volume of liquid can be in the region of 250:1, as is the case for propane. It is therefore essential to vaporize the liquid at the sample point and then treat it as a gas sample from then on.

3.1.4.4 Typical equations

(1) $t = \frac{L}{S}$

t = time lag

S = velocity (m/s)
L = line length (m)

(2) General gas law for ideal gases:

$$\frac{pv}{T} = \frac{8314 \times W}{10^5 \times M}$$

p = pressure
T = abs. temperature (K)
v = volume (l)
W = mass (g)
M = molecular weight

(3) Line volume:

$$\frac{\pi d^2}{4} = V_{\text{I}}$$

d = internal diameter of tube (mm)
V_{I} = volume (ml/m)

(4)

$$t = \frac{6L \times V_{\text{I}}}{100F}$$

L = line length (m)
V_{I} = internal volume of line (ml/m)
F = sample flow rate (l/min)
t = time lag (s)

(For an example of a fast loop calculation see Section 3.3.2.2 (Table 3.1.)

3.1.4.5 Useful data

Internal volume per metre (V_{I}) of typical sample lines:

⅛ in OD × 0.035 wall	= 1.5 ml/m
¼ in OD × 0.035 wall	= 16.4 ml/m
⅜ in OD × 0.035 wall	= 47.2 ml/m
½ in OD × 0.065 wall	= 69.4 ml/m
½ in nominal bore steel pipe (extra strong) (13.88 mm ID)	= 149.6 ml/m
3 mm OD × 1 mm wall	= 0.8 ml/m
6 mm OD × 1 mm wall	= 12.6 ml/m
8 mm OD × 1 mm wall	= 28.3 ml/m
10 mm OD × 1 m wall	= 50.3 ml/m
12 mm OD × 1.5 mm wall	= 63.6 ml/m

3.1.5 Construction materials

Stainless steel (Type 316 or 304) has become one of the most popular materials for the construction of sample systems due to its high resistance to corrosion, low surface adsorption (especially moisture), wide operating temperature range, high-pressure capability and the fact that it is easily obtainable. Care must be taken when there are materials in the sample which cause corrosion, such as chlorides and sulphides, in which case it is necessary to change to more expensive materials such as Monel.

When atmospheric sampling is carried out for trace constituents, teflon tubing is frequently used, as the surface adsorption of the compounds is less than stainless steel, but it is necessary to check that the compound to be measured does not diffuse through the wall of the tubing.

For water analysis (e.g. pH and conductivity) it is possible to use plastic (such as PVC or ABS) components, although materials such as Kunifer 10 (copper 90%, nickel 10%) are increasing in popularity when chlorides (e.g. salt water) are present, as they are totally immune to chloride corrosion.

3.2 Sample system components

3.2.1 Probes

The most important function of a probe is to obtain the sample from the most representative point (or points) in the process line.

3.2.1.1 Sample probe

A typical probe of this type for sampling all types of liquid and gases at low pressure is shown in Figure 3.1. It can be seen that the probe which is made of 21 mm OD (11.7 mm ID) stainless steel pipe extends to the centre of the line being sampled. However, if the latter is more than 500 mm OD the probe intrusion is kept at 250 mm to avoid vibration in use.

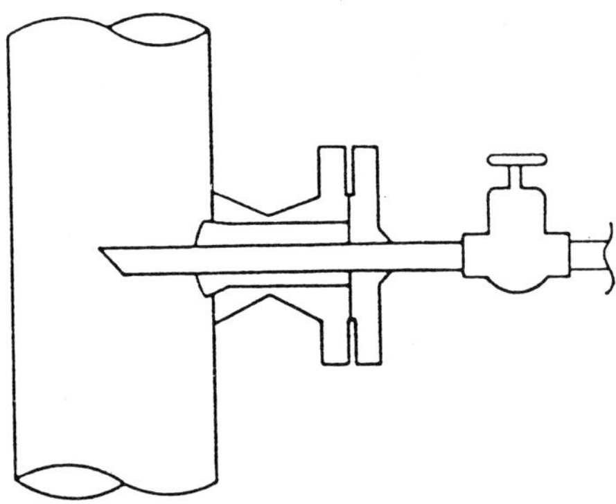

Figure 3.1 Sample probe (courtesy Ludlam Sysco).

3.2.1.2 Small-volume sample probe

This probe is used for sampling liquids which require

to be vaporized or for high-pressure gases (Figure 3.2). Typically, a 6 mm OD × 2 mm ID tube is inserted through the centre of a probe of the type described in section 3.2.1.1. The probe may be withdrawn through the valve for cleaning.

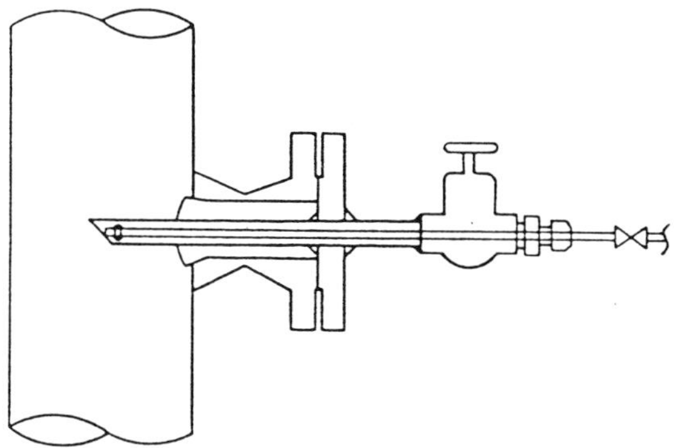

Figure 3.2 Small-volume sample probe (courtesy Ludlam Sysco).

3.2.1.3 Furnace gas probes

Low temperature probe Figure 3.3 shows a gas sampling probe with a ceramic outside filter for use in temperatures up to 400°C.

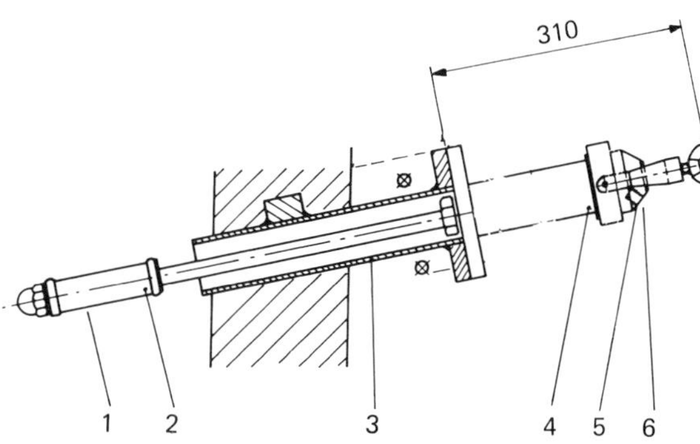

Figure 3.3 Gas-sampling probe (courtesy Hartmann and Braun). 1 Gas intake; 2 ceramic intake filter; 3 bushing tube with flange; 4 case with outlet filter; 5 internal screwthread; 6 gas outlet.

Water-wash probe This probe system is used for sampling furnace gases with high dust content at high temperature (up to 1600°C). (Figure 3.4). The wet gas sampling probe is water cooled and self priming. The water/gas mixture passes from the probe down to a water trap, where the gas and water are separated. The gas leaves the trap at a pressure of approximately 40 m bar, and precautions should be taken to avoid condensation in the analyser, either by ensuring that the analyser is at a higher temperature than the water trap or by passing the sample gas through a sample cooler at 5°C to reduce the humidity.

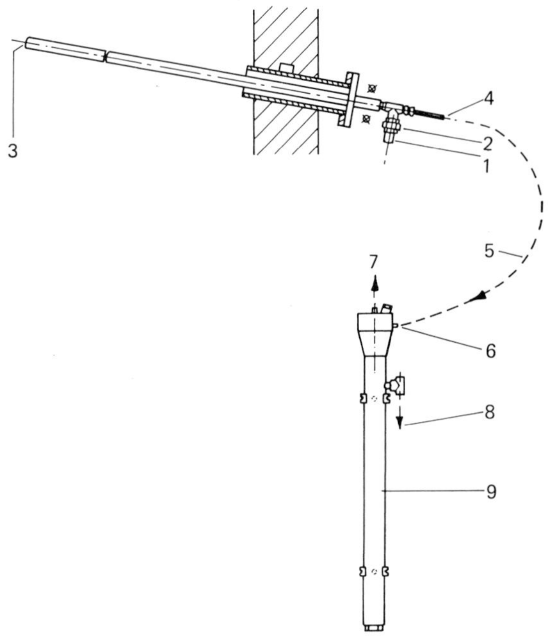

Figure 3.4 Water-wash probe (courtesy Hartmann and Braun). 1 Water intake; 2 water filter; 3 gas intake; 4 gas–water outlet; 5 connecting hose; 6 gas–water intake; 7 gas outlet; 8 water outlet; 9 water separator.

Note that this probe is not suitable for the measurement of water-soluble gases such as CO_2, SO_2 or H_2S.

Steam ejector The steam ejector illustrated in Figure 3.5 can be used for sample temperatures up to 180°C and, because the condensed steam dilutes the condensate present in the flue gas, the risk of corrosion of the sample lines when the steam/gas sample cools to the dew point is greatly reduced.

Dry steam is supplied to the probe and then ejected through a jet situated in the mouth of a Venturi. The flow of steam causes sample gas to be drawn into the probe. The steam and gas pass out of the probe and down the sample line to the analyser system at a positive pressure. The flow of steam through the sample line prevents the build-up of any corrosive condensate.

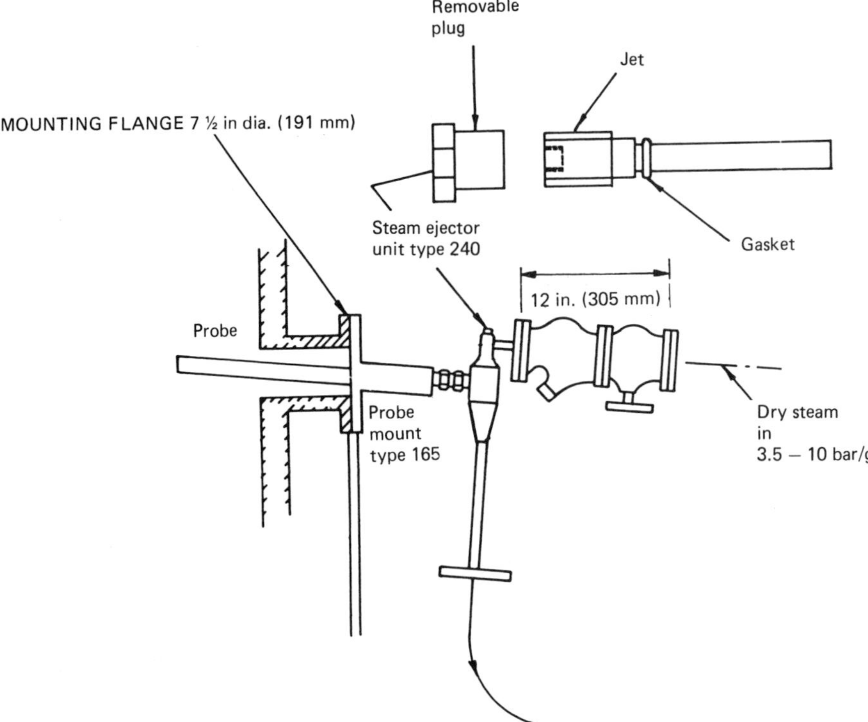

Figure 3.5 Steam ejection probe (courtesy Servomex).

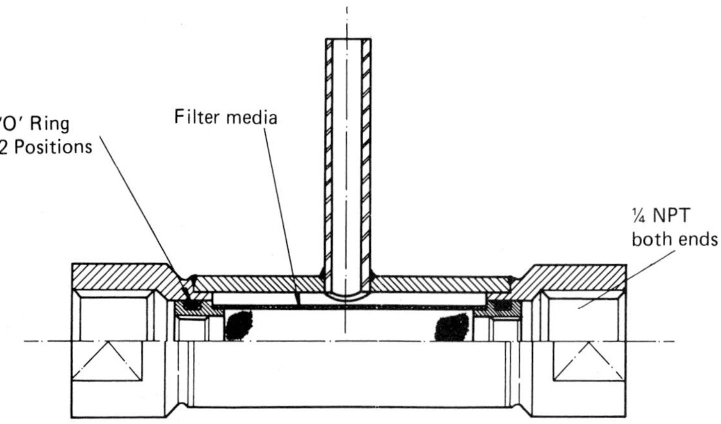

Figure 3.6 In-line filter (courtesy Microfiltrex).

3.2.2 Filters

3.2.2.1 'Y' strainers

'Y' strainers are available in stainless steel, carbon steel and bronze. They are ideal for preliminary filtering of samples before pumps or at sample points to prevent line scale entering sample lines. Filtration sizes are available from 75 to 400 μ (200 to 40 mesh). The main application for this type of filter is for liquids and steam.

3.2.2.2 In-line filters

This design of filter is normally used in a fast loop configuration and is self cleaning (Figure 3.6). Filtration is through a stainless steel or a ceramic element. Solid particles tend to be carried straight on in the sample stream so that maintenance time is very low. Filtration sizes are available from 150 μ (100 mesh) down to 5 μ. It is suitable for use with liquids or gases.

3.2.2.3 Filters with disposable glass microfibre element

These filters are available in a wide variety of sizes and porosities (Figure 3.7). Bodies are available in stainless steel, aluminium or plastic. Elements are made of glass microfibre and are bonded with either resin or fluorocarbon. The fluorocarbon-bonded filter is particularly useful for low-level moisture applications because of the low adsorption/desorption characteristic.

The smallest filter in this range has an internal volume of only 19 ml and is therefore suitable when a fast response time is required.

3.2.2.4 Miniature in-line filter

These are used for filtration of gases prior to pressure reduction and are frequently fitted as the last component in the sample system to protect the analyser (Figure 3.8).

Figure 3.7 Filter with disposable element (courtesy Balston).

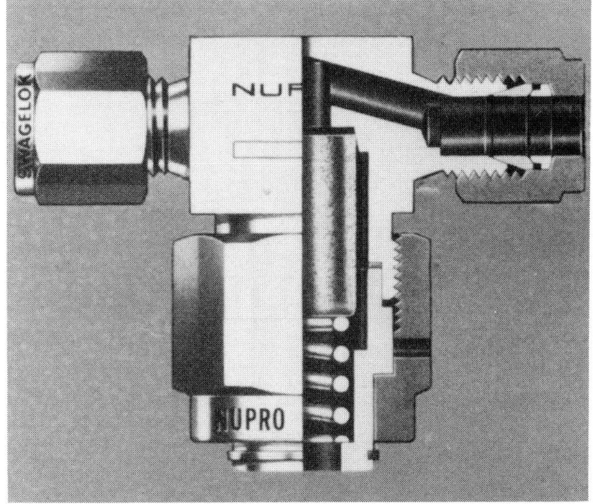

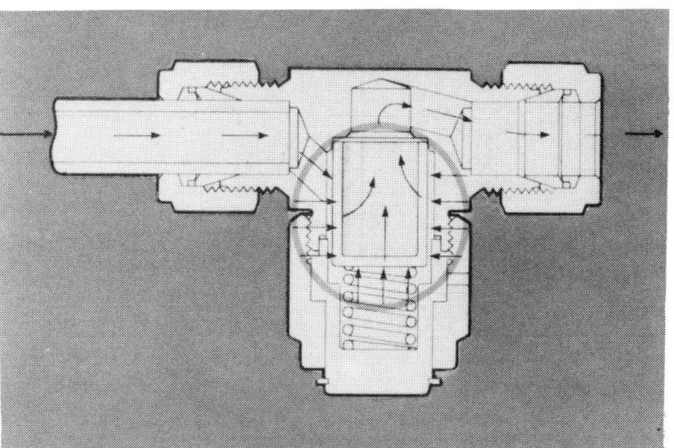

Figure 3.8 Miniature in-line filter (courtesy Nupro).

3.2.2.5 Manual self-cleaning filter

This type of filter works on the principle of edge filtration using discs usually made of stainless steel and fitted with a manual cleaning system (Figure 3.9). The filter is cleaned by rotating a handle which removes any deposits from the filter element while the sample is flowing. The main uses are for filtration of liquids where filter cleaning must be carried out regularly without the system being shut down; it is especially suitable for waxy material which can rapidly clog up normal filter media.

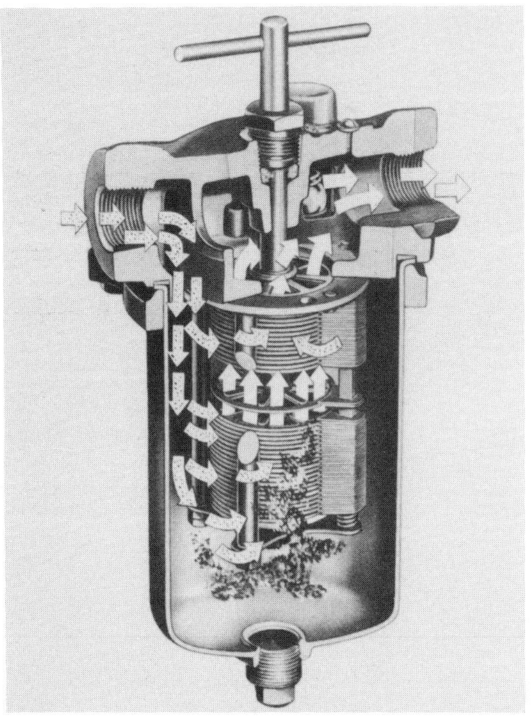

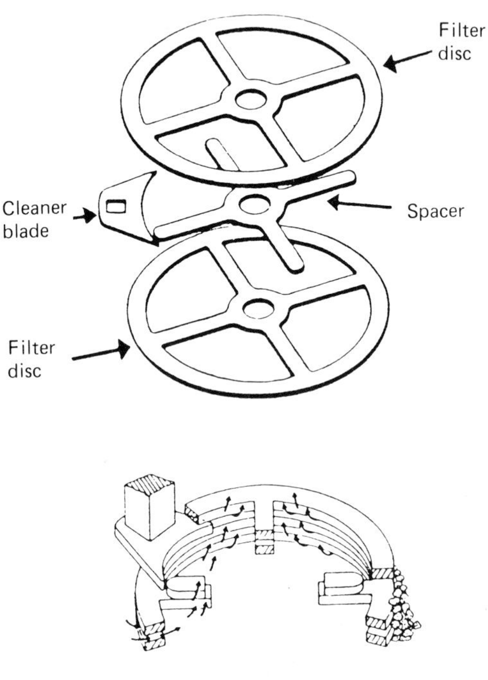

Figure 3.9 Manual self-cleaning filter (courtesy AMF CUNO).

3.2.3 Coalescers

Coalescers are a special type of filter for separating water from oil or oil from water (Figure 3.10). The incoming sample flows from the centre of a specially treated filter element through to the outside. In so doing, the diffused water is slowed down and coalesced, thus forming droplets which, when they reach the outer surface, drain downwards as the water is denser than the hydrocarbon. A bypass stream is taken from the bottom of the coalescer to remove the water. The dry hydrocarbon stream is taken from the top of the coalescer.

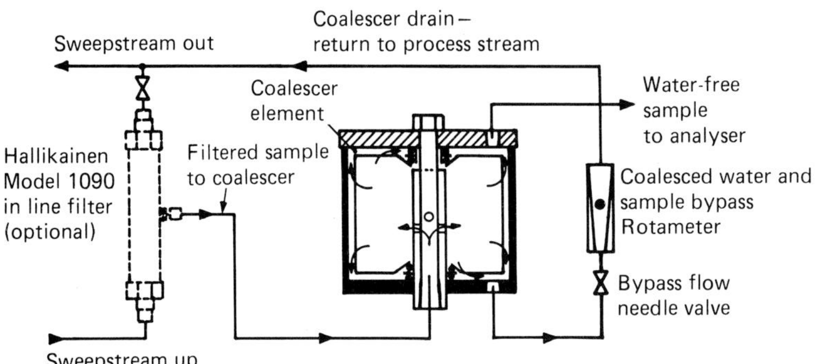

Figure 3.10 Coalescer (courtesy Fluid Data).

3.2.4 Coolers

3.2.4.1 Air coolers

These are usually used to bring the sample gas temperature close to ambient before feeding into the analyser.

3.2.4.2 Water-jacketed coolers

These are used to cool liquid and gas samples and are available in a wide range of sizes (Figure 3.11).

3.2.4.3 Refrigerated coolers

These are used to reduce the temperature of a gas to a fixed temperature (e.g. +5°C) in order to condense the water out of a sample prior to passing the gas into the analyser. Two types are available; one with an electrically driven compressor type refrigerator and another using a Peltier cooling element. The compressor type has a large cooling capacity whereas the Peltier type, being solid state, needs less maintenance.

3.2.5 Pumps, gas

Whenever gaseous samples have to be taken from sample points which are below the pressure required by the analyser a sample pump of some type is required. The pumps that are available can broadly be divided into two groups:

(1) The eductor or aspirator type; and
(2) The mechanical type.

3.2.5.1 Eductor or aspirator type

All of these types of pump operate on the principle of using the velocity of one fluid which may be liquid or gas to induce the flow in the sample gas. The pump may be fitted before or after the analyser, depending on the application. A typical application for a water-operated aspirator (similar to a laboratory vacuum pump) is for taking a sample of flue gas for oxygen measurement. In this case the suction port of the aspirator is connected directly to the probe via a sample line and the water/gas mixture from the outlet feeds into a separator arranged to supply the sample gas to the analyser at a positive pressure of about 300 mm water gauge.

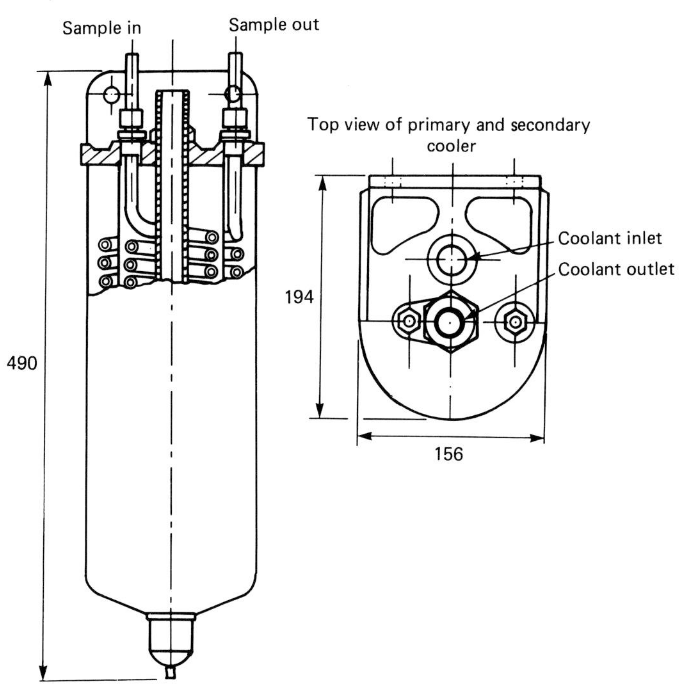

Figure 3.11 Water-jacketed cooler (courtesy George E. Lowe). Dimensions are shown in mm.

In cases where water will affect the analysis it is sometimes possible to place the eductor or aspirator after the analyser and draw the sample through the system. In these cases the eductor may be supplied with steam, air or water to provide the propulsive power.

3.2.5.2 Mechanical gas pumps

There are two main types of mechanical gas pump available:

(1) Rotary pumps; and
(2) Reciprocating piston or diaphragm pump.

Rotary pumps Rotary pumps can be divided into two categories, the rotary piston and the rotating fan types, but the latter is very rarely used as a sampling pump.

The rotary piston pump is manufactured in two configurations. The Rootes type has two pistons of equal size which rotate inside a housing with the synchronizing carried out by external gears. The rotary vane type is similar to those used extensively as vacuum pumps. The Rootes type is ideal where very large flow rates are required and, because there is a clearance between the pistons and the housing, it is possible to operate them on very dirty gases.

The main disadvantage of the rotary vane type is that, because there is contact between the vanes and the housing, lubrication is usually required, and this may interfere with the analysis.

Reciprocating piston and diaphragm pump Of these two types the diaphragm pump has become the most popular. The main reason for this is the improvement in the types of material available for the diaphragms and the fact that there are no piston seals to leak. The pumps are available in a wide variety of sizes from the miniature units for portable personnel protection analysers to large heavy duty industrial types.

A typical diaphragm pump (Figure 3.12) for boosting the pressure of the gas into the analyser could have an all stainless steel head with a Terylene reinforced viton diaphragm and viton valves. This gives the pump a very long service life on critical hydrocarbon applications.

Many variations are possible; for example, a Teflon-coated diaphragm can be fitted where viton

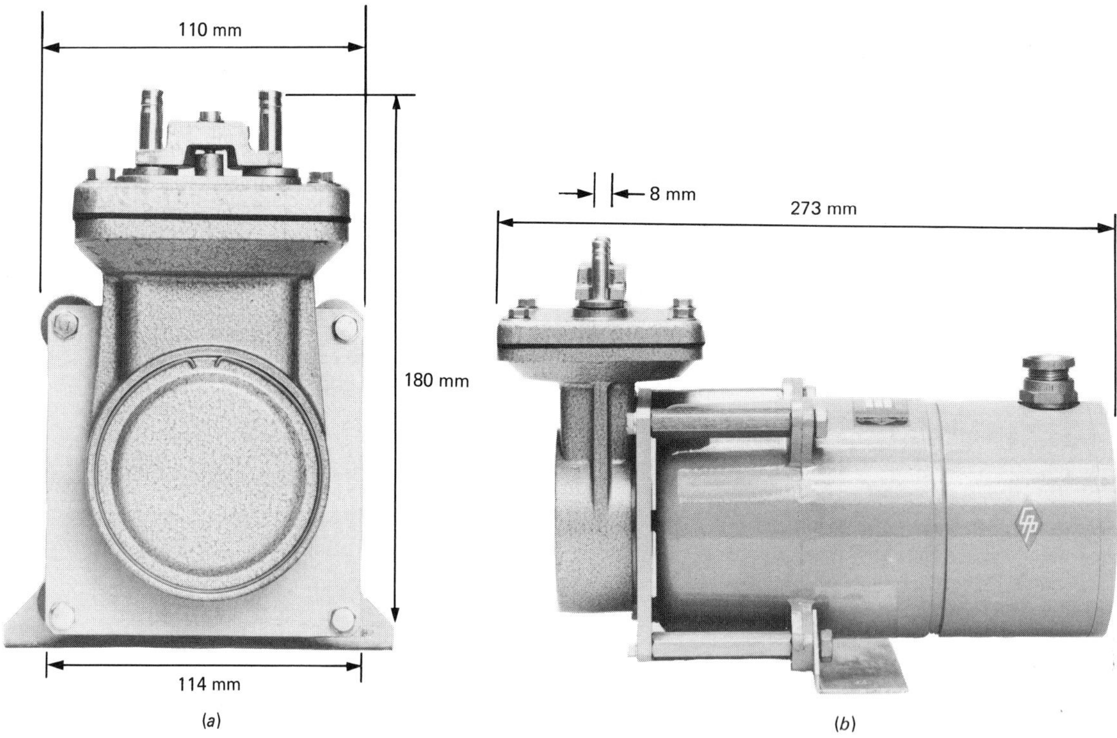

Figure 3.12 Diaphragm pump (courtesy Charles Austen Pumps).

may not be compatible with the sample and heaters may be fitted to the head to keep the sample above the dew point.

The piston pump is still used in certain cases where high accuracy is required in the flow rate (for example, gas blending) to produce specific gas mixtures. In these cases the pumps are usually operated immersed in oil so that the piston is well lubricated and there is no chance of gas leaks to and from the atmosphere.

3.2.6 Pumps: liquid

There are two situations where pumps are required in liquid sample systems:

(1) Where the pressure at the analyser is too low because either the process line pressure is too low, or the pressure drop in the sample line is too high or a combination of both.
(2) When the process sample has to be returned to the same process line after analysis.

The two most common types of pumps used for sample transfer are:

(1) Centrifugal (including turbine pump);
(2) Positive displacement (e.g. gear, peristaltic, etc.).

3.2.6.1 Centrifugal

The centrifugal and turbine pumps are mainly used when high flow rates of low-viscosity liquids are required. The turbine pumps are similar to centrifugal pumps but have a special impellor device which produces a considerably higher pressure than the same size centrifugal. In order to produce high pressures using a centrifugal pump there is a type available which has a gearbox to increase the rotor speed to above 20 000 rev/min.

3.2.6.2 Positive-displacement pumps

Positive-displacement pumps have the main characteristic of being constant flow devices. Some of these are specifically designed for metering purposes where an accurate flow rate must be maintained (e.g. process viscometers). They can take various forms:

(1) Gear pump;
(2) Rotary vane pump;
(3) Peristaltic pump.

Gear pumps Gear pumps are used mainly on high-viscosity products where the sample has some lubricating properties. They can generate high pressures for low flow rates and are used extensively for hydrocarbon samples ranging from diesel oil to the heaviest fuel oils.

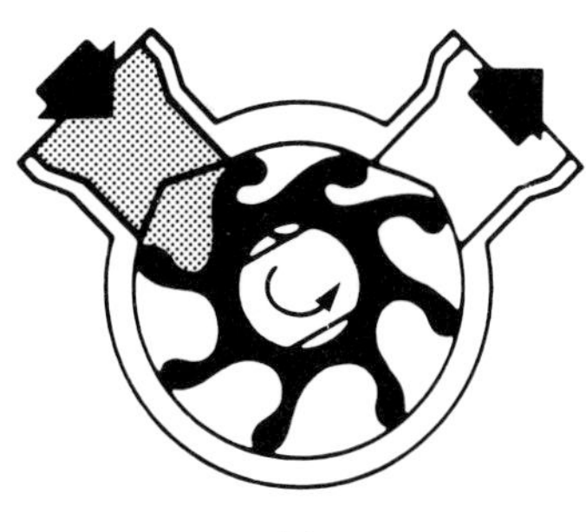

(a)

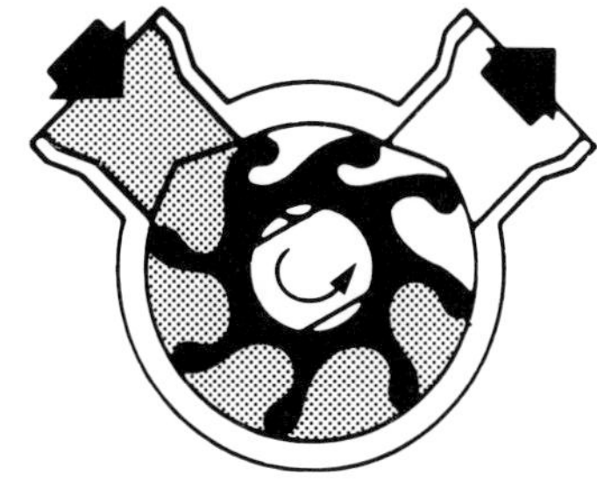

(b)

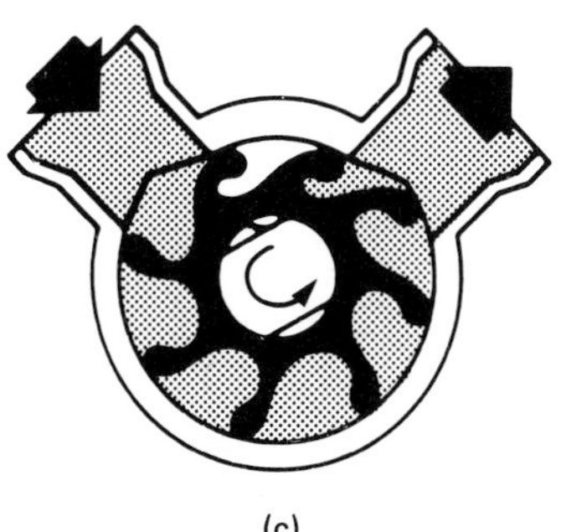

(c)

Figure 3.13 Flexible impeller pump (courtesy ITT Jabsco). (a) Upon leaving the offset plate the impeller blade straightens and creates a vacuum, drawing in liquid—instantly priming the pump. (b) As the impeller rotates it carries the liquid through the pump from the intake to outlet port, each successive blade drawing in liquid. (c) When the flexible blades again contact the offset plate they bend with a squeezing action which provides a continuous, uniform discharge of liquid.

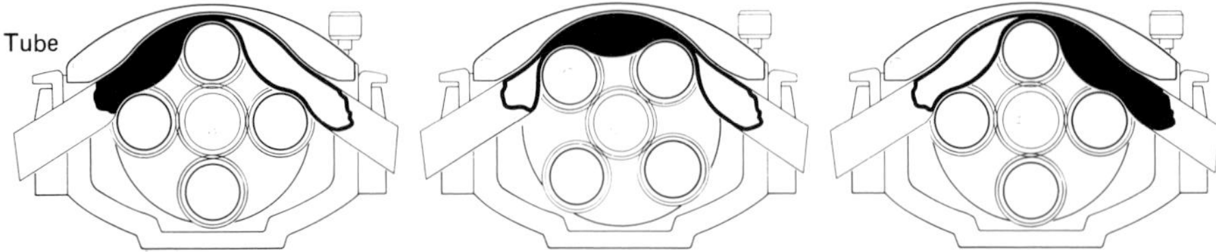

Figure 3.14 Peristaltic pump (courtesy Watson-Marlow). The advancing roller occludes the tube which, as it recovers to its normal size, draws in fluid which is trapped by the next roller (in the second part of the cycle) and expelled from the pump (in the third part of the cycle). This is the peristaltic flow-inducing action.

Rotary vane pumps These pumps are of two types, one having rigid vanes (usually metal) and the other fitted with a rotor made of an elastomer such as nitrile rubber or viton. The metal vane pumps have characteristics similar to the gear pumps described above, but can be supplied with a method of varying the flow rate externally while the pump is operating.

Pumps manufactured with the flexible vanes (Figure 3.13) are particularly suitable for pumping aqueous solutions and are available in a wide range of sizes but are only capable of producing differential pressures of up to 2 bar.

Peristaltic pumps Peristaltic pumps are used when either accurate metering is required or it is important that no contamination should enter the sample. As can be seen from Figure 3.14, the only material in contact with the sample is the special plastic tubing, which may be replaced very easily during routine servicing.

3.2.7 Flow measurement and indication

Flow measurement on analyser systems falls into three main categories:

(1) Measuring the flow precisely where the accuracy of the analyser depends on it;
(2) Measuring the flow where it is necessary to know the flow rate but it is not critical (e.g. fast loop flow);
(3) Checking that there is flow present but measurement is not required (e.g. cooling water for heat exchangers).

It is important to decide which category the flowmeter falls into when writing the specification, as the prices vary over a wide range, depending on the precision required.

The types of flowmeter available will be mentioned but not the construction or method of operation, as this is covered in *Instrument Technology*, Volume 1, Chapter 1.

3.2.7.1 Variable-orifice meters

The variable-orifice meter is extensively used in analyser systems because of its simplicity, and there are two main types.

Glass tube This type is the most common as the position of the float is read directly on the scale attached to the tube and it is available calibrated for liquids or gases. The high-precision versions are available with an accuracy of ±1 per cent full-scale deflection (FSD), whereas the low-priced units have a typical accuracy of ±5 per cent FSD.

Metal tube The metal tube type is used mainly on liquids for high-pressure duty or where the liquid is flammable or hazardous. A good example is the fast loop of a hydrocarbon analyser. The float has a magnet embedded in it and the position is detected by an external follower system. The accuracy of metal tube flowmeters varies from ±10 per cent FSD to ±2 per cent FSD, depending on the type and whether individual calibration is required.

3.2.7.2 Differential-pressure devices

On sample systems these normally consist of an orifice plate or preset needle valve to produce the differential pressure, and are used to operate a gauge or liquid-filled manometer when indication is required or a differential pressure switch when used as a flow alarm.

3.2.7.3 Spinner or vane-type indicators

In this type the flow is indicated either by the rotation of a spinner or by the deflection of a vane by the fluid. It is ideal for duties such as cooling water flow, where it is essential to know that a flow is present but the actual flow rate is of secondary importance.

3.2.8 Pressure reduction and vaporization

The pressure-reduction stage in a sample system is often the most critical, because not only must the reduced pressure be kept constant but also provision must be made to ensure that under faulty conditions dangerously high pressures cannot be produced. Pressure reduction can be carried out in a variety of ways.

3.2.8.1 Simple needle valve

This is capable of giving good flow control if upstream and downstream pressures are constant.

Advantage: Simplicity and low cost.
Disadvantage: Any downstream blockage will allow pressure to rise.

They are only practical if downstream equipment can withstand upstream pressure safely.

3.2.8.2 Needle valve with liquid-filled lute

This combination is used to act as a pressure stabilizer and safety system combined. The maintained pressure will be equal to the liquid head when the needle valve flow is adjusted until bubbles are produced (Figure 3.15).

It is essential to choose a liquid which is not affected by sample gas and also does not evaporate in use and cause a drop in the controlled pressure.

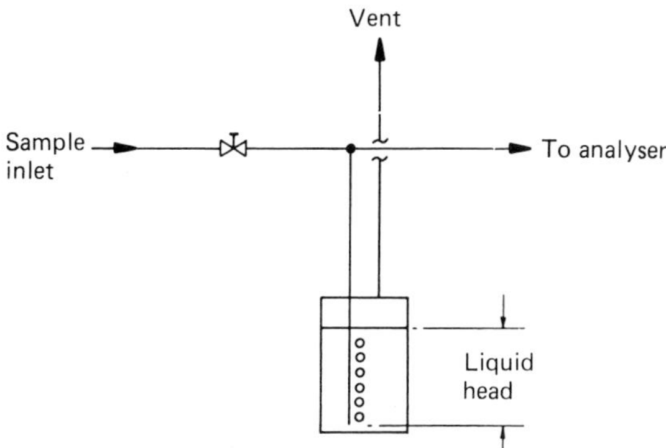

Figure 3.15 Lute-type pressure stabilizer (courtesy Ludlam Sysco).

3.2.8.3 Diaphragm-operated pressure controller

These regulators are used when there is either a very large reduction in pressure required or the downstream pressure must be accurately controlled (Figure 3.16). They are frequently used on gas cylinders to provide a controllable low-pressure gas supply.

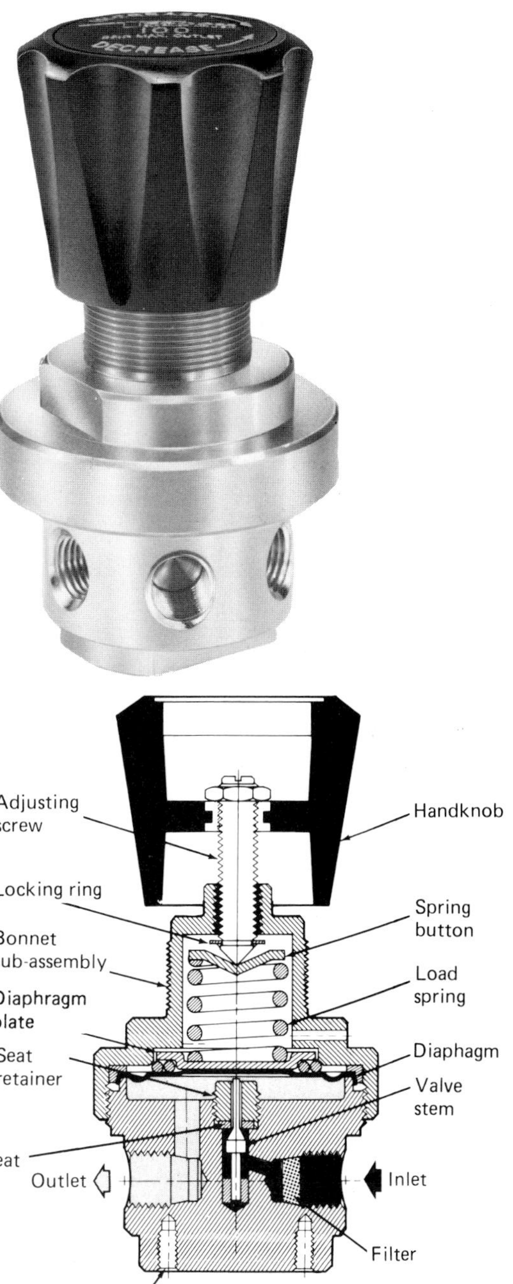

Figure 3.16 Diaphragm-operated pressure controller (courtesy Tescom).

3.2.8.4 Vaporization

There are cases when a sample in the liquid phase at high pressure has to be analysed in the gaseous phase. The pressure reduction and vaporization can be carried out in a specially adapted diaphragm-operated pressure controller as detailed above, where provision is made to heat the complete unit to replace the heat lost by the vaporization.

3.2.9 Sample lines, tube and pipe fitting

3.2.9.1 Sample lines

Sample lines can be looked at from two aspects: first, the materials of construction, which are covered in Section 3.1.5, and, second, the effect of the sample line on the process sample, which is detailed below.

The most important consideration is that the material chosen must not change the characteristics of the sample during its transportation to the analyser. There are two main ways in which the sample line material can affect the sample.

Adsorption and desorption Adsorption and desorption occur when molecules of gas or liquid are retained and discharged from the internal surface of the sample line material at varying rates. This has the effect of delaying the transport of the adsorbed material to the analyser and causing erroneous results.

Water and hydrogen sulphide at low levels are two common measurements where this problem is experienced. An example is when measuring water at a level of 10 ppm in a sample stream, where copper tubing has an adsorption/desorption which is twenty times greater than stainless steel tubing, and hence copper tubing would give a very sluggish response at the analyser.

Where this problem occurs it is possible to reduce the effects in the following ways:

(1) Careful choice of sample tube material;
(2) Raising the temperature of the sample line;
(3) Cleaning the sample line to ensure that it is absolutely free of impurities such as traces of oil;
(4) Increasing the sample flow rate to reduce the time the sample is in contact with the sample line material.

Permeability Permeability is the ability of gases to pass through the wall of the sample tubing. Two examples are:

(1) Polytetrafluoroethylene (PTFE) tubing is permeable to water and oxygen.
(2) Plasticized polyvinyl chloride (PVC) tubing is permeable to the smaller hydrocarbon molecules such as methane.

Permeability can have two effects on the analysis:

(1) External gases getting into the sample such as when measuring low-level oxygen using PTFE tubing. The results would always be high due to the ingress of oxygen from the air.
(2) Sample gases passing outwards through the tubing, such as when measuring a mixed hydrocarbon stream using plasticized PVC. The methane concentration would always be too low.

3.2.9.2 Tube, pipe and method of connection

Definition

(1) Pipe is normally rigid and the sizes are based on the nominal bore.

    Typical materials:
    Metallic: carbon steel, brass, etc.
    Plastic: UPVC, ABS, etc.

(2) Tubing is normally bendable or flexible, and the sizes are based on the outside diameter and wall thickness.

    Typical materials:
    Metallic: carbon steel, brass, etc.
    Plastic: UPVC, ABS, etc.

Methods of joining

Pipe (metallic):	(1) Screwed (2) Flanged (3) Welded (4) Brazed or soldered
Pipe (plastic):	(1) Screwed (2) Flanged (3) Welded (by heat or use of solvents)
Tubing (metallic):	(1) Welding (2) Compression fitting (3) Flanged
Tubing (plastic):	(1) Compression (2) Push-on fitting (especially for plastic tubing) with hose clip where required to withstand pressure.

General The most popular method of connecting metal tubing is the compression fitting, as it is capable of withstanding pressures up to the limit of the tubing itself and is easily dismantled for servicing as well as being obtainable manufactured in all the most common materials.

3.3 Typical sample systems

3.3.1 Gases

3.3.1.1 High-pressure sample to a process chromatograph

The example taken is for a chromatograph analysing the composition of a gas which is in the vapour phase at 35 bar (Figure 3.17). This is the case described in section 3.1.4.3, where it is necessary to reduce the pressure of the gas at the sample point in order to obtain a fast response time with a minimum wastage of process gas.

The sample is taken from the process line using a low-volume sample probe (section 3.2.1.2) and then flows immediately into a pressure reducing valve to drop the pressure to a constant 1.5 bar, which is measured on a local pressure gauge. A pressure relief valve set to relieve at 4 bar is connected at this point to protect downstream equipment if the pressure-reducing valve fails.

After pressure reduction the sample flows in small-bore tubing (6 mm OD) to the main sample system next to the analyser, where it flows through a filter (such as shown in section 3.2.2.3) to the sample selection system.

The fast loop flows out of the bottom of the filter body, bypassing the filter element, and then through a needle valve and flowmeter to an atmospheric vent on a low-pressure process line.

The stream selection system shown in Figure 3.17 is called a block and bleed system, and always has two or more three-way valves between each stream and the analyser inlet. The line between two of the valves on the stream which is not in operation is vented to atmosphere, so guaranteeing that the stream being analysed cannot be contaminated by any of the other streams. A simple system without block and bleed valve is described in section 3.3.2.1 below.

After the stream-selection system the sample flows through a needle valve flowmeter and a miniature in-line filter to the analyser sample inlet. The analyser sample outlet on this system flows to the atmospheric vent line.

3.3.1.2 Furnace gas using steam-injection probe inside the flue

This system utilizes a Venturi assembly located inside the flue (Figure 3.18). High-pressure steam enters the Venturi via a separate steam tube and a low-pressure region results inside the flue at the probe head. A mixture of steam and sample gas

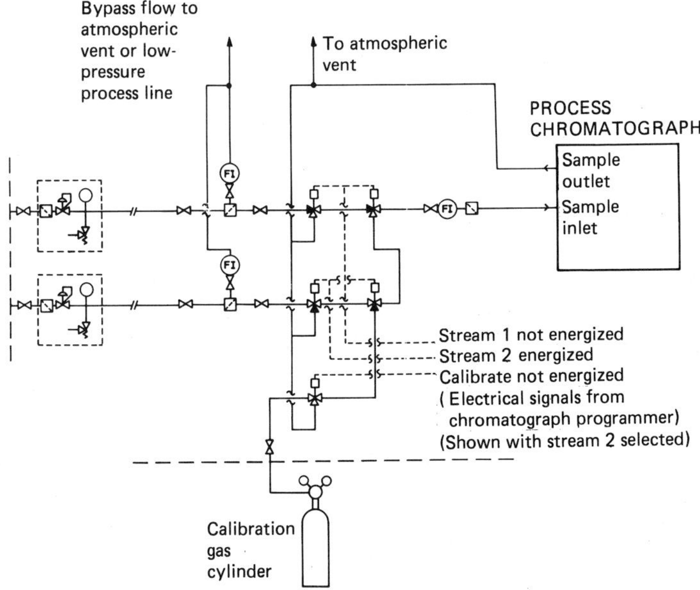

Figure 3.17 Schematic: high-pressure gas sample to chromatograph (courtesy Ludlam Sysco).

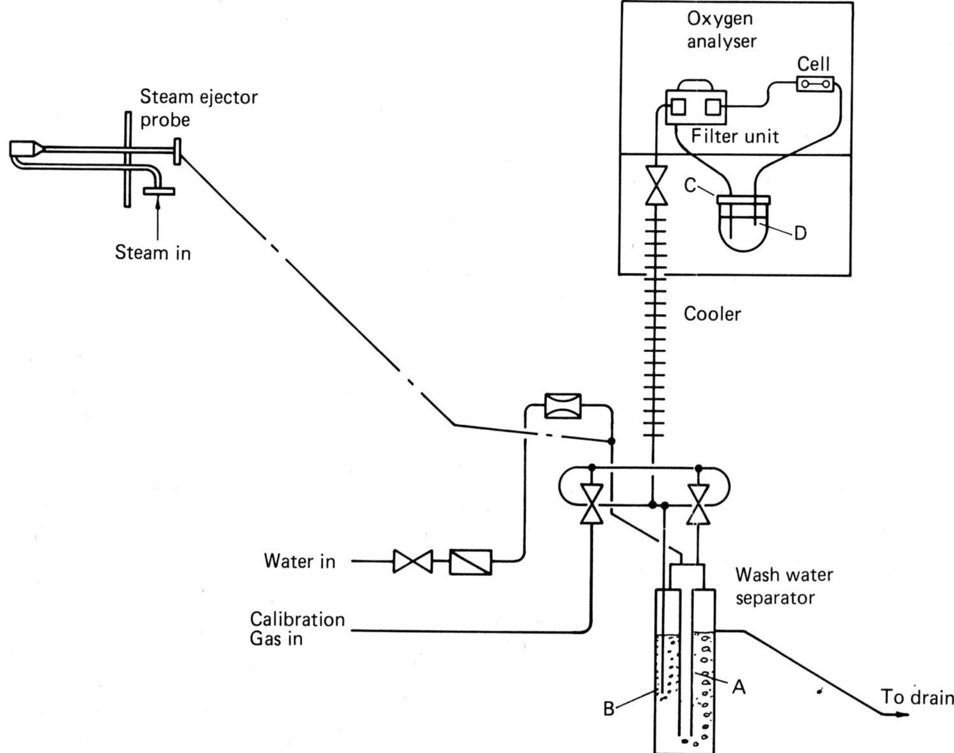

Figure 3.18 Schematic: furnace gas sampling (courtesy Servomex).

passes down the sample line. Butyl or EDPDM rubber-lined steam hose is recommended for sample lines, especially when high-sulphur fuels are used. This will minimize the effects of corrosion.

At the bottom end of the sample line the sample gas is mixed with a constant supply of water. The gas is separated from the water and taken either through a ball valve or a solenoid valve towards the sample loop, which minimizes the dead volume between each inlet valve and the analyser inlet.

The water, dust, etc. passes out of a dip leg (A) and to drain. It is assumed that the gas leaves the separator saturated with water at the temperature of the water. In the case of a flue gas system on a ship operating, for example, in the Red Sea this could be at 35°C. The system is designed to remove condensate that may be formed because of lower temperatures existing in downstream regions of the sample system.

At the end of the loop there is a second dip leg (B) passing into a separator. A 5 cm water differential pressure is produced by the difference in depth of the two dip legs, so there is always a continuous flow of gas round the loop and out to vent via dipleg (B).

The gas passes from the loop to a heat exchanger, which is designed so that the gas leaving the exchanger is within 1 K of the air temperature. This means that the gas leaving the heat exchanger can be at 36°C and saturated with water vapour. The gas now passes into the analyser which is maintained at 60°C.

The gas arrives in the analyser and enters the first chamber, which is a centrifugal separator in a stainless steel block at 60°C. The condensate droplets will be removed at this point and passed down through the bottom end of the separator into a bubbler unit (C). The bubbles in this tube represent the bypass flow. At the same time the gas is raised from 36°C to 60°C inside the analyser.

Gas now passes through a filter contained in the second chamber, the measuring cell and finally to a second dip leg (D) in the bubbler unit. The flow of gas through the analyser cell is determined by the difference in the length of the two legs inside the bubbler unit and cannot be altered by the operator.

This system has the following operating advantages:

(1) The system is under a positive pressure right from inside the flue, and so leaks in the sample line can only allow steam and sample out and not air in.
(2) The high speed steam jet scours the tube preventing build-up.
(3) The steam maintains the whole of the sample probe above the dew point and so prevents corrosive condensate forming on the outside of the probe.
(4) The steam keeps the entire probe below the temperature of the flue whenever the temperature of the flue is above the temperature of the steam.
(5) The actual sampling system is intrinsically safe as no electrical pumps are required.

3.3.1.3 Steam sampling for conductivity

The steam sample is taken from the process line by means of a special probe and then flows through thick-wall 316 stainless steel tubing to the sample system panel (Figure 3.19). The sample enters the sampling panel through a high-temperature, high-pressure isolating valve and then flows into the cooler, where the steam is condensed and the condensate temperature is reduced to a suitable temperature for the analyser (typically 30°C).

After the cooler, the condensate passes to a pressure-control valve to reduce the pressure to about 1 bar gauge. The temperature and pressure of the sample are then measured on suitable gauges and a pressure-relief valve (set at 2 bar g) is fitted to protect downstream equipment from excess pressure if a fault occurs in the pressure control valve. The constant-pressure, cooled sample passes through a needle valve, flowmeter and three-way valve into the conductivity cell and then to drain.

Facilities are provided for feeding water of known conductivity into the conductivity cell through the three-way valve for calibration purposes. The sample coolers are normally supplied with stainless steel cooling coils which are suitable where neither the sample nor the coolant contain appreciable chloride which can cause stress corrosion cracking.

When chlorides are known to be present in the sample or cooling water, cooling coils are available, made of alternative materials which are resistant to chloride-induced stress corrosion cracking.

3.3.2 Liquids

3.3.2.1 Liquid sample to a process chromatograph

The example taken is for a chromatograph measuring butane in gasoline (petrol) (Figure 3.20). The chromatograph in this case would be fitted with a liquid inject valve so that the sample will remain in the liquid phase at all times within the sample system.

In a liquid inject chromatograph the sample flow rate through the analyser is very low (typically 25 ml/min), so that a fast loop system is essential.

The sample flow from the process enters the sample system through an isolating valve, then through a pump (if required) and an in-line filter,

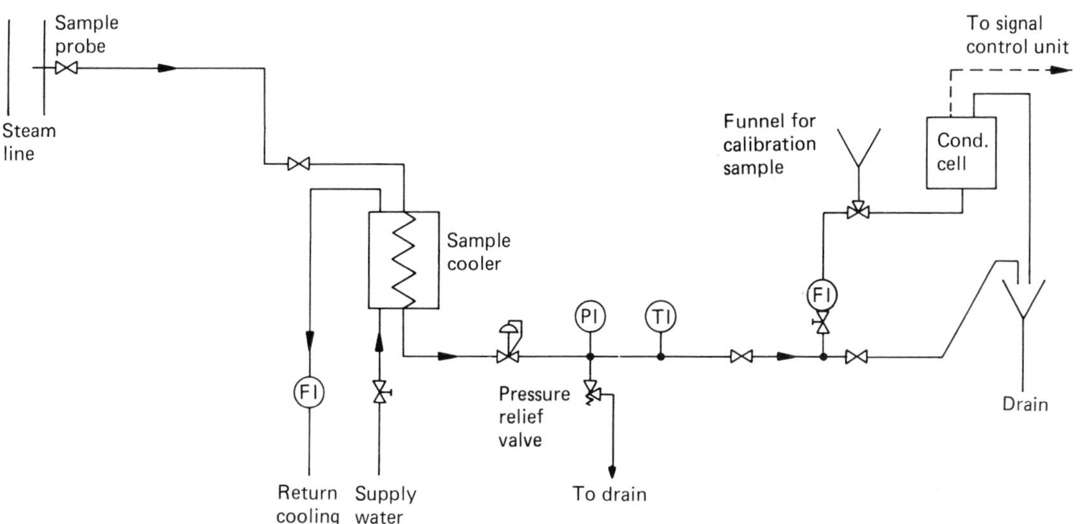

Figure 3.19 Schematic: steam sampling for conductivity (courtesy Ludlam Sysco).

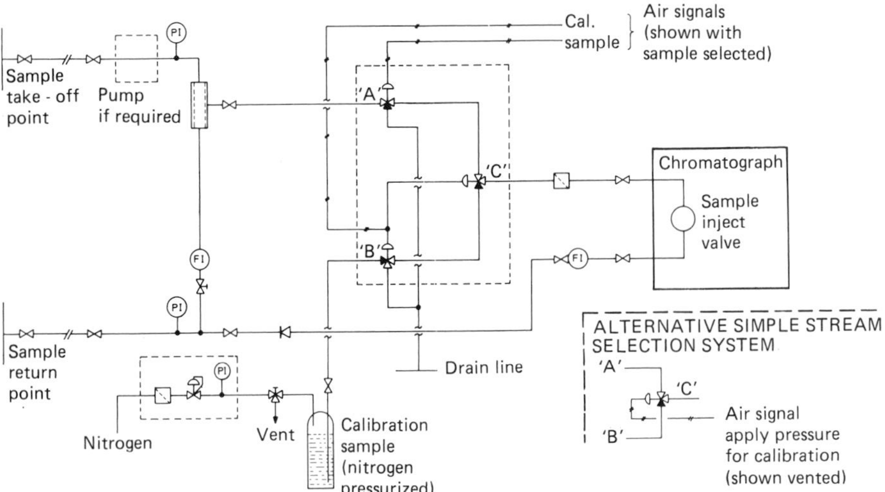

Figure 3.20 Schematic: liquid sample to process chromatograph (courtesy Ludlam Sysco).

from which the sample is taken to the analyser. After the filter the fast loop flows through a flowmeter followed by a needle valve, then through an isolating valve back to the process. Pressure gauges are fitted, one before the in-line filter and one after the needle valve, so that it is possible at any time to check that the pressure differential is sufficient (usually 1 bar minimum) to force the sample through the analyser.

The filtered sample flows through small-bore tubing (typically, 3 mm OD) to the sample/calibration selection valves. The system shown is the block and bleed configuration as described in Section 3.3.1.1. Where there is no risk of cross contamination the sample stream-selection system shown in the inset of Figure 3.20 may be used.

The selected sample flows through a miniature in-line filter (section 3.2.2.4) to the analyser, then through the flow control needle valve and non-return valve back to the fast loop return line.

When the sample is likely to vaporize at the sample return pressure it is essential to have the flow control needle valve after the flowmeter in both the fast loop and the sample through the analyser. This is done to avoid the possibility of any vapour flashing off in the needle valve and passing through the flowmeter, which would give erroneous readings.

The calibration sample is stored in a nitrogen-pressurized container and may be switched either manually or automatically from the chromatograph controller.

3.3.2.2 Gas oil sample to a distillation point analyser

In this case the process conditions are as follows (Figure 3.21):

Sample tap: Normal pressure: 5 bar g
Normal temperature: 70°C
Sample line length: 73 m

Sample return: Normal pressure: 5 bar g
Return line length: 73 m

This is a typical example of an oil-refinery application where, for safety reasons, the analyser has to be positioned at the edge of the process area and consequently the sample and return lines are relatively long. Data to illustrate the fast loop calculation, based on equations in Crane's Publication No. 410 M, are given in Table 3.1.

An electrically driven gear pump is positioned immediately outside the analyser house which pumps the sample round the fast loop and back to the return point. The sample from the pump enters the sample system cabinet and flows through an in-line filter from which the sample is taken to the analyser, through a needle valve and flowmeter back to the process. The filtered sample then passes through a water-jacketed cooler to reduce the temperature to that required for the coalescer and analyser. After the cooler the sample is pressure reduced to about 1 bar with a pressure-control valve.

The pressure is measured at this point and a relief valve is fitted so that, in the event of the pressure

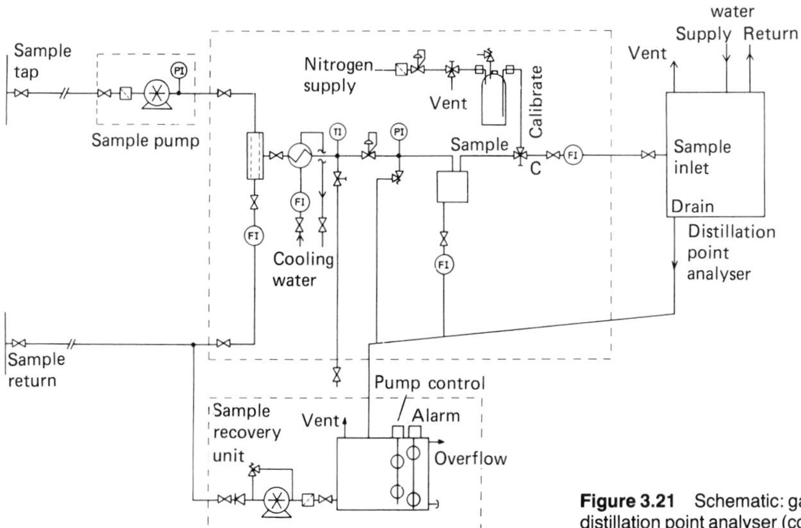

Figure 3.21 Schematic: gas oil sample to distillation point analyser (courtesy Ludlam Sysco).

Table 3.1 Fast-loop calculation for gas oil sample

Customer	Demo.
Date	Jan. 1986
Order No.	ABC 123
Tag number	Gas oil (sample line)
Density	825.00 kg/m^3
Viscosity	3.00 centipoise
Response time	39.92 s
Flow rate	16.60 l/min (1 m^3/h)
Length	73.00 m
Diameter (ID)	13.88 mm (½ in nominal bore (extra strong))
Velocity	1.83 m/s
RE=	6979
Flow	TURB
Friction factor	0.038
Delta P.	278.54 kPa (2.7854 bar)
Customer	Demo.
Date	Jan. 1986
Order No.	ABC 123
Tag number	Gas oil (return line)
Density	825.00 kg/m^3
Viscosity	3.00 centipoise
Response time	71.31 s
Flow rate	16.60 l/min (1 m^3/h)
Length	73.00 m
Diameter (ID)	18.55 mm (¾ in nominal bore (extra strong))
Velocity	1.02 m/s
RE=	5222
Flow	TURB
Friction factor	0.040
Delta P.	67.85 kPa (0.6785 bar)

control valve failing open, no downstream equipment will be damaged.

The gas oil sample may contain traces of free water and, as this will cause erroneous readings on the analyser, it is removed by the coalescer. The bypass sample from the bottom of the coalescer flows through a needle valve and flowmeter to the drain line. The dry sample from the coalescer flows through a three-way ball valve for calibration purposes and then a needle valve and flowmeter to control the sample flow into the analyser.

The calibration of this analyser is carried out by filling the calibration vessel with the sample which had previously been accurately analysed in the laboratory. The vessel is then pressurized with nitrogen to the same pressure as that set on the pressure-control valve and then the calibration sample is allowed to flow into the analyser by turning the three-way ball valve to the calibrate position.

The waste sample from the analyser has to flow to an atmospheric drain and, to prevent product wastage, it flows into a sample recovery unit along with the sample from the coalescer bypass and the pressure relief valve outlet.

The sample recovery unit consists of a steel tank from which the sample is returned to the process intermittently by means of a gear pump controlled by a level switch. An extra level switch is usually fitted to give an alarm if the level rises too high or falls too low.

A laboratory sample take-off point is fitted to enable a sample to be taken for separate analysis at any time without interfering with the operation of the analyser.

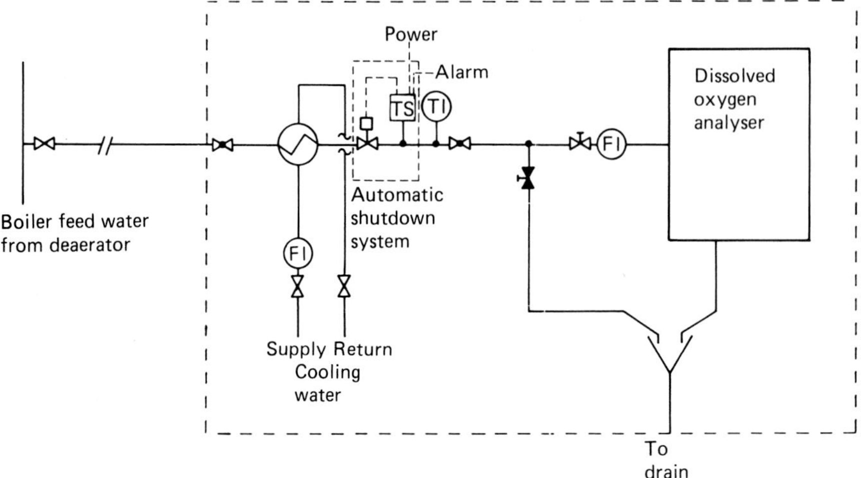

Figure 3.22 Schematic: water sample system for dissolved oxygen analyser (courtesy Ludlam Sysco).

3.3.2.3 Water-sampling system for dissolved oxygen analyser

Process conditions:

Sample tap: Normal pressure: 3.5 bar
Normal temperature: 140°C
Sample line length: 10 m

This system (Figure 3.22) illustrates a case where the sample system must be kept as simple as possible to prevent degradation of the sample. The analyser is measuring 0–20 µg/l oxygen and, because of the very low oxygen content, it is essential to avoid places in the system where oxygen can leak in or be retained in a pocket. Wherever possible ball or plug valves must be used, as they leave no dead volumes which are not purged with the sample.

The only needle valve in this system is the one controlling the flow into the analyser, and this must be mounted with the water flowing vertically up through it so that all air is displaced.

The sample line, which should be as short as possible, flows through an isolating ball valve into a water-jacketed cooler to drop the temperature from 140°C to approximately 30°C, and then the sample is flow controlled by a needle valve and flowmeter. In this case, it is essential to reduce the temperature of the water sample before pressure reduction otherwise the sample would flash off as steam. A bypass valve to drain is provided so that the sample can flow through the system while the analyser is being serviced.

When starting up an analyser such as this it may be necessary to loosen the compression fittings a little while the sample pressure is on to allow water to escape, and fill the small voids in the fitting and then finally tighten them up again to give an operational system.

An extra unit that is frequently added to a system such as this is automatic shutdown on cooling-water failure to protect the analyser from hot sample. This unit is shown dotted on Figure 3.22, and consists of an extra valve and a temperature detector, either pneumatic or electronically operated, so that the valve is held open normally but shuts and gives an alarm when the sample temperature exceeds a preset point. The valve would then be reset manually when the fault has been corrected.

3.4 References

CORNISH, D.C. *et al. Sampling Systems for Process Analysers*, Butterworths, London (1981)

Flow of Fluids, Publication No. 410M, Crane Limited (1982)

MARKS, J.W. *Sampling and Weighing of Bulk Solids*, Transtech Publications, Clausthal-Zellerfeld (1985)

4 Signal processing

M.L. SANDERSON

4.1 Introduction

This chapter is concerned with the application of electronic signal-processing techniques to the signals generated by transducers and instruments. The techniques employed in analogue signal processing, digital-to-analogue conversion and analogue-to-digital conversion are considered together with time and frequency domain analysis of signals using specialized equipment such as frequency analysers, phase-sensitive detectors, correlators and multichannel analysers. The chapter concludes with a section on the use of computer-based systems in instrumentation.

Although the signals generated by most transducers are analogue, increasingly, with the advent of cheaper computing power in the form of microprocessors and microcomputers, the transmission and processing of much data and information is undertaken in a digital form. Digital systems show several advantages over analogue systems. They are not subject to drift; they suffer much less from the problems of data corruption during transmission; and that can be easily reduced to acceptable levels by the application of simple error-checking codes to the transmitted data. The level of signal degradation which can be tolerated in a digital system before the signal is no longer recoverable is considerably greater, and thus digital systems can operate with lower signal-to-noise ratios than comparable analogue systems. In terms of signal-processing, modification of the algorithm provided by the digital-processing scheme can usually be fairly easily effected by means of software changes or, at most, simple hardware changes. Thus the bandwidth and central frequency of a digital filter can be altered by simply adjusting the sampling frequency either by a software or a hardware modification. In an analogue filter the modification can usually only be undertaken by changing several components within the filter.

Analogue electronics are essential in the processing of either high-frequency or low-level signals. In general, they are capable of providing a larger dynamic range and greater resolution than their digital counterparts.

Hybrid systems combining both analogue and digital electronics can offer significant advantages. The performance of analogue signal processing can generally be improved by using digital electronics to supply control and computational facilities. These enable the overall system to be provided with such functions as auto-zeroing, online calibration and self diagnostics. Such combinations are often referred to as 'smart' or 'intelligent'.

4.2 Analogue signal processing

Transducers can be characterized in a number of ways, either by the fundamental physical principle they employ or by the quantity they measure (Jones, 1977; Arbel, 1980). From a signal-processing point of view, transducers can be classified as to whether they produce outputs which are voltage, current or charge; whether these quantities are unidirectional, bidirectional, alternating or transient in nature; whether the information is contained within the signal as a level, or as an amplitude, frequency or phase modulation of a carrier wave; and whether the relationship between the measured quantity and the output from the transducer is linear or non-linear. Associated with the signal there is an output impedance. The purpose of analogue signal conditioning is often to convert the output of the transducer into a voltage; to effect any impedance changes that are required; and to provide such operations as amplification, filtering, demodulation and linearization.

4.2.1 Operational amplifiers

One of the most common elements in any signal-conditioning scheme is the operational amplifier. By this is simply meant a high-gain d.c. coupled amplifier, which is used with negative feedback such that the closed-loop performance is defined by the feedback elements and not by the amplifier. It is usually, although not always, a differential input/single-ended output device as shown in Figure

4.1(a). The ideal operational amplifier characteristics are infinite gain and bandwidth, infinite common mode rejection ratio, infinite input impedance and zero output impedance and zero input offset voltage and bias currents, and that it provides noise-free gain. Figure 4.1(b) shows the internal structure of the general-purpose 741 integrated circuit operational amplifier. Table 4.1 gives the parameters of three operational amplifiers produced by different integrated circuit technologies. Figures 4.1(c) and 4.1(d) illustrate the two basic methods of applying feedback to the operational amplifier. Figure 4.1(c) shows the inverting mode which employs shunt feedback and Figure 4.1(d) the non-inverting mode which employs series feedback. Assuming that the amplifiers show ideal characteristics, then since they have infinite gain there can be no potential between the two inputs of the amplifier for any finite output, and since the amplifiers require no bias current and have infinite input impedance, then $i_1 = i_f$.

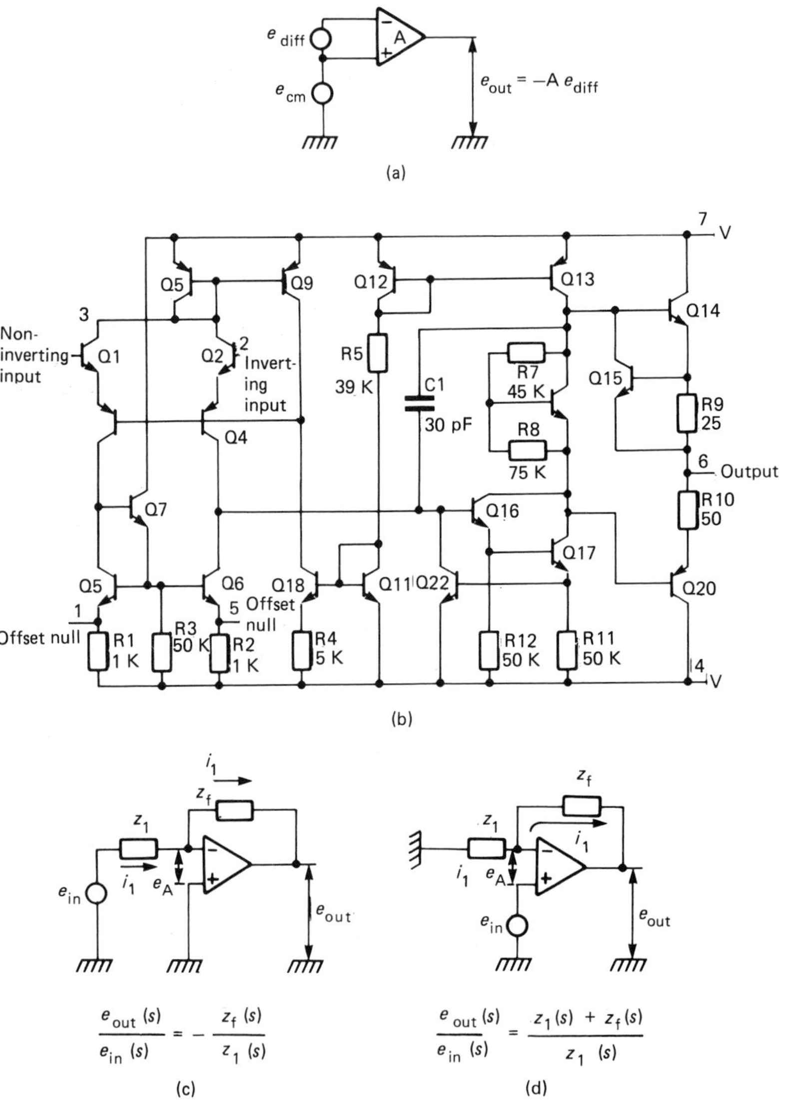

Figure 4.1 (a) Schematic diagram of an operational amplifier; (b) the internal structure of a 741 operational amplifier; (c) inverting mode feedback; (d) non-inverting mode feedback.

Table 4.1 Specifications of three operational amplifiers

Device	*741 Bipolar*	*μAF355 JFET*	*T071CP BIFET*
Supply voltage	±3 V to ±18 V	±4 V to ±18 V	±3 V to ±18 V
Open-loop gain	106 dB	106 dB	106 dB
Input resistance	2 MΩ	10^{12} Ω	10^{12} Ω
Offset voltage	1 mV	3 mV	3 mV
Offset voltage temperature coefficient	5 μV/K	5 μV/K	20 μV/K
Bias current	80 nA	30 pA	30 pA
Offset bias current	20 nA	10 pA	5 pA
Offset bias temperature coefficient	0.5 nA/K	doubles for every 20K	doubles for every 20K
CMRR	90 dB	100 dB	76 dB
Slew rate	0.5 V/μs	5 V/μs	13 V/μs
Full-power bandwidth	10 kHz	60 kHz	150 kHz
Supply voltage rejection ratio	30 μV/V	10 μV/V	158 μV/V

Thus for the inverting amplifier the transfer function between the input and output is given by:

$$\frac{e_{out}(s)}{e_{in}(s)} = \frac{-z_f(s)}{z_1(s)} = 1 - \frac{1}{\beta(s)};$$

$$\beta(s) = \frac{z_1(s)}{z_1(s) + z_f(s)} \tag{4.1}$$

where $\beta(s)$ is known as the feedback factor. Since the potential of the non-inverting input of the ideal amplifier does not change with input voltage it is called a 'virtual earth', and consequently the input impedance of the non-inverting amplifier is $z_1(s)$. Its output impedance is zero.

For the non-inverting amplifier:

$$\frac{e_{out}(s)}{e_{in}(s)} = \frac{z_1(s) + z_f(s)}{z_1(s)} = \frac{1}{\beta(s)} \tag{4.2}$$

The input impedance of the non-inverting amplifier is infinite since the input voltage is being applied to the non-inverting input of the operational amplifier. The closed-loop amplifier has zero output impedance. When $z_1(s) \rightarrow \infty$ or $z_f(s) \rightarrow 0$ then the closed-loop gain of the non-inverting amplifier $\rightarrow 1$, and the amplifier has the characteristics of a voltage follower, i.e. unity gain, infinite input impedance and zero output impedance.

It can be seen that by the application of feedback the closed-loop transfer function provided by the ideal operational amplifier is determined by the feedback elements and not the amplifier. By suitable choice of components, both linear and non-linear, for z_1 and z_f it is possible to produce a wide variety of signal-conditioning units. Tobey *et al.* (1971), Graeme (1973) and Clayton (1979) provide a wide range of examples of the use of operational amplifiers for signal processing. Figure 4.2 shows some commonly used operational amplifier circuits for linear signal processing and Figure 4.3 the application of operational amplifiers to non-linear signal processing providing half-wave and full-wave precision rectification, phase-sensitive detection and logarithmic and antilogarithmic amplification.

The following sections examine the effects of non-ideal operational amplifier characteristics on the closed-loop performance.

4.2.1.1 Gain and bandwidth

In practice, operational amplifiers do not have infinite gain or bandwidth, and consequently they produce phase shift which may interact with the phase shift within the feedback loop to produce overall positive feedback around the loop. If the amplifier is represented by a transfer function $A(s)$ then, re-analysing the inverting and non-inverting circuits in Figures 4.1(b) and 4.1(c) with:

$$e_A(s) = -\frac{e_{out}(s)}{A(s)} \tag{4.3}$$

then:

$$\frac{e_{out}(s)}{e_{in}(s)} = \text{ideal transfer function } \frac{1}{1 + 1/(A(s).\beta(s))} \tag{4.4}$$

where $A(s).\beta(s)$ is the loop gain.

For the closed-loop amplifier performance to be governed by the feedback components it is required that $|A(s).\beta(s)| >> 1$, i.e. that the loop gain should be significantly greater than unity. Stability of the closed-loop system requires that the roots of the characteristic equation, $1 + A(s).\beta(s)$, lie in the open left-half s plane. Closed-loop stability assessment for operational amplifiers and frequency compensation is generally undertaken using Bode diagrams (Clayton, 1979).

Many operational amplifiers can be approximated by a transfer function having a single low-frequency pole. Thus the transfer function $A(s)$ can be represented by:

$$A(s) = \frac{A_o}{(1 + s\tau_o)} \tag{4.5}$$

where A_o is the low-frequency gain of the amplifier and where the 3 dB break frequency is given by $f_o = 1/2\pi\tau_o)$. This is shown in Figure 4.4. Typically, A_o is 100 dB and f_o is under 10 Hz.

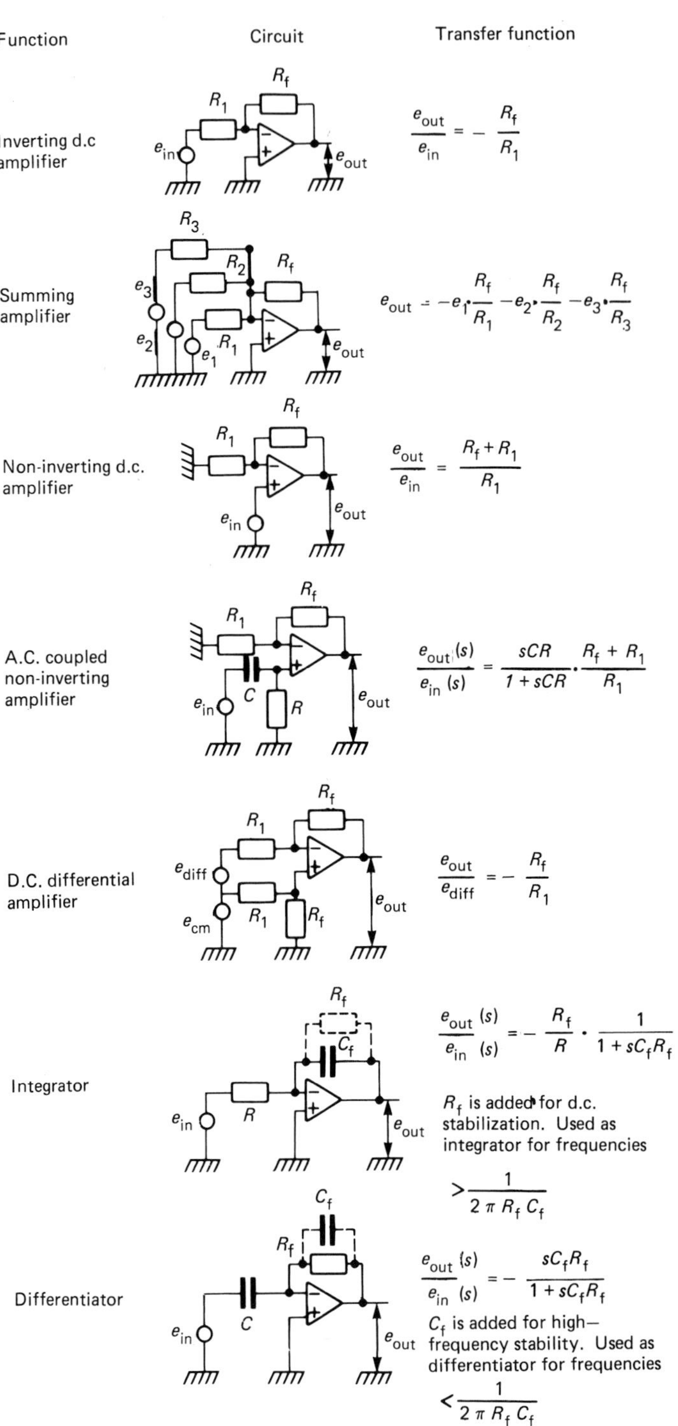

Figure 4.2 Linear signal processing using operational amplifiers.

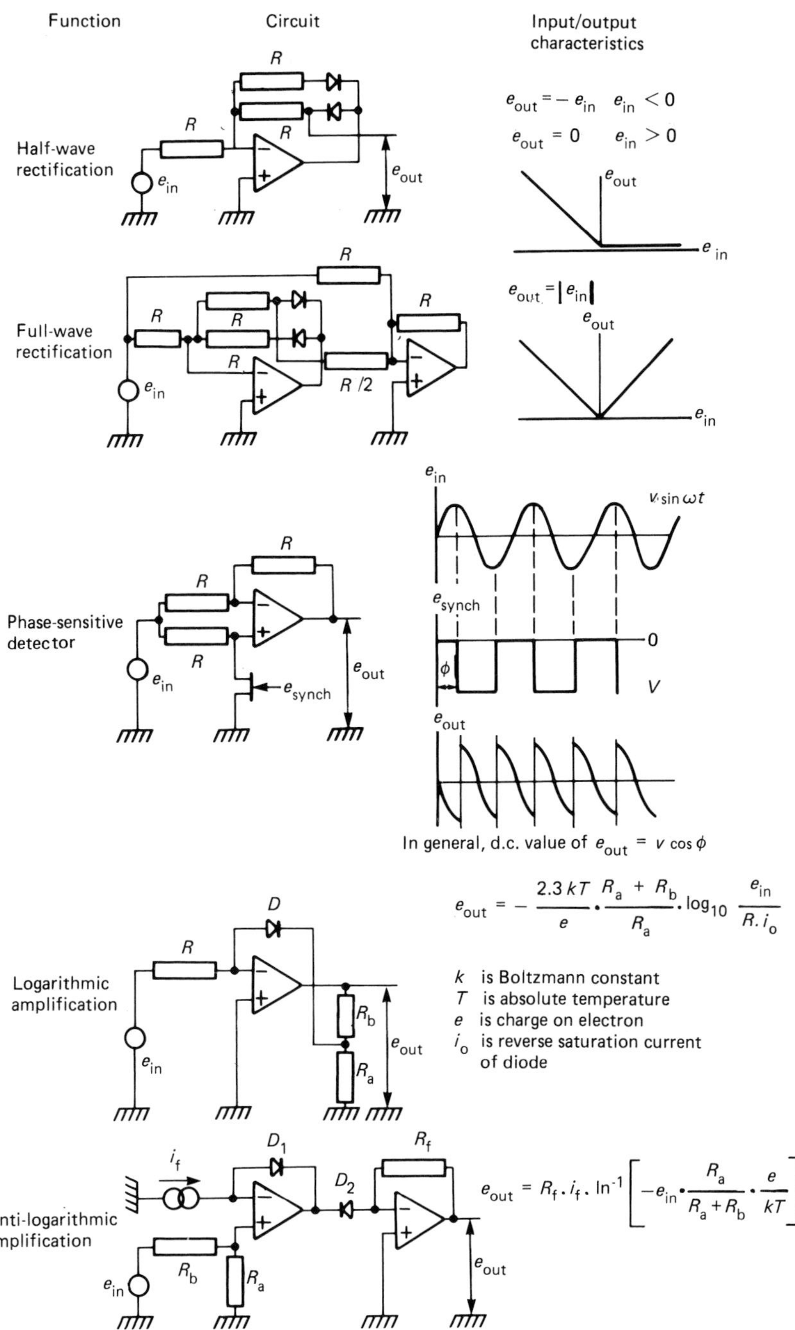

Figure 4.3 Non-linear signal processing using operational amplifiers.

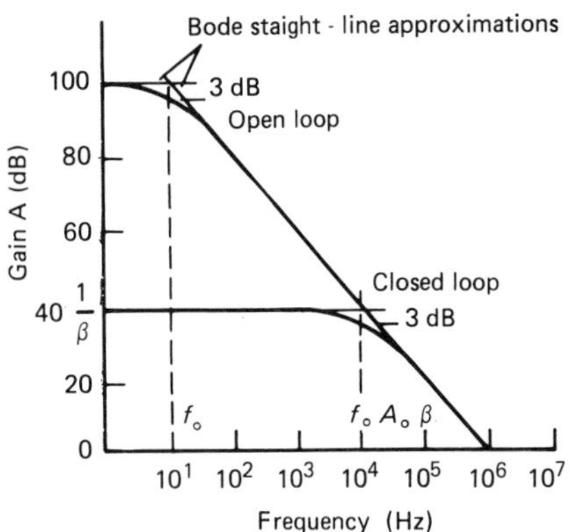

Figure 4.4 Gain–bandwidth product relationships in an operational amplifier.

If the amplifier is used as a non-inverting amplifier with resistive feedback, i.e. if $\beta(s)$ is real, then the closed-loop transfer function is given by:

$$A_{cl}(s) = \frac{e_{out}(s)}{e_{in}(s)} = \frac{1}{\beta} \cdot \frac{A_o\beta}{((A_o\beta + 1) + s\tau_o)} \tag{4.6}$$

and the 3 dB closed-loop break frequency, f_{cl}, is given by:

$$f_{cl} = \frac{(A_o\beta + 1)}{2\pi\tau_o} \simeq A_o\beta . f_o \; ; \quad A_o\beta >> 1 \tag{4.7}$$

Thus the gain $\times$ bandwidth product for both the open-loop and closed-loop amplifiers is $A_o . f_o$, and the gain of the open-loop amplifier has been traded against the bandwidth of the closed-loop amplifier.

A two-pole approximation to the open-loop transfer function of an operational amplifier is given by:

$$A(s) = \frac{A_o}{(1 + \tau_o s)(1 + \tau_1 s)} \tag{4.8}$$

If such an amplifier, with $\tau_o >> \tau_1$, is employed in a non-inverting feedback amplifier configuration with a resistive feedback factor, then the closed-loop amplifier transfer function $A_{cl}(s)$ is given by:

$$A_{cl}(s) \simeq \frac{1}{\beta} \cdot \frac{A_o\beta}{\tau_o\tau_1[s^2 + (1/\tau_1)s + (A_o\beta/\tau_o\tau_1)]} \tag{4.9}$$

which can be compared with the standard second-order transfer function

$$H(s) = \frac{H_o\omega_n^2}{s^2 + 2\xi\omega_n s + \omega_n^2} \tag{4.10}$$

where H_o is the low-frequency gain, ω is the natural frequency and ξ is the damping factor, to give:

$$H_o = \frac{1}{\beta} \tag{4.11}$$

$$\omega_n = \sqrt{\left(\frac{A_o\beta}{\tau_o\tau_1}\right)} \tag{4.12}$$

$$\xi = \frac{1}{2}\sqrt{\left(\frac{\tau_o}{A_o\beta\tau_1}\right)} \tag{4.13}$$

If $\xi < 1$ the amplifier is said to be underdamped and the system has a response to a unit step input of the form:

$$e_{out}(t) = \frac{1}{\beta}\left[1 - \exp\left\{\frac{(-\xi\omega_n t)}{\sqrt{(1 - \xi^2)}}\right\}\right] \times \sin(\omega_n\sqrt{(1 - \xi^2)}.t + \cos^{-1}\xi)\Big\} \tag{4.14}$$

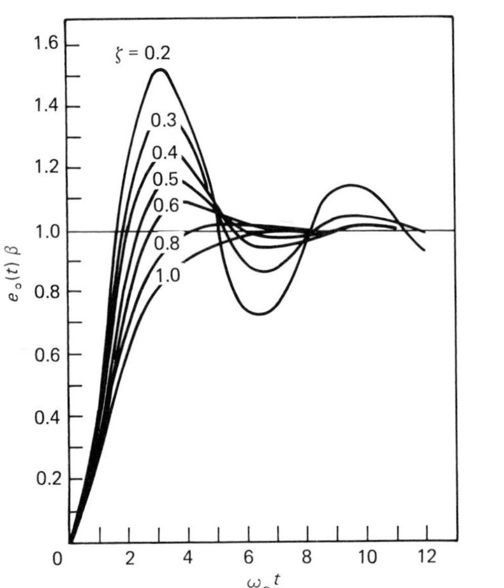

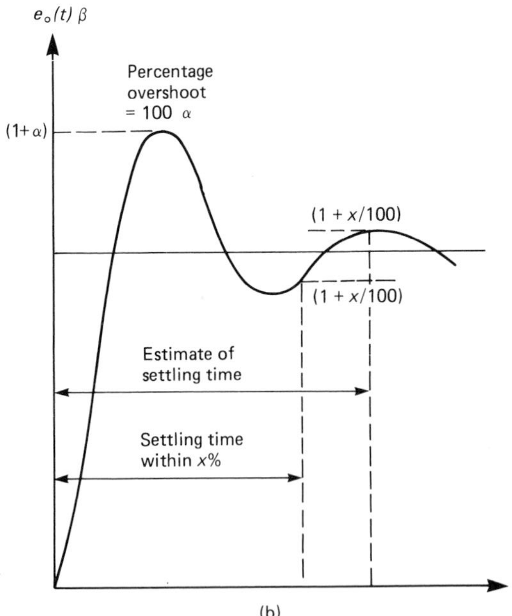

Figure 4.5 (a) Step responses for a second-order system with varying damping factor; (b) percentage overshoot and settling time for a second-order system.

The response of the system for various values of damping factor is shown in Figure 4.5. The maximum percentage overshoot (PO) is given by:

$$PO = 100 \exp\left[\frac{-\xi\pi}{\sqrt{(1-\xi^2)}}\right];\ \xi < 1 \qquad (4.15)$$

and an estimate of the time for the amplifier to settle to within $x\%$ of its final value is given by:

$$t_s = \frac{n\pi\sqrt{(1-\xi^2)}}{\omega_n} \qquad (4.16)$$

where the value of n is the smallest value which satisfies the equation:

$$100 \exp - \left[\frac{\xi n\pi}{\sqrt{(1-\xi^2)}}\right] \leqslant x \qquad (4.17)$$

As shown in Figure 4.5, this is generally an overestimate of the settling time.

For large-signal step changes the transient response of the closed-loop amplifier is governed by non-linear factors which arise as a consequence of the internal circuit design of the amplifier. Slew-rate limitation occurs, since there is a maximum rate at which the output of the amplifier can change. Figure 4.6 shows a typical large-signal step response. The

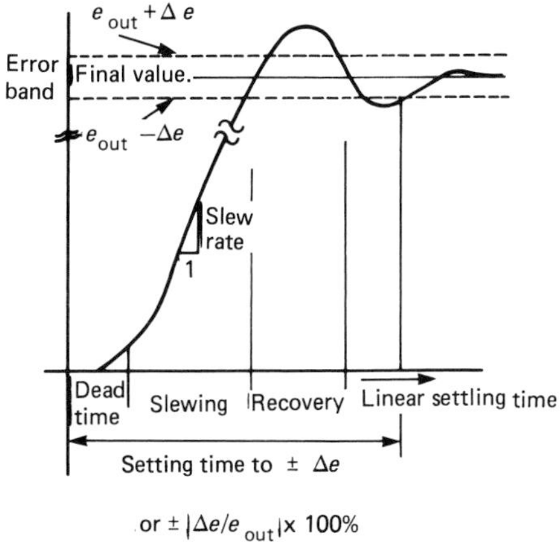

Figure 4.6 Large-signal step response.

settling time includes an initial propagation delay, together with the times required for the amplifier output to slew from its initial value to the vicinity of its final value, to recover from slew-rate limited overload and to settle to a given error in the linear range. The settling time is typically defined as the period required for an amplifier to swing from 0 V to full scale, typically 10 V, and settle within a specified percentage of the final output voltage. It is generally measured under conditions of unity gain, relatively low impedance levels and with no capacitive loading of the amplifier output.

4.2.1.2 Common mode rejection ratio (CMRR)

The operational amplifier in Figure 4.1(a) ideally should respond only to the differential signal e_{diff} applied between its input terminals and not to the common mode signal e_{cm}. CMRR is a measure of the ability of the amplifier to respond only to the differential signal and not to the common mode signal. It is defined as:

$$CMRR = 20 \log_{10} \frac{A_{diff}}{A_{cm}} \qquad (4.18)$$

where A_{diff} is the gain to the differential signal and A_{cm} is the gain to the common mode signal.

The common mode characteristic of the amplifier only causes error when the amplifier is being used in its non-inverting mode, since in the inverting mode there is no common mode signal applied to the amplifier. The CMRR is a function of several variables, including frequency, power supply, input signal level and temperature. Typically, an amplifier will have a common mode rejection of 100–120 dB at low frequencies.

4.2.1.3 Input and output impedances

Operational amplifiers, being differential devices, have both common mode and differential input impedances, as shown in Figure 4.7. The common

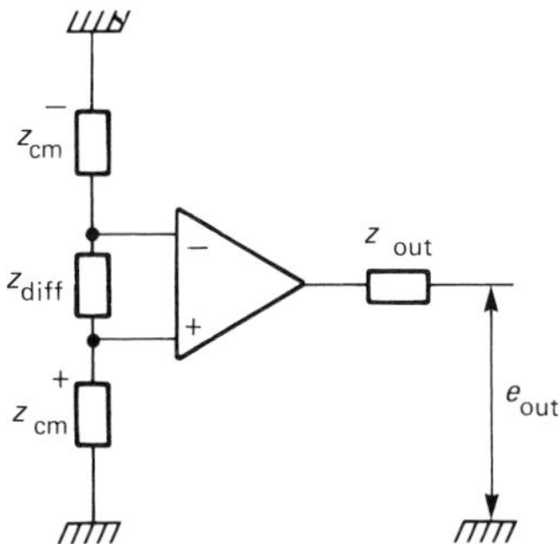

Figure 4.7 Input and output impedances for an operational amplifier.

mode input impedances $z_{cm}{}^{+}$ and $z_{cm}{}^{-}$ are the impedances between each input and ground or the power supply common. z_{diff} is the input impedance measured between the inputs. The dynamic impedances can be represented by resistance in parallel with capacitance. $R_{cm}{}^{+}$ and $R_{cm}{}^{-}$ are generally larger than R_{diff} by a factor of 100. Interaction of the input impedances with the feedback components to change the feedback can be minimized by employing feedback components with impedances significantly lower than the input impedances.

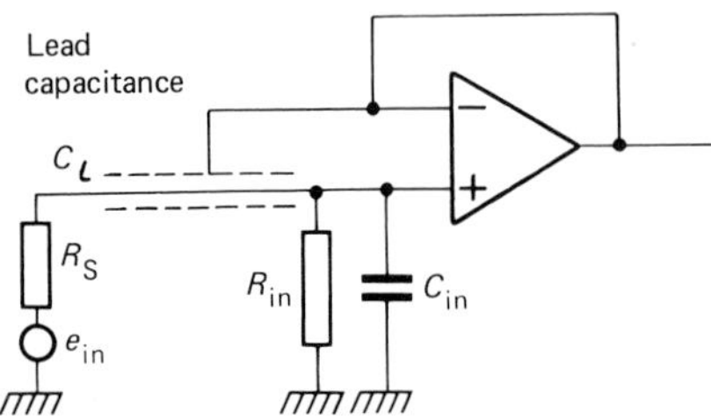

Figure 4.8 Driven shield for reducing the effect of lead capacitance.

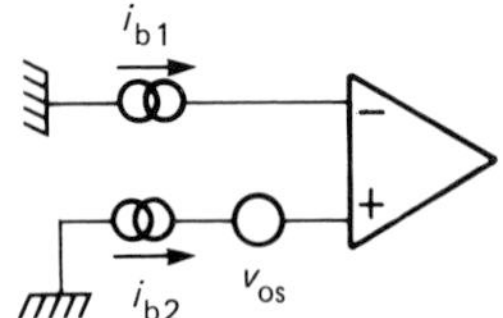

Figure 4.9 Input offset voltage and bias currents in an operational amplifier.

For the non-inverting amplifier the input impedance is the common mode input impedance between the non-inverting input and ground, since the effect of the differential input impedance is increased by a factor $A(s).\beta(s)$. FET operational amplifiers can achieve common mode input impedances of up to $10^{15}\,\Omega$ in parallel with capacitances in the region of 1 or 2 pF, which makes them suitable for use as electrometer amplifiers, since, additionally, such amplifiers have low bias currents. In order to preserve the high input impedance such amplifiers provide it is often necessary to apply driven-shield techniques to the cable connecting the source to the input of the amplifier and to guard the input pins of the amplifier. Figure 4.8 shows a typical driven-shield arrangement. The effect of the lead capacitance has been eliminated by driving its outer sheath from the output of the voltage follower. If it is assumed that the amplifier is ideal then the overall amplifier has a transfer function given by:

$$\frac{e_{out}(s)}{e_{in}(s)} = \frac{1}{(1 + sR_sC_{in})} \tag{4.19}$$

Guld (1974) examines the use of such techniques and also the use of positive feedback techniques to eliminate the input capacitance of the amplifier.

The open-loop output impedance of the amplifier can usually be represented by a resistance. Typically, this has a value of between 100 and 500 Ω. Feedback reduces this output impedance by a factor $1/(A(s)\beta(s))$.

4.2.1.4 Input voltage offset and bias current

Because of mismatch in the components making up the differential input stage the amplifier gives a d.c. output for zero input. This is represented in the model of the real amplifier, as shown in Figure 4.9, by a voltage source, v_{os} in series with the non-inverting input of the ideal amplifier. v_{os} has a value equal to the voltage which, when applied to the input, would bring the output to zero. This offset voltage typically is 0.1–30 mV. It is a function of temperature, power supply and time.

Most operational amplifiers have offset null adjustment pins which enable the initial offset to be nulled out. In precision d.c. measurements it is the temperature drift of the offset voltage which is of greater importance. The offset voltage temperature coefficient over a given range may be specified as:

$$\frac{\Delta v_{os}}{\Delta T} = \frac{v_{osH} - v_{osL}}{T_H - T_L} \tag{4.20}$$

where v_{osH} and v_{osL} are the measured values of the offset voltage measured at temperatures T_H and T_L. This is only an average measure of the temperature coefficient over the specified temperature range and, since the offset voltage is a non-linear function of temperature, it may be an over- or underestimate at any point, and it cannot be used to estimate the temperature drift from a given point in the temperature range. Some manufacturers (Analog Devices, 1982) use a butterfly specification of temperature coefficient, as shown in Figure 4.10, which allows bounds to be set on the offset voltage drift from some reference temperature T_{ref} at which it has been nulled. Using this technique, the offset voltage drift from the reference temperature T_{ref} to the working ambient temperature T_A is guaranteed to be less than $(T_{ref} - T_A)$ multiplied by the specified temperature coefficient. Typical values for the temperature coefficient of the offset voltage are in the range 0.5–20 μV/K.

It should be noted that offset nulling using the internal circuitry can considerably increase the offset voltage temperature coefficient, and it is recommended that in critical situations external nulling techniques should be employed. Generally, all offset voltage temperature specifications are for steady-state thermal conditions. Under transient thermal conditions such as warm-up or under conditions of thermal shock the value of offset voltage may be considerably increased.

The offset voltage is also a function of power supply voltage and time. Its variation with power supply voltage is specified as $\Delta v_{os}/\Delta V$ (in μV/V).

The drift of offset voltage with time occurs as a consequence of ageing. It is specified as μV/day, μV/month or μV/year, and is generally not linear with time. Extrapolation can often be made on the basis of a square-root estimate. The drift for any

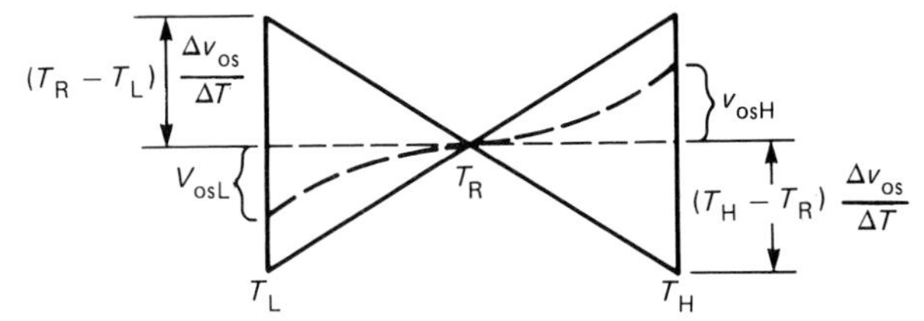

True butterfly specification

$$\frac{\Delta v_{os}}{\Delta T} \leqslant \frac{v_{osH}}{T_H - T_R} \text{ or } \frac{v_{osL}}{T_L - T_R}$$

Modified butterfly specification

$$\frac{\Delta v_{os}}{\Delta T} = \frac{|v_{osH}| + |v_{osL}|}{T_H - T_L}$$

$(T_R - T_L)\dfrac{\Delta v_{os}}{\Delta T}$ v_{osL} T_R v_{osH} $(T_H - T_R)\dfrac{\Delta v_{os}}{\Delta T}$ T_L T_H

$\dfrac{\Delta v_{os}}{\Delta T}$ is the max. drift coefficient permissible

Figure 4.10 Butterfly specification of the offset voltage temperature coefficient.

period is thus obtained by taking the product of the specified drift over a given period and multiplying it by the square root of the ratio of the time period for which the drift is required to the time period for which the drift is specified. The data for time variations tend to be somewhat more scanty than those for the temperature and power-supply variations.

The input stages of the operational amplifier have to be supplied with bias current. It is therefore necessary to provide d.c. bias paths through which these currents can flow. These bias currents are represented as shown in Figure 4.9 by two current generators, i_{b1} and i_{b2}, having values which are the average of the bias current into the positive and negative terminals. These current generators can have values from 10^{-7}A to 10^{-15}A, dependent on the technology employed in the fabrication of the operational amplifier. The bias currents are a function of temperature and power supply voltage.

The effect of offset voltage and bias currents on the output of an operational amplifier can be assessed in any circuit by shorting-out inductors, open-circuiting capacitors, short-circuiting voltage sources and open-circuiting current sources. Figure 4.11 shows the effect of the voltage offset and bias current on an inverting operational amplifier. The output offset due to bias currents can be minimized by making the source resistances at the two inputs equal, i.e.

$$R_s = \frac{R_1 \cdot R_f}{R_1 + R_f}$$

Under such conditions the offset is now a function of the difference current $i_d = i_{b1} - i_{b2}$. This, in general, will be almost an order of magnitude smaller than either i_{b1} or i_{b2}, and since the two bias currents track each other with temperature the temperature coefficient for i_d will also be considerably smaller.

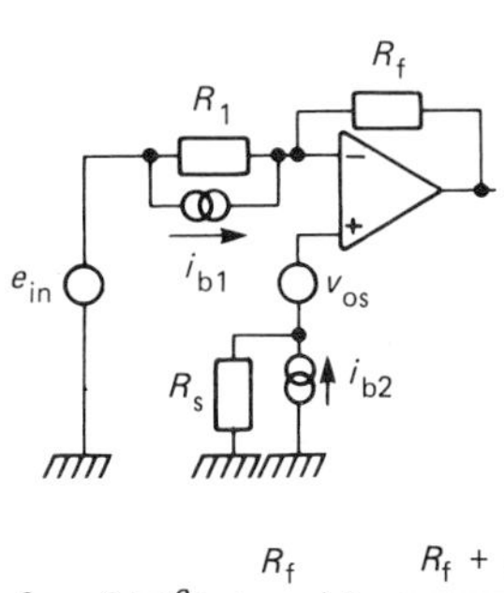

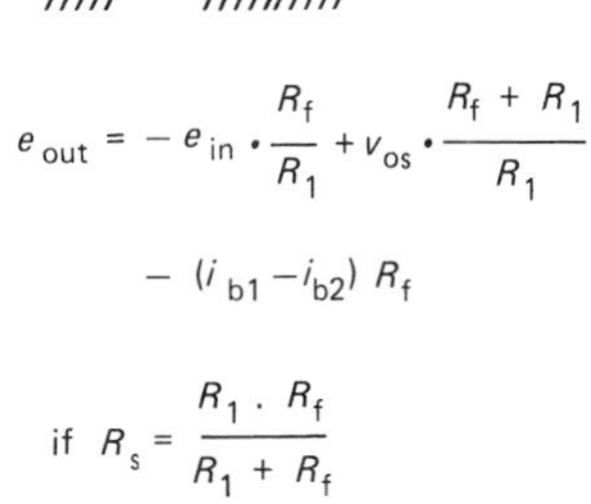

$$e_{out} = -e_{in} \cdot \frac{R_f}{R_1} + v_{os} \cdot \frac{R_f + R_1}{R_1} - (i_{b1} - i_{b2}) R_f$$

$$\text{if } R_s = \frac{R_1 \cdot R_f}{R_1 + R_f}$$

Figure 4.11 Effects of offset voltage and bias current on the output of an operational amplifier.

4.2.1.5 Noise

In the detection of low-level signals the noise performance of the operational amplifier is extremely important, and it is therefore necessary to be able to calculate and minimize the noise contribution of the amplifier using data obtained from the manufacturers' specifications. Figure 4.12 shows the representation of the noise sources in an operational amplifier. The voltage source has an r.m.s. value given by e_n and the current generators have r.m.s. values given by i_n. The resistors in the circuit each have associated with them a thermal noise voltage e_R whose r.m.s. value is given by:

$$e_R = \sqrt{(4kTRf)} \tag{4.21}$$

where k is the Boltzmann constant, T is the absolute

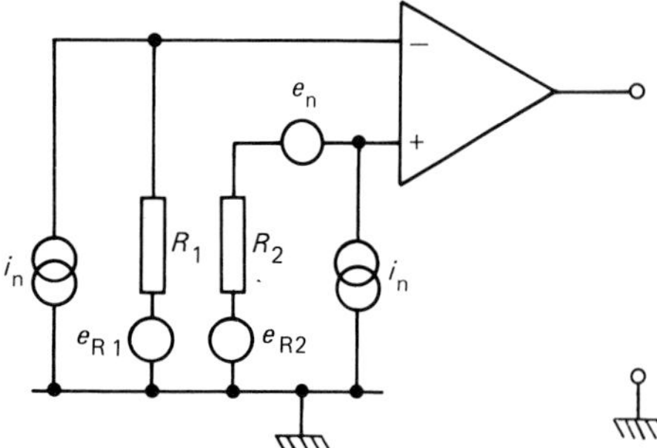

Figure 4.12 Noise sources in an operational amplifier.

temperature, R is the resistance and f is the bandwidth over which the measurement is made.

It is therefore possible to calculate the total r.m.s. noise e_{ntot} referred to the input of the amplifier. It is given by:

$$e_{ntot} = \sqrt{(e_n^2 + R_1^2 i_n^2 + R_2^2 i_n^2 + 4kTR_1 f + 4kTR_2 f)} \tag{4.22}$$

The first term represents the voltage noise, the second and third terms the effect of the current noise interacting with the resistances associated with each input and the last two terms represent the thermal noise associated with the resistances. The addition is performed in a mean square sense, since it is assumed that the sources are statistically independent.

Manufacturers provide graphical representations of the r.m.s. level of the noise referred to the input as a function of the source resistance for a series of bandwidths, typically 10 Hz–100 kHz, 10 Hz–10 kHz or 10 Hz–1 kHz. Figure 4.13 shows such plots for a 741 operational amplifier. The peak-to-peak noise can be estimated to be $6.6e_{ntot}$, where e_{ntot} is the r.m.s. value of the noise which is assumed to be Gaussian.

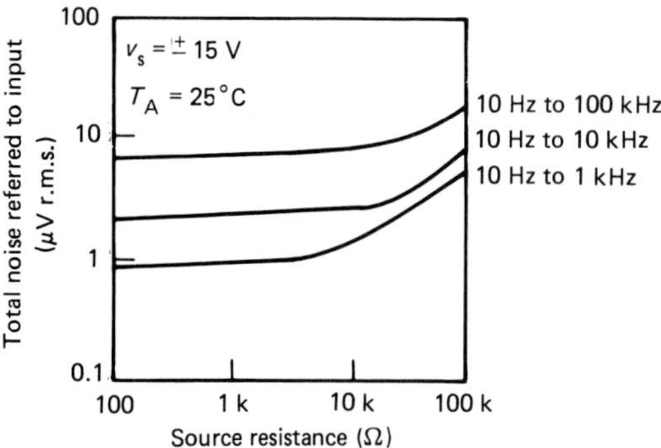

Figure 4.13 Noise characteristics of a 741 operational amplifier.

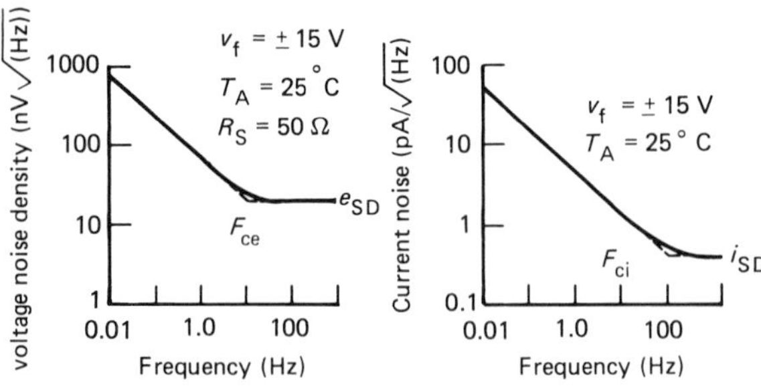

Figure 4.14 Voltage and current noise spectral densities for an OP-14 operational amplifier.

Manufacturers also provide spectral data on the voltage noise source and the current noise source. Figure 4.14 shows typical curves for the voltage spectral density in nV/√(Hz) and the current spectral density in pA/√(Hz) for a Precision Monolithics OP-14 operational amplifier. At high frequencies both the voltage and current noise exhibit white noise characteristics, i.e. have equal power in equal bandwidths. At low frequencies they exhibit a $1/f$ characteristic called flicker noise. This is characterized by having equal power in each decade of the bandwidth. By integrating these power spectra over a given frequency band it is possible to calculate the total r.m.s. noise in that band. Thus the r.m.s. value of the voltage noise e_n in a band as shown in Figure 4.14 can be calculated as:

$$e_n = e_{sd}\sqrt{\left[f_{ce}.\log_e\left(\frac{f_H}{f_L}\right) + (f_H - f_L)\right]} \tag{4.23}$$

where f_{ce} is the corner frequency of the voltage noise, f_H and f_L are the upper and lower frequencies of the bandwidth over which the noise is being measured and e_{sd} is the spectral density of the voltage noise at high frequencies.

A similar calculation can be performed for the r.m.s. value of the current i_n:

$$i_n = i_{sd}\sqrt{\left[f_{ci}\log_e\left(\frac{f_H}{f_L}\right) + (f_H - f_L)\right]} \tag{4.24}$$

where f_{ci} is now the corner frequency of the current noise and i_{sd} is the spectral density of the current noise at high frequencies.

It is possible to modify the spectral densities to take into account the frequency response of the amplifier in order to determine the noise at the output of the amplifier (Tobey *et al.*, 1971).

An alternative approach in noise assessment is to specify the amplifier in terms of a noise figure, NF (Arbel, 1980) and seek by noise matching of the source to the amplifier to minimize the noise figure. This approach is less useful in instrumentation applications, since it does not lead to the best signal-to-noise ratio at the output of the amplifier.

4.2.1.6 Operating parameters

In addition to the parameters specified above, there are also parameters specified for the operational amplifier which are designed to keep it within its linear regime. These include such parameters as input and output voltage swings and output drive current capability, which arise as a consequence of internal circuit design and which place limitations on the load and feedback impedances that the amplifier can drive. The full-power bandwidth of the amplifier is determined by the slew rate of the amplifier. It is specified as the maximum bandwidth at unity closed-loop gain for which a sinusoidal input signal will produce full rated output at rated load without exceeding a given level of distortion. Distortion in the amplifier is measured in terms of total harmonic distortion (THD). Overload recovery measures the ability of the amplifier to recover from a saturation condition caused by a specified amount of overdrive. For further details of these parameters the reader is referred to the manufacturers' amplifier specifications, which give the values of these parameters for particular amplifiers together with specifications of the conditions under which they are measured.

4.2.2 Instrumentation amplifiers

The single-ended inverting and non-inverting amplifiers shown in Figures 4.1(c) and 4.1(d) are not suitable for use as general-purpose instrumentation amplifiers, since in many transducers the low-level signal may be superimposed on a large-amplitude common mode signal, as in the case of the output signal from a strain gauge bridge or a line frequency interference signal, as shown in Figure 4.15(a). Measurement of the signal by the use of a single-ended amplifier leads to amplification of the

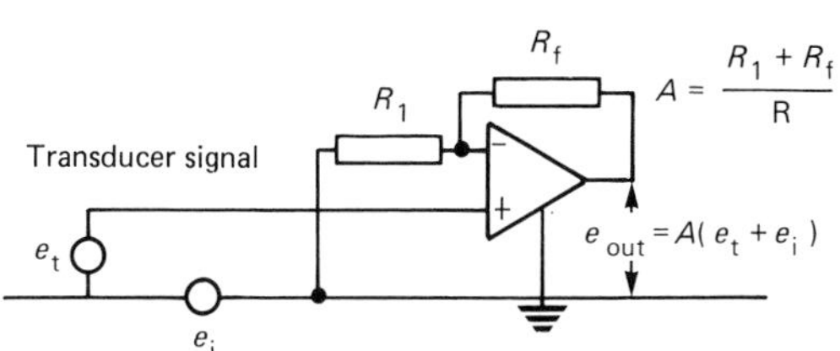

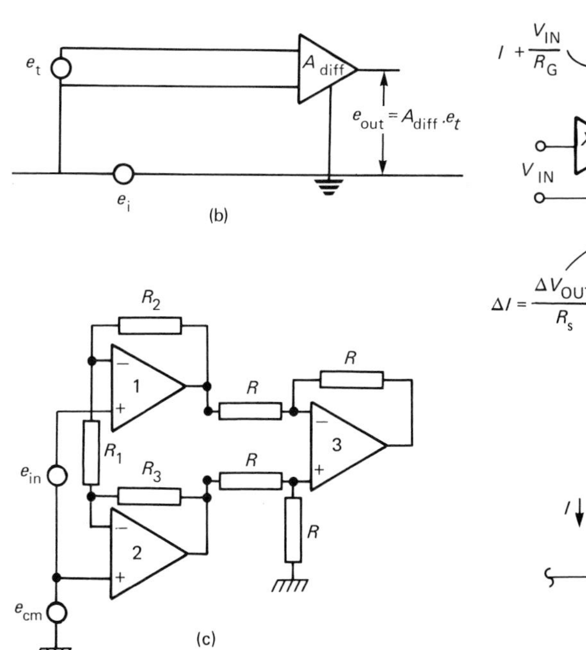

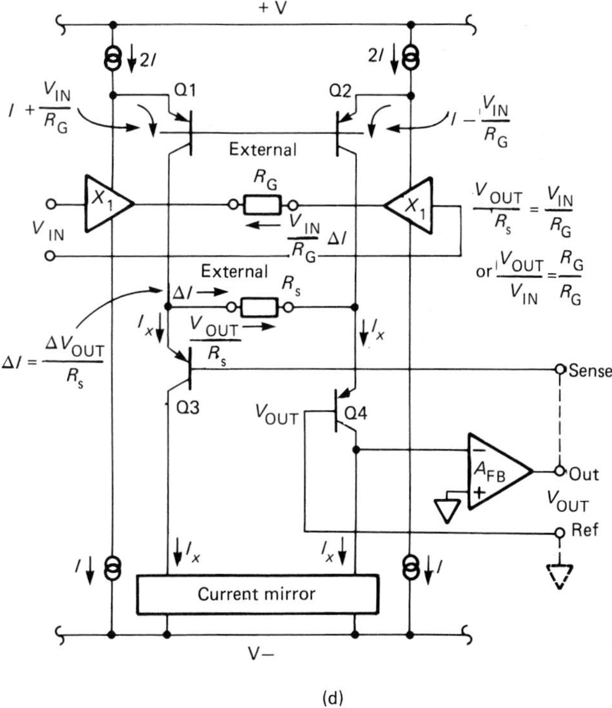

Figure 4.15 (a) Effect of common mode signals on a single-ended input amplifier; (b) the use of a differential amplifier to reduce the effects of common mode signals; (c) an instrumentation amplifier using three operational amplifiers; (d) the internal construction of a commercially available instrumentation amplifier AD.

common mode signal as well as the transducer signal. By using the differential amplifier shown in Figure 4.15(b), the CMRR of the amplifier reduces the effect of common mode signals. Instrumentation amplifiers are wideband, high input impedance differential amplifiers, having adjustable and stable differential gain, high common mode rejection ratio, low input drift characteristics and low output impedance. They are used for the amplification of signals from thermocouples, strain gauge bridges, current shunts and biological probes.

Figure 4.15(c) shows an instrumentation amplifier employing three operational amplifiers. Amplifiers A1 and A2 provide only unity gain to the common mode signal and amplifier A3 acts as a differential amplifier. The differential gain of the overall amplifier is given by:

$$A_{\text{diff}} = \frac{R_1 + R_2 + R_3}{R_1} \tag{4.25}$$

The common mode rejection ratio is governed by the common mode rejection ratio of the amplifiers making up the instrumentation amplifier and the matching of the resistors in the differential amplifier A3.

Figure 4.15(d) shows the internal construction of a commercially available instrumentation amplifier (Analog Devices AD521). The differential voltage e_{diff} appears across R_G and causes an imbalance in the currents flowing through the transistors Q_1 and Q_2. The current mirror consisting of Q_3 and Q_4 forces this imbalance current to flow through R_S. The output voltage e_{out} is given by R_S/R_G. Differential gains from 1 to 1000 can be provided by adjusting R_G. The characteristics of this amplifier are given in Table 4.2. Instrumentation amplifiers are available with software programmable gains.

Table 4.2 Instrumentation amplifier specification

Gain G	1–1000
Small-signal bandwidth	
$G = 1$	>2 MHz
$G = 1000$	40 kHz
Differential input voltage	±10 V
Common mode rejection ratio	
$G = 1$	70 dB min
$G = 1000$	100 dB min
Input impedances	
Differential	$3 \times 10^9\,\Omega \| 1.8\,\text{pF}$
Common mode	$6 \times 10^{10}\,\Omega \| 3.0\,\text{pF}$
Voltage offsets	
Input	3 mV max
vs temp.	15 μV/K max
Output	400 mV max
vs temp.	400 μV/K max
Input bias current	
Initial	80 nA max
vs temp.	1 nA/K
Noise	
Voltage noise wrt output	
0.1 Hz to 10 Hz	$\sqrt{[(0.5G)^2 + (225)^2]}$ μV p-p
10 Hz to 10 kHz	$\sqrt{[(1.2G)^2 + (50)^2]}$ μV r.m.s.
Input current noise	
10 Hz to 10 kHz	15 pA r.m.s.

4.2.3 Isolation amplifiers

The amplifier shown in Figure 4.15(d) can only allow the rejection of common mode signals which are within its power rails. By using an isolation technique as shown in Figure 4.16, which provides galvanic isolation of the front-end amplifier from the power supply and subsequent stages, it is possible to construct an amplifier which is capable of providing isolation capable of withstanding several kV. Isolation is generally provided by transformer coupling. In such amplifiers the primary source of leakage between input and output circuits is the capacitance between the windings of the transformer.

A power oscillator provides isolated power to the input amplifier, together with a carrier which is modulated by the amplified input signal and coupled across the isolation barrier. In the output section this signal is demodulated and filtered. The amplifier output is provided via a buffer amplifier. A second demodulator in the input stage is used to provide the input stage with feedback.

Applications for such amplifiers include the measurement of low-level d.c. and low-frequency voltage or current in the presence of high common mode voltages and the reception of signals transmitted at high impedance in a noisy environment. Isolation amplifiers are widely used in medical electronics where, for reasons of patient safety, it is necessary to limit d.c. and line frequency leakage currents. Table 4.3 gives the specification of a commercially available isolation amplifier (Analog Devices AD293).

4.2.4 Chopper-stabilized amplifiers and commutating auto-zero amplifiers

There is often a requirement to produce amplifiers which have a low offset voltage and also a low offset voltage temperature coefficient. Two amplifiers with such characteristics are chopper-stabilized amplifiers and commutating auto-zero (CAZ) amplifiers. These are shown in Figures 4.17(a) and 4.17(b), respectively. In the chopper-stabilized amplifier (Giacoletto, 1977) the signal is split into two paths on a frequency basis. The d.c. and low-frequency signals are routed via a low-pass filter to a modulator. This modulated signal (which is now an a.c. signal) is then amplified by means of an a.c.

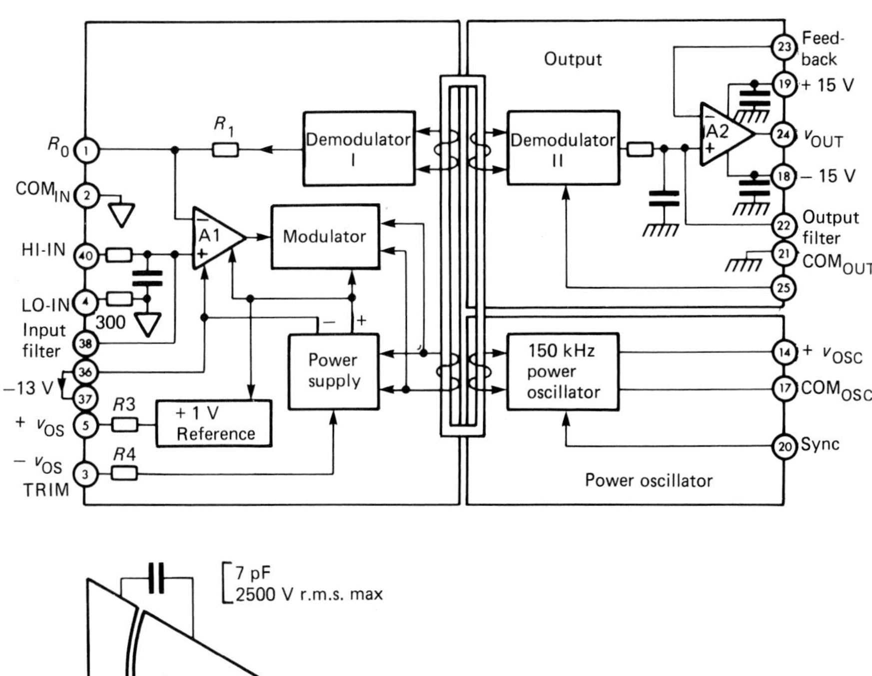

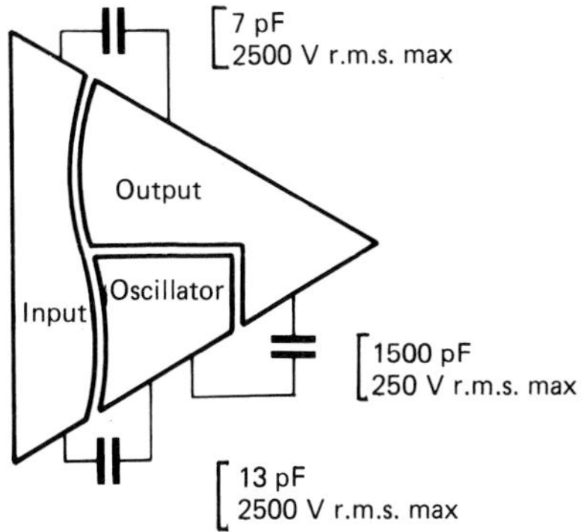

Figure 4.16 Isolation amplifier.

amplifier. After amplification it is demodulated, filtered and passed into the main amplifier. Thus the d.c. and low-frequency signals are amplified by an a.c. amplifier which ideally has no d.c. offset (the only offset being introduced by non-ideal modulation and demodulation of the signal). If the effective gain of the chopper stage is A_{chop} and the offset of the main amplifier is v_{osm}, then, referred to the overall amplifier input, the effective offset of the amplifier is v_{osm}/A_{chop}, since the d.c. signals have been given a d.c. offset-free gain of A_{chop} before they are applied to the main amplifier. Typically, such amplifiers have an offset voltage of between 15 and 50 μV and a temperature coefficient of between 0.1 and 1.0 μV/K, with a long-term stability of order 2 μV/month, 5 μV/year. They are normally used with heavy overall feedback to remove the effects of variations in the open-loop frequency response.

The commutating auto-zero amplifier consists of two operational amplifiers situated on the same substrate (Intersil, 1979). The amplifier is a two-state device and these two states are shown in Figure 4.17(b). In the state 1 operational amplifier 1 is being used as the active amplifier with the capacitor C_1 in series with its non-inverting input. Amplifier 2 is switched so that its offset is being stored on C_2. After a fixed period of time (typically 3 ms) the roles of the two amplifiers are reversed. The offset on amplifier 1 is now measured and the offset on amplifier 2 is removed by placing the capacitor C_2 in series with its non-inverting input. The commutation back to state 1 then occurs after a further 3 ms. CAZ amplifiers typically can have an initial offset voltage of 2 μV, a temperature coefficient of 0.05 μV/K and a time variation of the offset of 0.2 μV/year. CAZ amplifiers generate noise spikes at the commutation frequency, and thus it is necessary to limit the frequency of operation to one tenth of the commutation frequency.

Table 4.3 Isolation amplifier specification

Gain G	1–1000
Small-signal bandwidth	
($G = 1$ to 100)	2.5 kHz
Differential input voltage	±10 V
Max. common mode voltage	
(Inputs/Outputs)	
Continuous a.c. or d.c.	±2500 V peak
Common mode rejection	
(1 KΩ source impedance imbalance)	100 dB
Leakage current	
Input to output	
at 115 V a.c. 60 Hz	2 μA r.m.s. max
Input impedances $G = 1$	
Differential	$150\,\text{pG} \parallel 110^{8}\,\Omega$
Common mode	$30\,\text{pF} \parallel 5 \times 10^{10}\,\Omega$
Offset voltage referred to input	
initial	$(\pm 3 \pm 22/G_{in})$ mV
vs temp.	$(\pm 3 \pm 150/G_{in})$ μV/K
(G_{in} = gain of input stage)	
Input bias current	
Initial	2 nA
vs temp.	20 pA/K
Input noise	
Voltage	
0.05 Hz to 100 Hz	10 μV p-p
10 Hz to 1 kHz	5 μV r.m.s.
Current	
0.05 Hz to 100 Hz	50 pA p-p

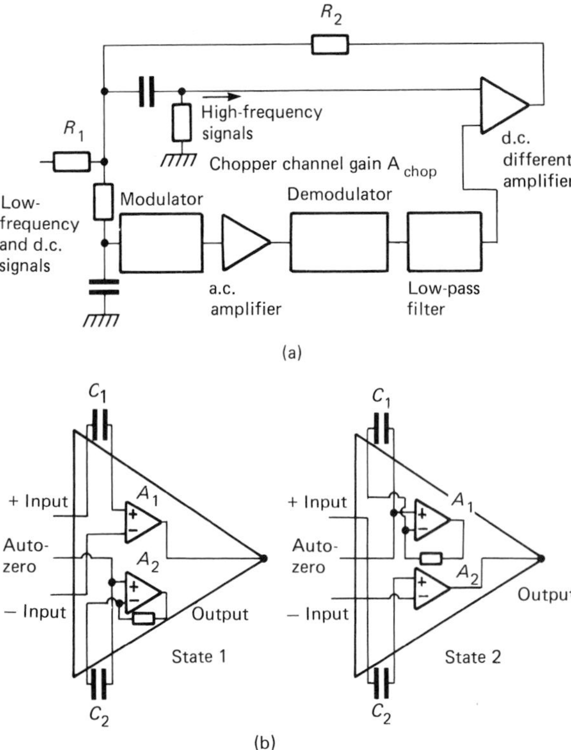

Figure 4.17 (a) Chopper-stabilized amplifier; (b) commutating auto-zero amplifier.

4.2.5 Charge and current amplifiers

Piezoelectric crystals, used in accelerometers, pressure transducers and load cells, produce charge outputs. A charge amplifier, as shown in Figure 4.18, can be used to convert the charge into a voltage. The non-inverting input of the amplifier acts as a virtual earth, and therefore the shunting effect of the capacitance of the cable connecting the crystal to the amplifier is removed, since there is no voltage drop across it. The large resistance R_f provides d.c. feedback for the amplifier and a path for its bias current. The charge amplifier has the advantage that its sensitivity and low-frequency cut-off are governed by the feedback components and not by the crystal. Typically, for a charge amplifier C_f and R_f will have values of 10 pF to 100 pF and 10^{11}–$10^{14}\,\Omega$, respectively. Using such feedback components it is possible to produce charge amplifiers which, for all practical purposes, have a response down to d.c.

Current-to-voltage conversion, for example, of the output of a photodiode can be provided by means of the current or transimpedance amplifier, as shown in Figure 4.19(a). The current from the

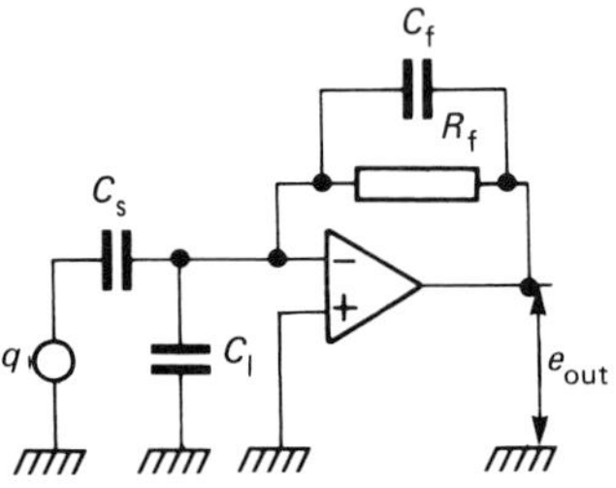

$$\frac{e_{out}(s)}{q(s)} = -\frac{sR_f}{1 + sR_f C_f}$$

if $sC_f R_f \gg 1$

$$\frac{e_{out}(s)}{q(s)} = -\frac{1}{C_f}$$

R_f is large resistance required for d.c. stabilization
C_s represents capacitance of source
C_l lead capacitance

Figure 4.18 Charge amplifier.

photodiode is detected under short-circuit conditions, since its cathode is connected to the virtual earth of the operational amplifier. The sensitivity of the amplifier is given by R_f. C_f is required for stability purposes and limits the bandwidth of the conversion. By the use of FET operational amplifiers with large values of R_f it is possible to measure currents of below 10^{-12}A. Since offset voltage and bias current errors can be nulled out, the measurement accuracy is then limited by the bias current temperature drift, which for FET amplifiers doubles for every 10K rise in temperature, and noise.

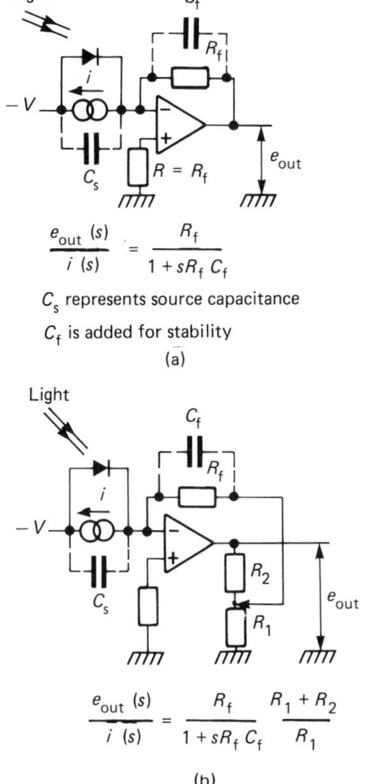

Figure 4.19 (a) Current (transimpedance) amplifier; (b) a current amplifier employing lower-value feedback resistors.

The need for large-feedback resistors can be eliminated by the use of the output divider circuit, as shown in Figure 4.19(b). This reduction in the value required for R_f is effected at the expense of a reduction in the amplifier loop gain and an increase in offset and noise gain.

4.2.6 Sample and hold amplifiers

Sample and hold (S and H) amplifiers, otherwise known as track and hold amplifiers, are used to maintain the input of an analogue-to-digital converter constant during the period in which the conversion is taking place. This is particularly required when the analogue signal is rapidly varying, when the signal is being quantized into a large number of levels or in systems where there is a high conversion throughput. Such an amplifier has two modes—the sample or track mode, in which the output follows the input, and the hold mode, in which the value is maintained at the value the input had at the instant at which the hold instruction was given. Logical signals, usually at TTL levels, determine which mode the amplifier is in at any one time.

A schematic diagram of such an amplifier is shown in Figure 4.20(a). In the sample or track mode the capacitor C is being charged or discharged by amplifier 1 at such a rate as to enable it to follow the input. The following action is ensured by means of the heavy overall feedback applied around the amplifier. In the hold mode the capacitor is isolated from amplifier 1 and it therefore retains its charge, being only discharged by the input bias current of amplifier 2, which acts as a follower. In the sampling or tracking mode ideally the capacitor should be small, since the maximum rate of change of voltage on the capacitor dV_c/dt is limited to i_{max}/C, where i_{max} is the maximum output current that amplifier 1 can supply. Thus for fast tracking the capacitor C should be small. In the hold mode the capacitor C should be large, since the droop rate is given by i_b/C, where i_b is the bias current drawn by amplifier 2. A compromise has therefore to be reached between these two conflicting requirements. The capacitor should be made of a material such as polystyrene or teflon in which dielectric absorption effects are small, thus minimizing errors due to 'creep'.

Figure 4.20(b) shows some of the specifications of the S and H amplifier which are of importance when the device is changing its state. The aperture time is the time delay between applying the hold command signal and the time at which the capacitor is isolated from amplifier 1. It is possible to allow for this time delay in precision timing circuits, but also associated with the aperture time there is a random uncertainty or jitter. Typically, the aperture time is 6–150 ns, dependent on the device. High-speed devices can have a jitter as low as 20 ps. After the settling time required for sample-to-hold transients to decay it is found that the signal in the hold mode has an offset with respect to the input signal. The major cause of this is charge transfer or an offset step, caused by capacitive coupling of the switching signal to the

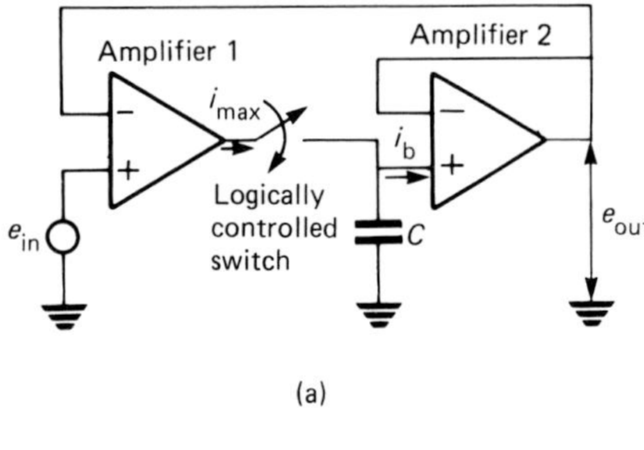

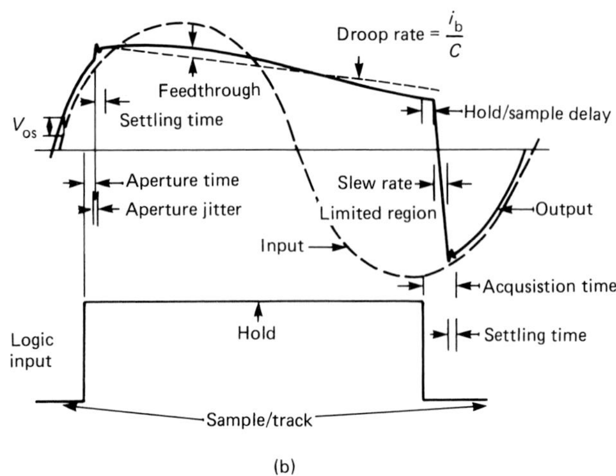

Figure 4.20 (a) Schematic diagram of a sample and hold amplifier; (b) specifications of a sample and hold amplifier.

hold capacitor. It can be reduced by using a large hold capacitor, at the expense of system response time, or cancelled by capacitively coupling a signal of the correct polarity to the hold capacitor. The signal in the hold mode will droop for the reasons stated above, and for a particular value of capacitor this is expressed in μV/μs or mV/μs. During the hold mode capacitive feedthrough of the input signal to the output will occur across the open switch, and this is usually measured as a rejection in dB for a signal at a given level and frequency. The acquisition time is the time for the output to reach its final value, within a specific error band, after the sample command has been given. For precision sample and hold amplifiers, typically this may be expressed as the time required to achieve an accuracy of ±0.01 per cent for a 10 V step. This time includes switching delay, slewing interval and settling time, and is dependent on the size of the hold capacitor employed. High speed S and H amplifiers can have acquisition times of order 250 ns.

4.2.7 Filtering

Filtering is used in signal conditioning in instrumentation systems to improve the signal-to-noise ratio by selectively reducing both random noise and also unwanted periodic signals such as line frequency interference. There are four types of filter—low pass, high pass, bandpass and bandstop. Figure 4.21 shows the ideal forms of these filters. In practice, it is not possible to have infinitely sharp transitions between the stop and pass bands, and the filter design problem thus becomes an approximation problem.

The simplest low-pass and high-pass filters are the single-pole filters whose transfer functions and amplitude and phase characteristics are shown in Figure 4.22(a). Such filters have a single real pole. Figure 4.22(b) shows the realizations of these filters using operational amplifiers.

Figure 4.23 shows the transfer functions and amplitude and phase characteristics of the four filter types using two-pole filters with complex conjugate pole pairs. Operational amplifiers are used extensively in the production of active filters having complex conjugate pole pairs. A wide variety of design techniques are available for such filters.

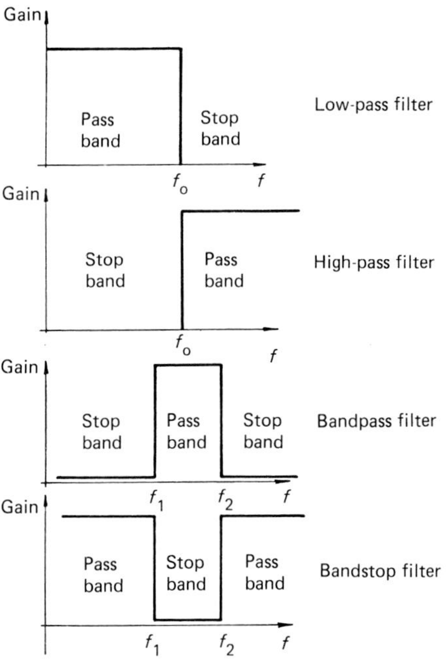

Figure 4.21 Ideal filters.

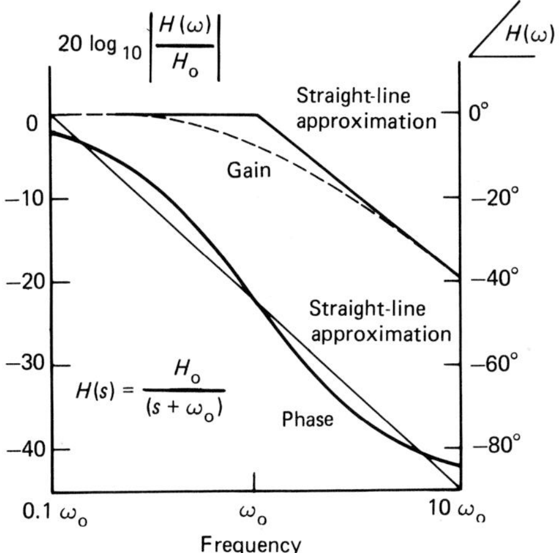

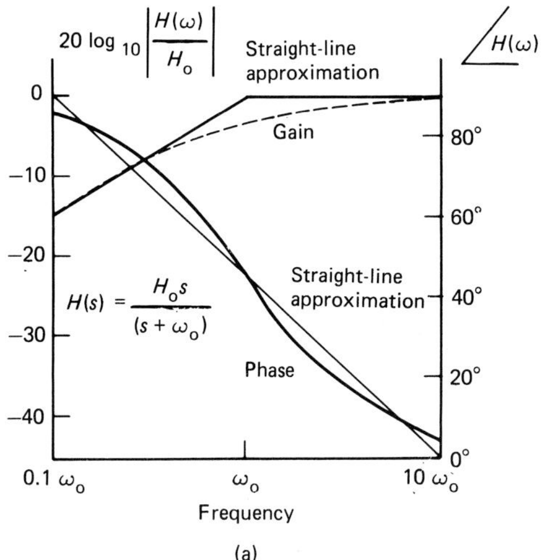

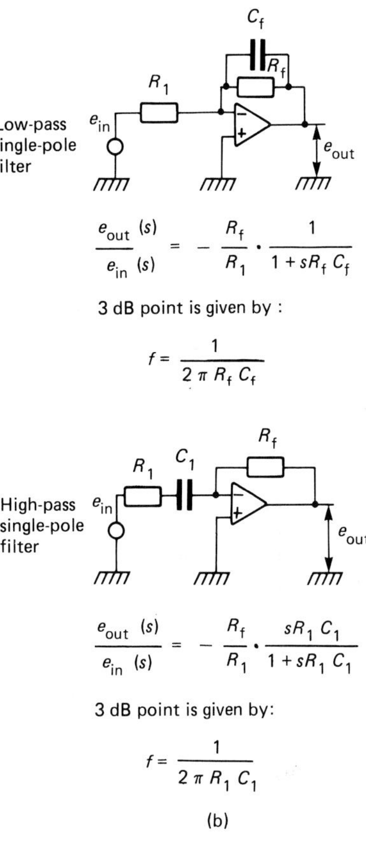

Figure 4.22 (a) Single-pole (a) low-pass and (b) high-pass filters; (b) realization of single-pole low-pass and high-pass filters using operational amplifiers.

Figure 4.24 shows two-pole complex conjugate filters realizations employing multiple feedback, voltage-controlled voltage source and state variable circuits. Tobey *et al.* (1971) and Bowron and Stephenson (1979) give detailed design procedures for the design of such filters.

In general, a filter can be represented by its transfer function $G(s)$, which can be represented as the ratio of two polynomials:

$$G(s) = \frac{K \prod_{i=1}^{m} (s - z_i)}{\prod_{j=1}^{n} (s - p_j)} \tag{4.26}$$

where in order for the filter to be realizable $n \geqslant m$.

The z_i are the zeros of the transfer function and the p_j are the poles of the transfer function. The number of poles of the transfer function is called the order of the filter, and, the larger the number of poles, the sharper the transition between the pass and stop bands. The problem in filter design is choosing the location of the poles according to some criteria. Figure 4.25 shows the amplitude characteristics of three approximations to the low-pass filter. These are Butterworth filters, which have a maximally flat response; Chebyshev filters, which have ripple in the pass band; and elliptic filters, which allow ripple in both the pass band and the stop band. In addition to such approximations, which are based on amplitude considerations, alternative filter realizations are available, such as the Thompson approximation, which provides a maximally flat

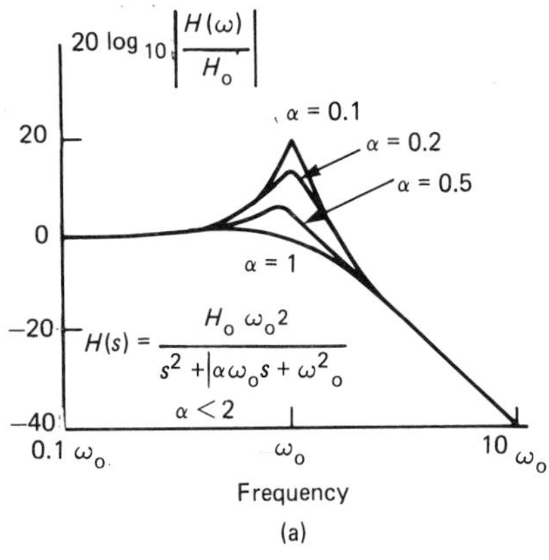

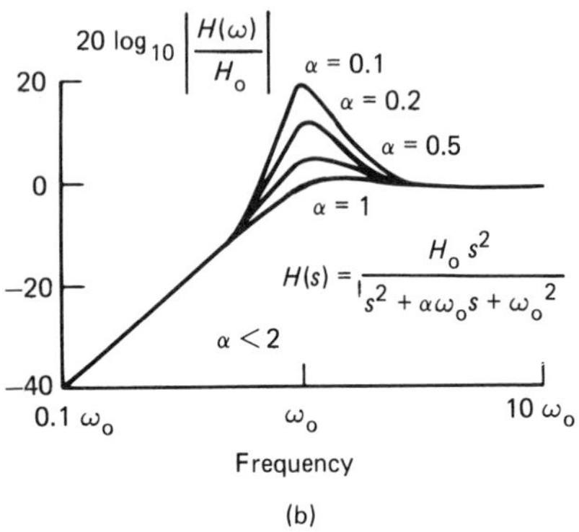

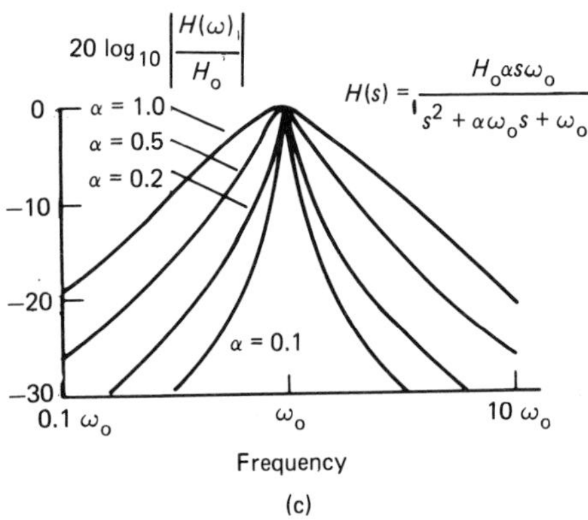

Figure 4.23 Amplitude and phase relations for filters. (a) low-pass, (b) high-pass, (c) bandpass and (d) bandstop filters employing two complex conjugate poles. (e) Phase relations corresponding to (a) (b) and (c); (f) phase relations corresponding to (d).

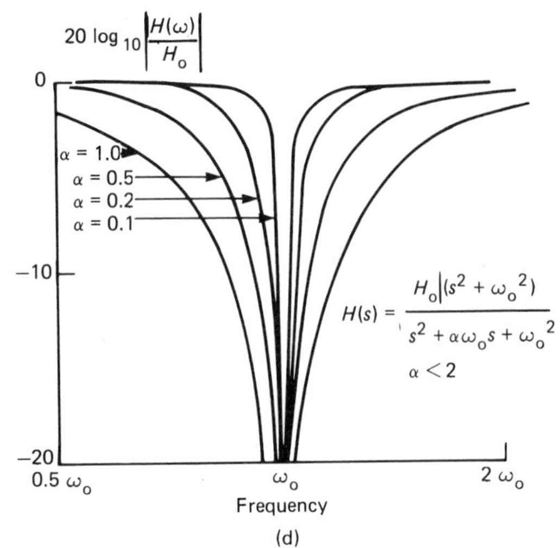

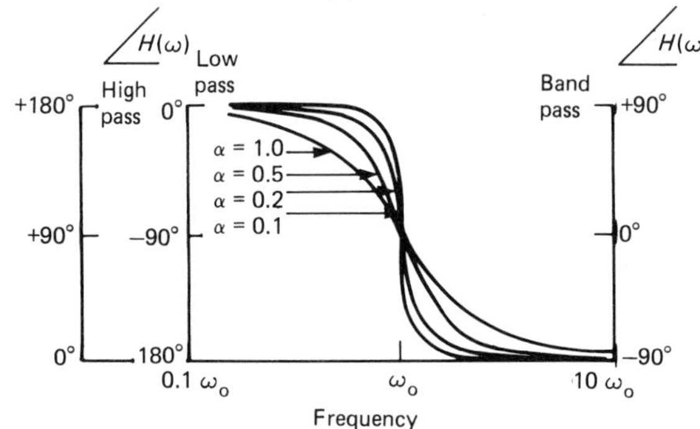

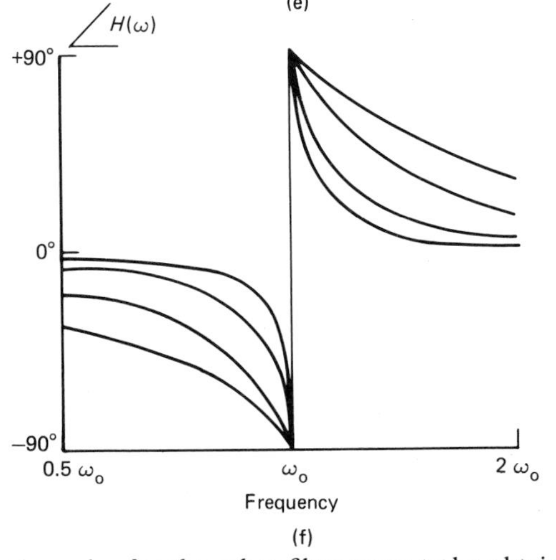

delay characteristic. Filters based on the Thompson approximation are of importance in digital transmission systems. Bowron and Stephenson (1979) give methods for locating the poles for low-pass filters using all the above approximations together with transformation techniques to enable the locations of the poles for the other filter types to be obtained. Tobey *et al.* (1971) give tables of the poles for low-pass Butterworth, Bessel and Chebyshev filters up to the tenth order.

Filters of order higher than two can be produced by cascading a series of active filters. Operational

$$\frac{e_{out}(s)}{e_{in}(s)} = \frac{-Y_1 Y_3}{Y_5(Y_1 + Y_2 + Y_3 + Y_4) + Y_3 Y_4}$$

Y_1, Y_2, Y_3, Y_4, Y_5 represent admittances of resistances and capacitances

	Element				
	1	2	3	4	5
Low pass	*R*	*C*	*R*	*R*	*C*
High pass	*C*	*R*	*C*	*C*	*R*
Bandpass	*R*	*R*	*C*	*C*	*R*

(a)

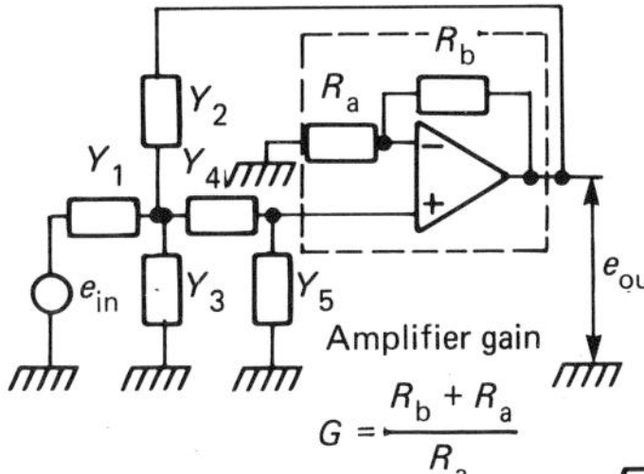

$$\frac{e_{out}(s)}{e_{in}(s)} = \frac{G Y_1 Y_4}{Y_5(Y_1 + Y_2 + Y_3) + Y_4(Y_1 + Y_2[1-G] + Y_3)}$$

Y_1, Y_2, Y_3, Y_4, Y_5 represent admittances of resistances and capacitances

G is gain of non-inverting amplifier

	Element				
	1	2	3	4	5
Low pass	*R*	*C*	-	*R*	*C*
High pass	*C*	*R*	-	*C*	*R*
Bandpass	*R*	*R*	-	*C*	*R* ‖ *C*

(b)

Low-pass filter:

$$\frac{e_{out\,1}(s)}{e_{in}(s)} = \frac{1}{b_o + b_1 s + b_2 s^2}$$

Bandpass filter:

$$\frac{e_{out\,2}(s)}{e_{in}(s)} = \frac{s}{b_o + b_1 s + b_2 s^2}$$

High-pass filter:

$$\frac{e_{out\,3}(s)}{e_{in}(s)} = \frac{s^2}{b_o + b_1 s + b_2 s^2}$$

(c)

Figure 4.24 Realization of two-pole complex conjugate filters using operational amplifiers. (a) Multiple feedback circuit; (b) voltage-controlled voltage source realization; (c) state-space realization.

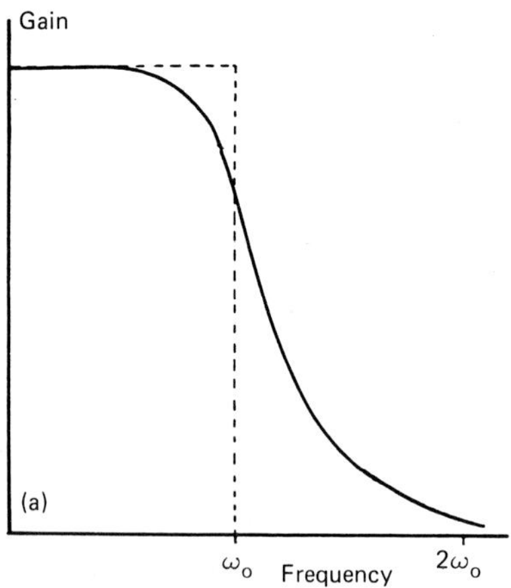

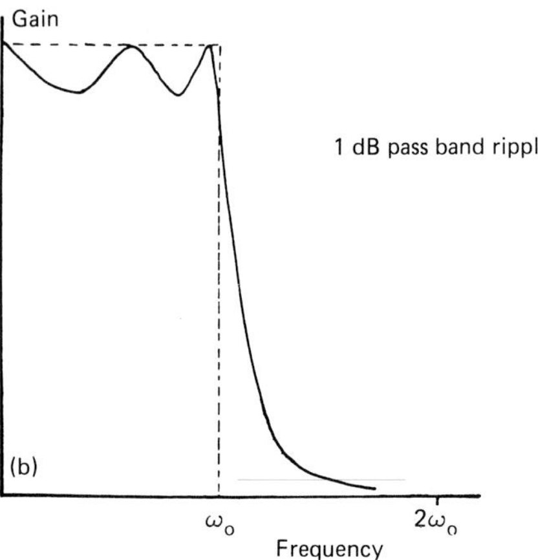

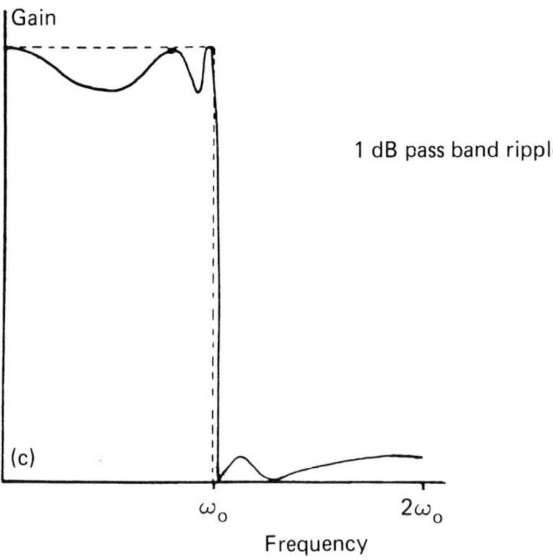

Figure 4.25 Fifth-order (a) Butterworth, (b) Chebyshev and (c) elliptic approximations to the low-pass filter.

amplifiers are ideally suited to such applications, since the low output impedance of the operational amplifier allows the filters to be cascaded with little interaction.

4.2.7.1 The Shannon sampling theorem and anti-aliasing filters

Data-transmission systems often operate by sampling the data from the transducer system, transmitting the sampled form of the data and reconstructing the original data at the other end of the data-transmission medium. The process of sampling the data modifies its spectrum as shown in Figure 4.26(a). If the original data has a maximum frequency content f_d, the question arises as to what is the slowest speed that the data can be sampled at for it to be still possible to reconstruct the data from the samples. The answer to this question is given by the Shannon sampling theorem, which states that for a band-limited signal, having frequencies up to f_d, in order to sample the data in such a manner that it is possible to reconstruct the data from the sampled form it is necessary to sample it with a frequency of at least $2f_d$. This is a theoretical limit and, as a

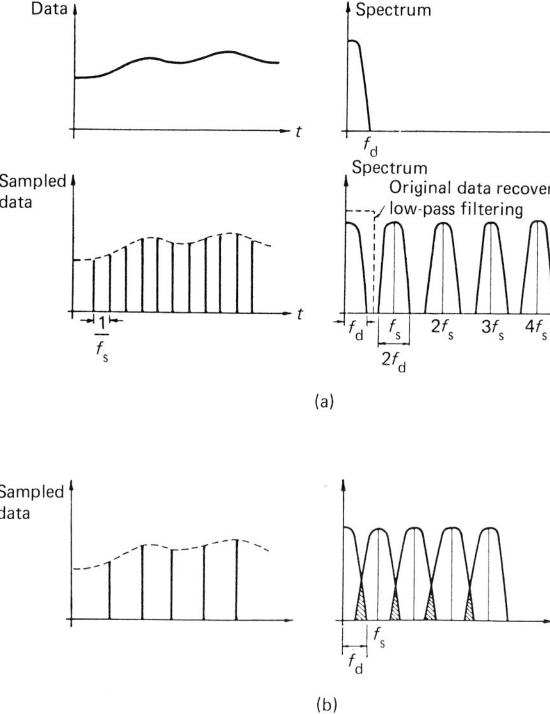

Figure 4.26 (a) Spectrum of sampled data; (b) aliasing errors in sampled data.

general rule of thumb, it is usual to sample signals with a frequency at least ten times the maximum frequency of interest. Figure 4.26(b) shows the effect of disobeying the Shannon sampling theorem. It can be seen that it is no longer possible to reconstruct the data by the application of a low-pass filter onto the sampled data. This effect caused by allowing the signal to have frequency components which have frequencies in excess of $f_s/2$ is called aliasing. It is usually prevented by the insertion of low-pass anti-aliasing filters prior to sampling the signal. The break frequencies of these filters are set according to the sampling rate.

4.2.8 Non-linear analogue signal processing

Although increasingly non-linear signal processing is provided by digital means, integrated circuits are available which enable the processing shown in Figures 4.27 and 4.28 to be applied to analogue signals.

Figure 4.27(a) shows the schematic diagram of a four-quadrant multiplier circuit. Four-quadrant devices allow both inputs to have either positive or negative polarity. The multiplier operates by converting the two input voltages to be multiplied into currents and generating an output current which is the ratio of the product of the two input currents to a reference current. Such multipliers provide typical multiplication errors of order 0.5 per cent of full scale and operate at frequencies in excess of 10 MHz. They can be used as modulators and demodulators, as gain control elements and in power measurement.

The multiplier can also be used to provide division and square rooting, as shown in Figures 4.27(b) and 4.27(c). The divider uses the multiplier in a feedback configuration. Division enables fixed or variable gain elements to be constructed and

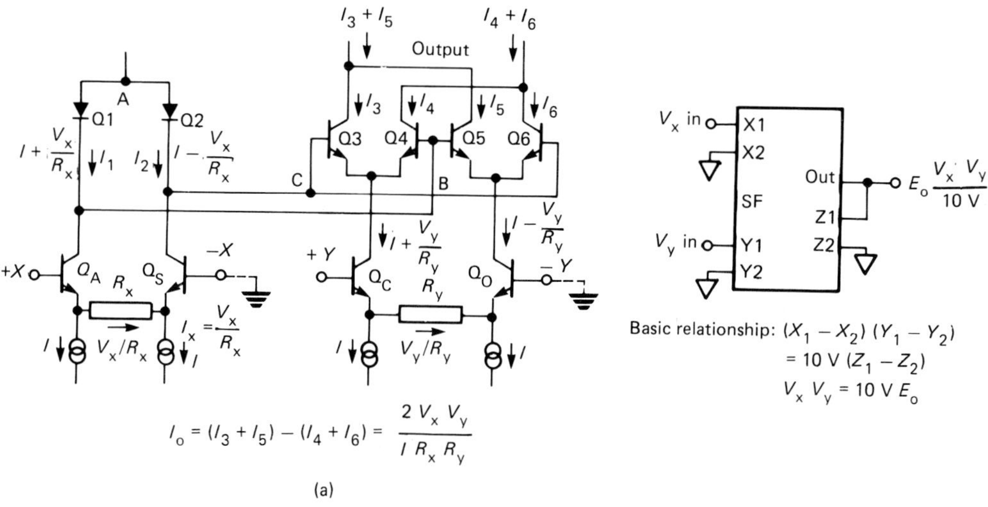

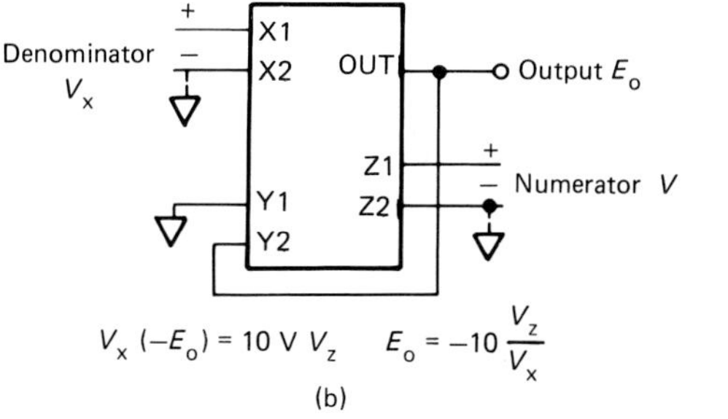

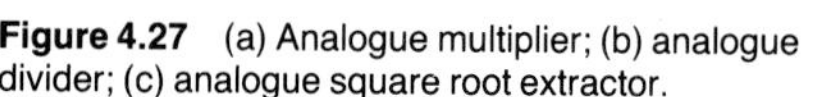

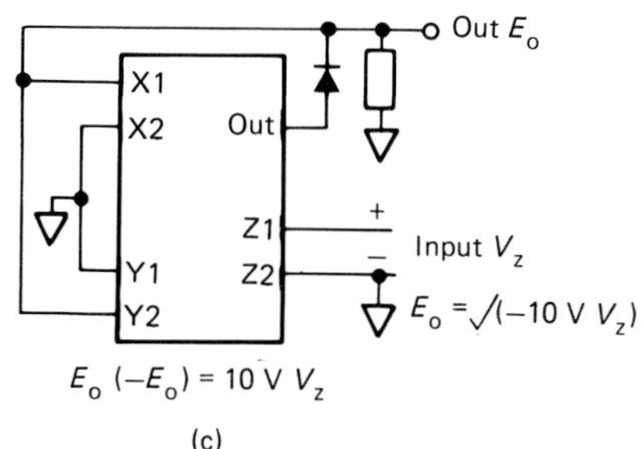

$E_o(-E_o) = 10\text{ V } V_z$

(c)

Figure 4.27 (a) Analogue multiplier; (b) analogue divider; (c) analogue square root extractor.

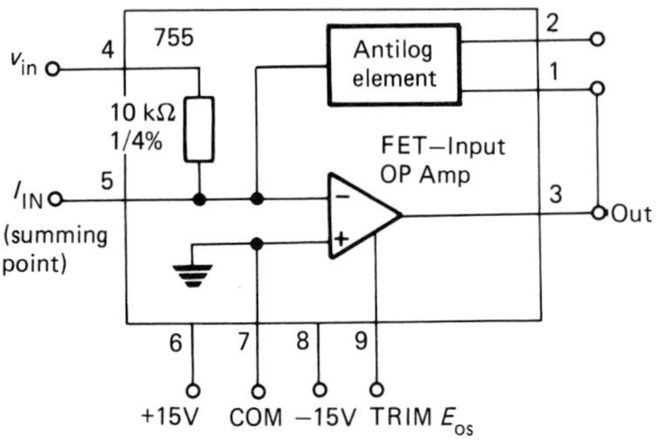

(a)

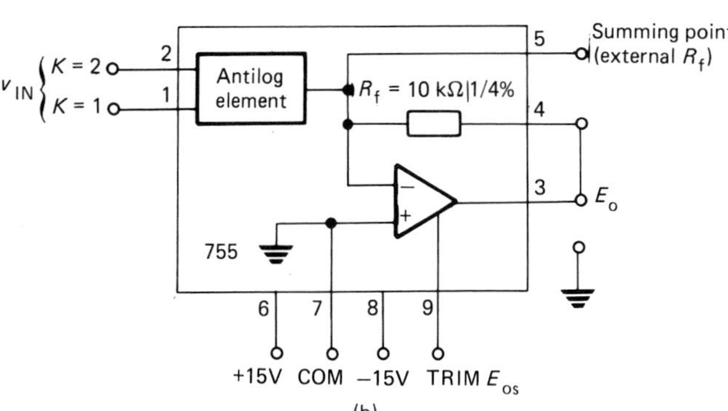

(b)

Figure 4.28 (a) Logarithmic amplifier; (b) antilogarithmic amplifier.

ratiometric measurements to be made. The square-root extractor, which is a single quadrant device allowing inputs of only one polarity, can be used in vector amplitude and r.m.s. computations and in linearizing the outputs from flowmeters based on differential pressure devices.

Integrated circuits are also available providing logarithmic and antilogarithmic amplification. They generally consist, as shown in Figures 4.28(a) and 4.28(b), of an operational amplifier and an exponential transconductance element. This element is usually provided by using the exponential current–voltage relationship of a transistor emitter–base junction. For logarithmic operation the element is applied in the feedback loop of the operational amplifier. In antilog operation the input voltage is applied directly to the input of the antilog element, which generates a current proportional to the exponential of the applied voltage. This current is then converted by the feedback resistance to a voltage at the output of the operational amplifier. Log-antilog amplifiers are available with a six-decade logarithmic conversion range and a typical log conformity error of 1.0 per cent. Logarithmic amplification is used for signal compression and for linearizing transducers with an exponential output characteristic. Antilogarithmic amplification is used to linearize transducers with a logarithmic output characteristic and in the expansion of compressed data.

4.3 Digital-to-analogue conversion

Decimal numbers can be represented in binary form as a series of bits which can take the value 1 or 0. Thus the number 191 is stored as an eight-bit binary number, as shown in Figure 4.29(a), and in general a decimal number, N, is represented in binary form by:

$$N = \sum_{n=0}^{M-1} a_n 2^n \tag{4.27}$$

where M is the number of bits used to represent the number and the constants a and n take the value 1 or 0.

To convert the digital number into an analogue voltage v_{out} requires the production of a voltage given by:

$$v_{out} = \frac{v_{ref}}{k} \sum_{n=0}^{M-1} a_n . 2^n \tag{4.28}$$

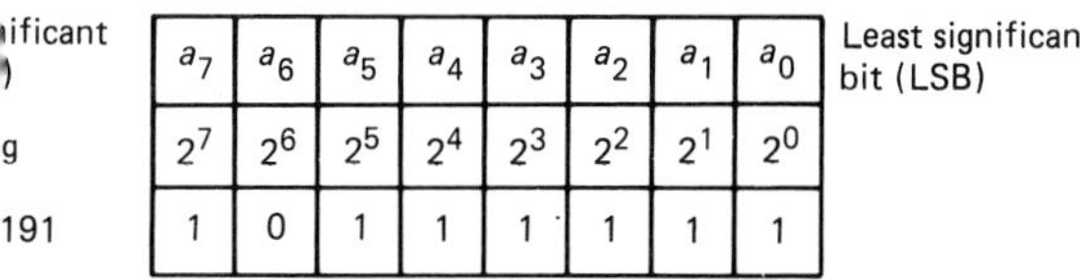

a_7	a_6	a_5	a_4	a_3	a_2	a_1	a_0
2^7	2^6	2^5	2^4	2^3	2^2	2^1	2^0
1	0	1	1	1	1	1	1

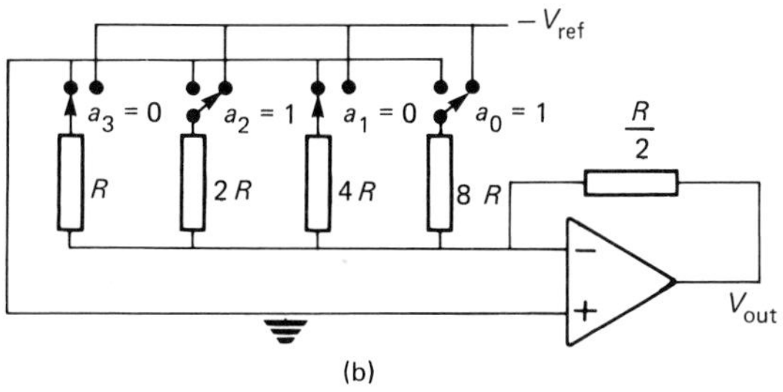

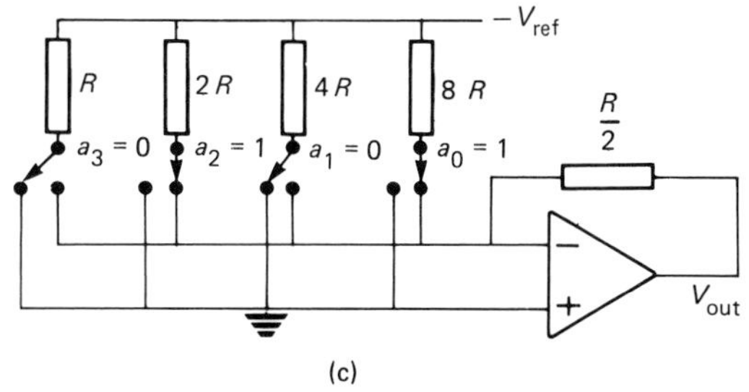

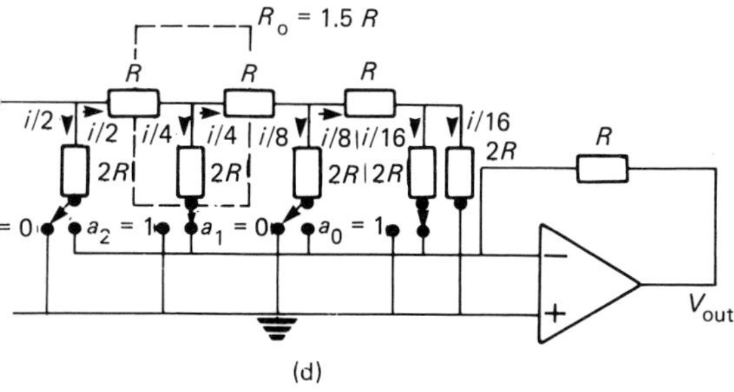

Figure 4.29 (a) Binary representation of a digital number; (b) voltage-switching DAC; (c) current-switching DAC; (d) *R-2R* ladder network.

where v_{ref} is the reference voltage of the digital-to-analogue converter (DAC) and k is a scaling constant. Thus an output voltage is produced by adding a series of weighted voltages together.

Figure 4.29(b) shows a voltage switching DAC using a weighted ladder network. The output from this device is given by:

$$v_{out} = v_{ref} \sum_{n=0}^{M-1} a_n . 2^{(n-M)} \tag{4.29}$$

The transient response of such a device depends largely on charging and discharging parasitic capacitances, and can be improved by using current switching instead of voltage switching. This is shown in Figure 4.29(c). In current switching the potentials of all the switch points are maintained irrespective of whether a particular element is representing a 1 or a 0. One major disadvantage of the weighted ladder technique is the spread of resistance values which are required. Even for an 8-bit DAC there is a 256:1 spread in the resistance values, and the problem gets progressively worse as the number of bits in the DAC increases. It is difficult to produce sets of resistors which are accurately matched and with temperature coefficients which track for such a large spread in values. Figure 4.29(d) shows the *R*-2*R* ladder solution to this problem. Since the iterative impedance of the network shown within the dotted lines is 1.5*R* then there is an equal division of the current at the indicated nodes. Thus the *R*-2*R* ladder technique achieves the required weightings with a spread of resistance values of 2:1, irrespective of the number of bits in the converter. This technique forms the basis of most commercially available DACs. Digital-to-analogue conversion employing capacitive rather than resistive divider techniques suitable for fully integrated DACs employing MOS fabrication techniques are available.

DACs are available in which the reference voltage v_{ref} is no longer fixed but can be varied, and thus the output can be scaled by adjusting v_{ref}. This provides multiplication of the digital input by an analogue value. Such devices are called 'multiplying DACs'. DACs having a non-linear transfer characteristic are used in signal compression/expansion systems in order to allow efficient representation of analogue signals having a wide dynamic range. Devices such as the Precision Monolithic DAC-76 provide a dynamic range of 72 dB equivalent to a sign + 12-bit DAC in a sign + 7-bit format. When used in a feedback configuration in an analogue-to-digital converter such a DAC provides logarithmic conversion of the signal.

4.3.1 Accuracy of DACs

Since each digital code applied to the DAC should give rise to a unique analogue output it is possible to specify an accuracy of the DAC in terms of the error between the theoretically determined analogue output for that particular digital code and the actual analogue output. The error is caused by such factors as gain or calibration errors, zero offset errors and non-linearity errors. Two accuracies are usually specified by manufacturers—absolute accuracy and relative accuracy. Absolute accuracy is a measure of the deviation of the output of the DAC from the theoretical value for that digital code. Relative accuracy is the deviation from the theoretical value after the full-scale range has been calibrated. Both of these accuracies are specified as a percentage or parts per million (p.p.m.) of full-scale range or fractions of the least significant bit (LSB).

The ideal transfer characteristic of a DAC should be a series of analogue values, each one corresponding to a digital value, which, when plotted as shown in Figure 4.30(a), lie on a straight line. Gain or calibration error will mean that the slope of the transfer characteristic between the analogue output and the digital input will not have the correct slope. The zero error will have the effect that the digital code corresponding to zero will not give rise to zero output. These errors are shown in Figure 4.30(b).

The actual output from a DAC when plotted in the same manner as shown in Figure 4.30(a) will have a transfer characteristic which, after the gain and zero errors are removed, will not be a straight line. There are two measures of non-linearity—integral and differential. These are shown in Figures 4.30(c) and 4.30(d), respectively. Integral non-linearity is the deviation between the analogue output at a point and a straight-line transfer characteristic. The straight line can be chosen in several ways. It may simply be the straight line joining the end points of the transfer characteristic or it may be a line constructed in such a manner as to equalize the maximum positive and negative deviations from the line. As shown in Figure 4.30(c), by carefully choosing the line it is possible to improve

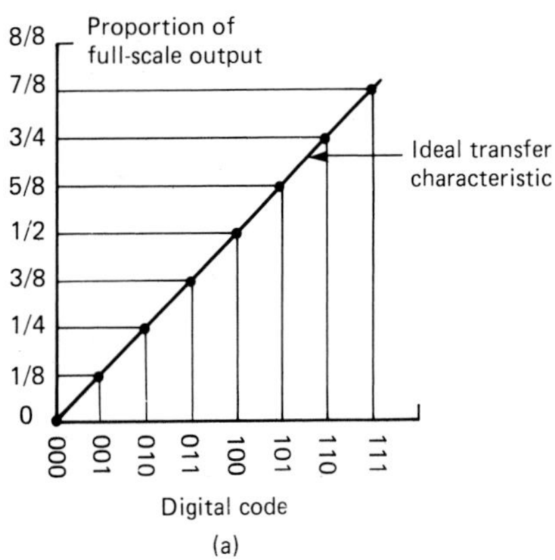

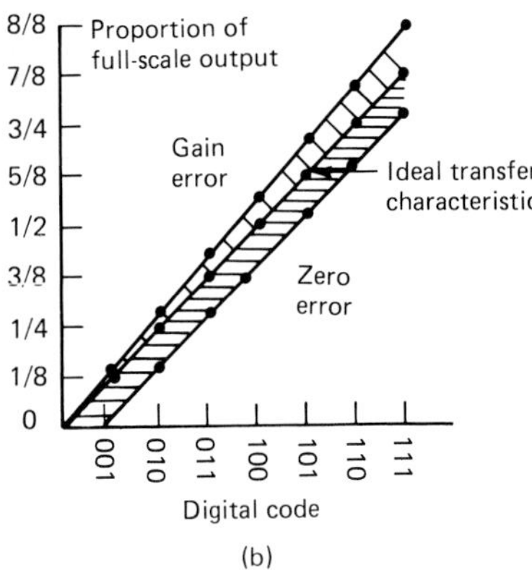

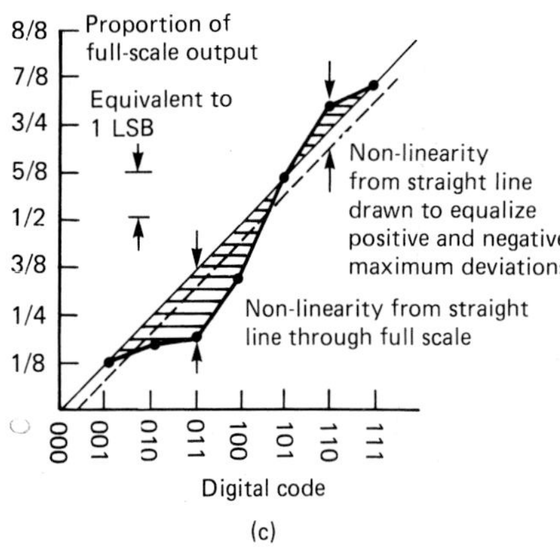

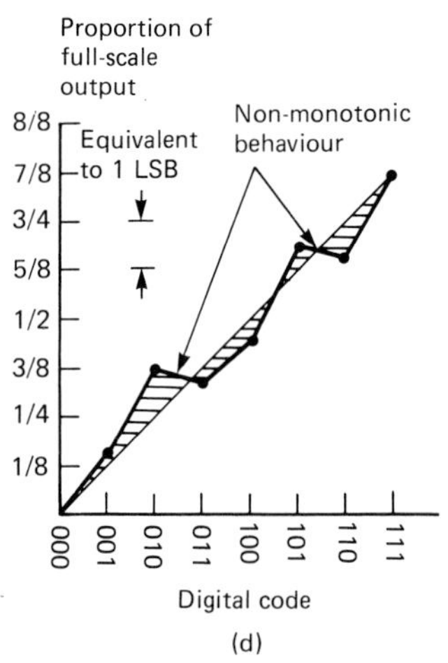

Figure 4.30 (a) Ideal transfer characteristic for DAC; (b) gain and zero error in a DAC; (c) integral non-linearity; (d) differential non-linearity.

the integral non-linearity specification. Integral non-linearity is expressed as a percentage or p.p.m. of full-scale range or as fractions of 1 LSB.

Ideally, as the digital input changes by 1 LSB the analogue output should change by a voltage equivalent to 1 LSB, no matter where on the digital input scale that change is effected. Differential non-linearity is the deviation of the change in the output, from the theoretical analogue output voltage equivalent to 1 LSB, as the digital input is changed by 1 LSB. It is usually expressed in fractions of 1 LSB. In order to ensure that the analogue output increases or remains constant as the digital input is increased, it is necessary that the differential non-linearity should be less than 1 LSB. If the differential non-linearity of a DAC is less than 1 LSB then the DAC is said to be monotonic. Monotonicity is particularly important when a DAC is used in an analogue-to-digital converter since non-monotonicity leads to missed codes in the analogue-to-digital conversion. It is also important in control applications where non-monotonicity can lead to 180 degrees of phase shifting of signals within the control loop, and can thus produce stability problems.

DACs are specified primarily by the number of bits they convert, the accuracy and linearity of conversion and the conversion time, which is typically measured by its settling time. This is the time required, following a prescribed data change, for the output of the device to reach and remain within a given fraction, usually ±½LSB, of its final value. The usual prescribed changes being full scale, 1 most significant bit (MSB) and 1 LSB at a major carry.

Table 4.4 DAC specification

Number of bits	8
Relative accuracy	±0.1% of FS
Monotonicity	Guaranteed
Settling time	250 ns
V_{ref}	−16.5 to +5.5 V
Output current	2 mA FS
Temperature coefficient of gain	20 p.p.m./K
CMOS or TTL compatible	

The output from a DAC may be either voltage or current and may be either unipolar or bipolar.

Manufacturers' specifications will also include the reference input, which can be internal or external, fixed or variable, single polarity or bipolar; the coding and data levels of the digital input of the DAC; the level, sense, loading and timing of control signals applied to the DAC; power supply requirements; output noise; offset; and the temperature coefficients of gain, linearity and offset. For further details of these the reader should consult Analog Devices (1984). Table 4.4 shows a typical specification for a medium-speed 8-bit DAC.

4.4 Analogue-to-digital conversion

Analogue-to-digital converters (ADCs) convert an analogue signal whose amplitude can vary continuously into a digital form which has a discrete number of levels. The number of levels is fixed by the number of bits employed in the conversion, and this sets the resolution of the conversion. For a binary code having n bits there are 2^n levels. Since the digital representation is discrete, there is a range of analogue values which all have the same digital representation. There is thus a quantization uncertainty in analogue-to-digital conversion of ±½LSB, and this is in addition to any other errors which may occur in the conversion itself. The methods which are available for analogue-to-digital conversion split into four general methods. These are voltage-to-time conversion, voltage-to-frequency conversion, feedback methods employing DACs and simultaneous comparison techniques (Owens, 1983; Arbel, 1980; Sheingold, 1977).

4.4.1 Voltage-to-time conversion

These techniques all employ some method of converting the voltage measurement into a corresponding time measurement. The available methods include voltage-to-pulsewidth conversion; single-slope conversion (which is sometimes called single-ramp conversion); and dual-slope conversion (which is also known as dual-ramp conversion). The voltage-to-pulsewidth converter in Figure 4.31(a) employs a voltage-controlled monostable to produce a pulse whose width is proportional to the input voltage. The width of this pulse is then measured by means of the reference clock. Thus the counter has within it at the end of the conversion a binary number which corresponds to the analogue input.

Two different single-ramp converters are shown in Figures 4.31(b) and 4.31(c). In Figure 4.31(b) the voltage to be measured is applied to the reference terminal of the comparator. The time measured is that for the ramp to climb from 0 V to the input voltage v_{in}. The start pulse enables the clock gate and the stop pulse, which is derived from the output of the comparator, disables it. This time is measured using the reference clock. In the converter in Figure 4.31(c) the input voltage to be measured is stored on a capacitor, and the time to be measured is that required to discharge the capacitor using a constant current source.

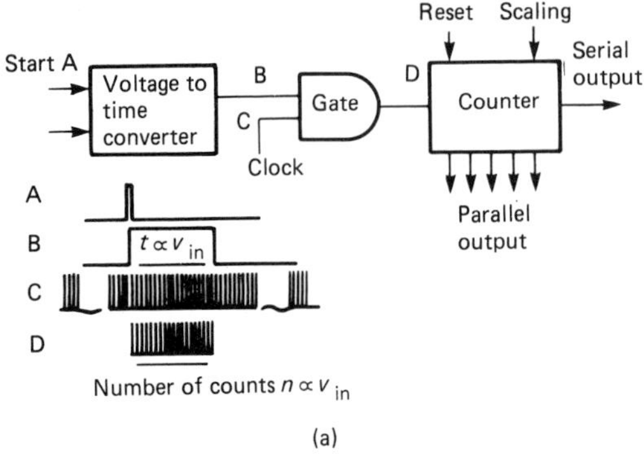

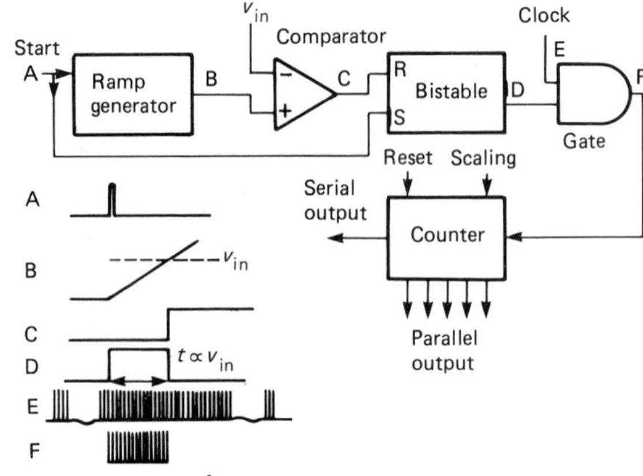

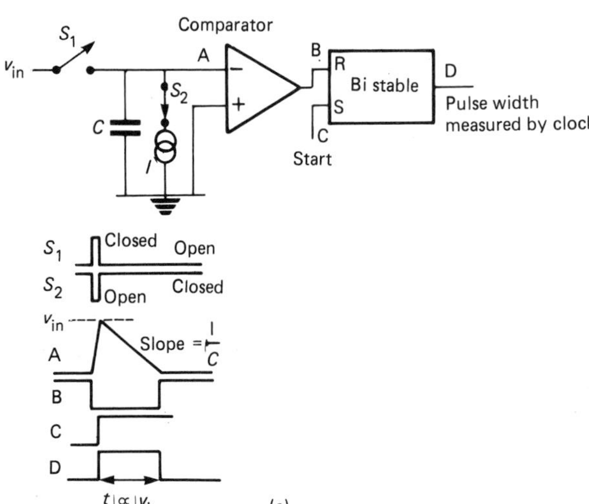

Figure 4.31 (a) Voltage-to-pulsewidth converter; (b) and (c) single-ramp converter; (d) dual-ramp converter.

The dual-ramp conversion technique shown in Figure 4.31(d) has the advantage of line frequency signal rejection. The operation of the converter is as follows.

The input voltage is electronically switched to the input of the integrator for a fixed period of time t_1, after which time the integrator output will be $-v_{in}t_1/RC$. The reference voltage $-v_{ref}$ is then applied to the integrator and the time is then measured for the output of the integrator to ramp back to zero. Thus:

$$\frac{v_{in}.t_1}{RC} = \frac{v_{ref}.t_2}{RC} \tag{4.30}$$

from which:

$$t_2 = \frac{v_{in}}{v_{ref}}.\ t_1 \tag{4.31}$$

If t_1 is a fixed number of counts, n_1, of a clock having a period t_c and t_2 is measured with the same clock, say, n_2 counts, then:

$$n_2 = \frac{v_{in}}{v_{ref}}.\ n_1 \tag{4.32}$$

The R and C components of the integrator do not appear in the defining equation of the ADC, neither does the frequency of the reference clock. The only variable which does appear in the defining equation is the reference voltage. The effect of offset voltage on the comparator will be minimized as long as its value remains constant over the cycle, and also providing it exhibits no hysteresis. Modifications of the technique employing quad slope integrators are available which reduce the effects of switch leakage current and offset voltage and bias current to second-order effects (Analog Devices, 1984). Errors caused by non-linearity of the integrator limit the conversion using dual-ramp techniques to five decades.

The rejection of line frequency is achieved as follows. If the input is a d.c. signal with an a.c. interference signal superimposed on it:

$$v_{in} = v_{d.c.} + v_{a.c.} \sin(\omega t + \phi) \quad (4.33)$$

where ϕ represents the phase of the interference signal at the start of the integration, then the value at the output of the integrator, v_{out}, at the end of the period t_1 is given by:

$$v_{out} = -\frac{v_{d.c.} t_1}{RC} - \frac{1}{RC} \int_0^{t_1} v_{a.c.} \sin(\omega t + \phi).dt \quad (4.34)$$

If the period, t_1 is made equal to the period of the line frequency then the integral of the line frequency signal or any harmonic of it over the period will be zero, as shown in Figure 4.31(d).

At any other frequency it is possible to find a value of ϕ such that the interference signal gives rise to no error. It is also possible to find a value ϕ_{max} such that the error is a maximum. It can be shown that the value of ϕ_{max} is given by:

$$\tan \phi_{max} = \frac{\sin \omega t_1}{(1 - \cos \omega t_1)} \quad (4.35)$$

The series mode rejection (SMR) of the ADC is given as the ratio of the maximum error produced by the sine wave to the peak magnitude of the sine wave. It is normally expressed in decibels as

series mode rejection (SMR) =

$$-20 \log_{10} \frac{\omega t_1}{\cos\phi_{max} - \cos(\omega t_1 + \phi_{max})} \quad (4.36)$$

A plot of the SMR of the ADC is shown in Figure 4.32. It can be seen that ideally the dual slope ADC provides infinite SMR for any frequency given by n/t_1, $n = 1,2,3...$. Practically, the amount of rejection such an ADC can produce is limited because of non-linear effects, due to the fact that the period t_1 can only be defined to a finite accuracy and that the frequency of the signal to be rejected may drift. However, such a technique can easily provide 40 dB of line-frequency rejection.

This technique is commonly used when low-speed conversion is required. Because of the integrating nature of the technique it is not suitable for rapidly changing or multiplexed signals. It is commercially available in integrated form, and forms the basis for most digital voltmeters.

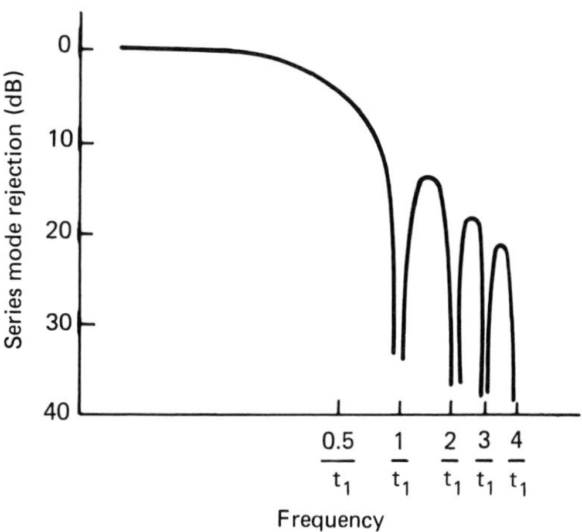

Figure 4.32 Series mode rejection for a dual-ramp converter.

4.4.2 Voltage-to-frequency conversion

Such techniques employ circuitry which converts the input voltage into a frequency which is linearly related to the input voltage. The analogue signal is converted to its digital equivalent by gating the frequency signal over a fixed period of time. Frequency transmission is often employed as a method of transmitting analogue data. A simple form of voltage-to-frequency conversion is shown in Figure 4.33(a). The input signal is integrated for the time that it takes the integrator output to go from 0 to $-v_{ref}$, i.e. for a time given by:

$$t = \frac{RC v_{ref}}{v_{in}} \quad (4.37)$$

If the discharge time for the capacitor is small, then the repetition frequency of the converter is given by:

$$f = \frac{v_{in}}{RC v_{ref}} \quad (4.38)$$

The accuracy of the conversion can be improved by using the frequency-to-voltage converter in a feedback configuration with a voltage-to-frequency converter (Owens, 1983).

Figure 4.33(b) shows a charge balance converter in which the output of the integrator is periodically reset, not by shorting it out but by injecting a charge onto it in the form of a current pulse containing a fixed charge. Thus over one cycle of operation the charge provided to the feedback capacitor by the current v_{in}/R exactly balances that supplied by the current pulse:

$$It_1 = \frac{v_{in}t_2}{R} \tag{4.39}$$

and

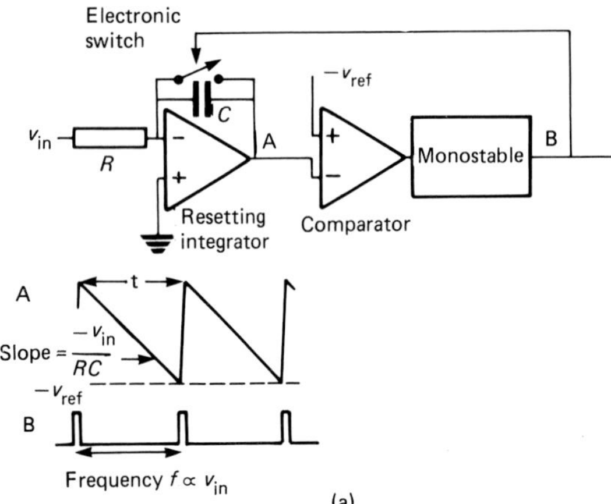

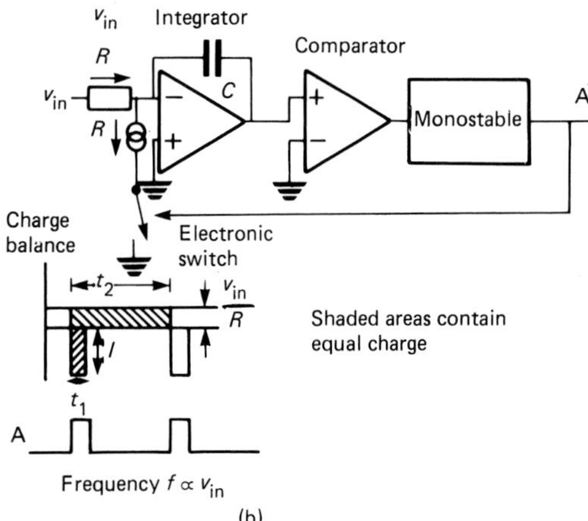

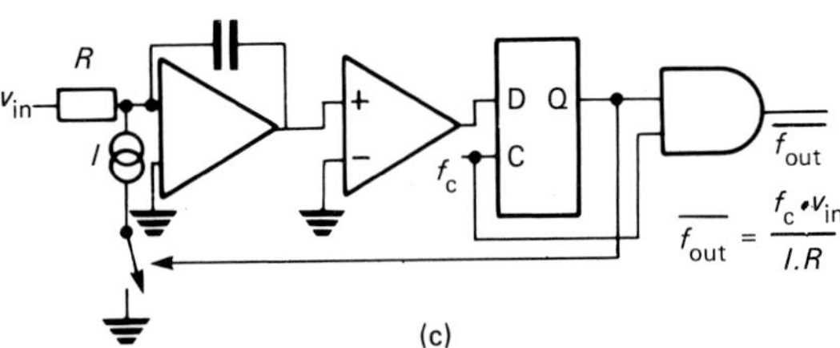

Figure 4.33 (a) Voltage-to-frequency converter; (b) charge balance converter; (c) delta–sigma modulation.

$$f = \frac{1}{t_2} = \frac{v_{in}}{R.I.t_1} \tag{4.40}$$

Delta–sigma modulation (Steele, 1975) is a form of voltage-to-frequency conversion which is often used in speech transmission. This is shown in Figure 4.33(c).

4.4.3 Feedback methods employing DACs

Feedback techniques adjust the digital input of a DAC in such a way as to find the digital input for the DAC whose analogue output most closely corresponds to the input voltage which is to be measured.

In the ramp or staircase generator shown in Figure 4.34(a) a counter is used to set the input of the DAC. Initially, the digital input is set to zero, and therefore the analogue output of the DAC is zero. The counter is then incremented by the clock. As the input to the DAC is incremented, the analogue output of the DAC also steps in value. Stepping continues until the output of the DAC exceeds the input voltage. The comparator output switches and inhibits further clock pulses from being fed into the counter. The counter now contains the digital equivalent of the analogue input. The conversion speed for this converter is dependent on the level of the input signal. The speed of conversion of slowly varying signals can be improved by the use of additional hardware and an up–down counter to produce a tracking ADC which will follow slowly changing signals.

The successive approximation technique shown in Figure 4.34(b) employs a decision-tree approach to the problem. The control circuitry on the first cycle of the conversion sets the MSB of the DAC to 1 and all the rest of the bits to 0. The output of the comparator is examined. If it is a 1, implying that the analogue input is greater than the output of the DAC, then the MSB of the DAC is maintained at a 1, otherwise it is changed to a 0. The next cycle determines whether the next most significant bit is a 1 or a 0. This process is then repeated for each bit of the DAC. The conversion period of the successive approximation analogue-to-digital conversion technique is fixed for a given ADC, irrespective of the signal level, and is equal to $n\tau$, where n is the number of bits and τ is the cycle time for determining a single bit. Integrated-circuit successive-approximation logic-generating chips are available to be used in conjunction with standard DACs and comparators to produce medium-speed DACs.

4.4.4 Simultaneous comparison

For high-speed conversion, the successive-approximation technique is often not fast enough,

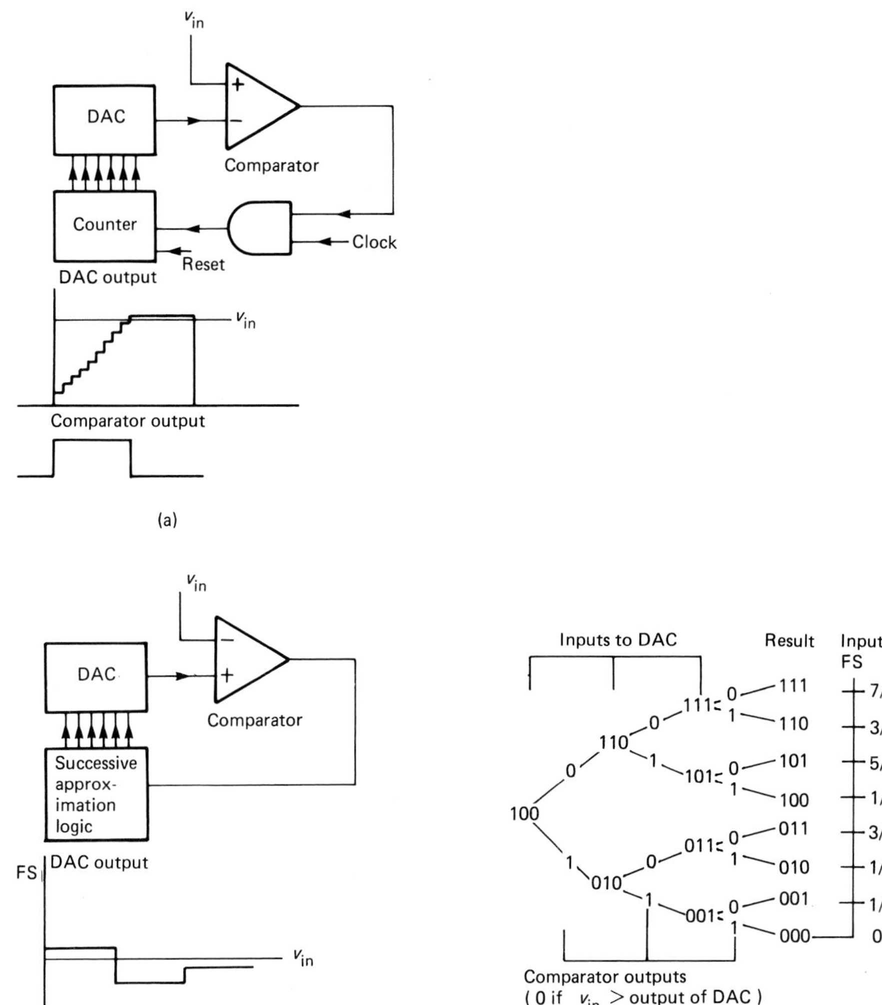

Figure 4.34 (a) Ramp or staircase generator; (b) successive approximation converter.

particularly in the digitization of video signals, and simultaneous comparison techniques are necessary. Such converters are called 'flash converters', since the conversion takes place in one cycle. Figure 4.35 shows the schematic diagram of a flash converter. The analogue values corresponding to each of the digital codes is simultaneously compared with the input. For an n-bit conversion, 2^{n-1} individual comparators are required. The logic then examines the output of the comparators and produces the digital code corresponding to the input. It is possible to reduce the number of comparators required in an n-bit conversion by means of subranging. In the first stage of the conversion the analogue signal is digitized using a set of comparators. This value is then stored in a latch and fed into a high-speed DAC. The output from this DAC is subtracted from the original analogue input and this difference or residue is amplified and redigitized using the same converters. By combining the two digitized values it is possible to produce an n-bit digital number corresponding to the analogue input.

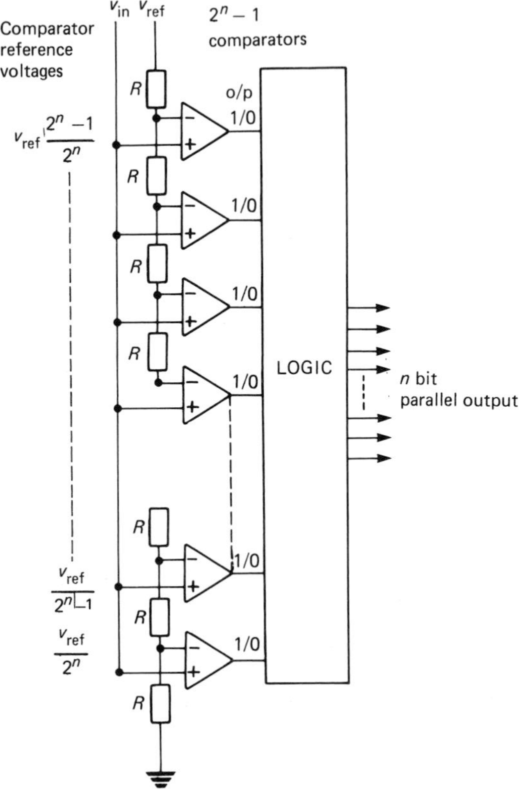

Figure 4.35 Flash converter.

4.4.5 ADC specifications

The most commonly encountered ADCs are dual-slope, successive-approximation and flash converters. These devices can be specified in terms of their analogue, digital and control sections, with the most important performance specifications being the resolution, accuracy and linearity of conversion, together with the conversion time or rate.

The analogue section of the ADC is usually specified in terms of the allowable analogue input signal range together with its associated source impedance. ADCs may accept either unipolar or bipolar inputs.

The digital section is specified by the technology employed and the output coding and format. The digital output may use TTL, CMOS or ECL technology. Unipolar inputs can be represented by binary coding. Bipolar inputs, which can have both positive and negative values, can be represented by a series of codings, including offset binary coding, two's complement coding (which is the technique used for representing negative numbers in most computers) or sign and magnitude coding. ADCs which are used for digital voltmeters often use BCD coding with sign and magnitude coding. Figure 4.36 shows the transfer characteristics of a unipolar ADC and a bipolar ADC using offset binary coding.

The formatting of the output is important from the point of view of interfacing the ADC to other equipment. The most common formats are parallel, serial and byte serial. The byte serial format is used particularly in microprocessor-compatible ADCs, where it may be necessary to communicate the output of a 12-bit ADC to an 8-bit microcomputer.

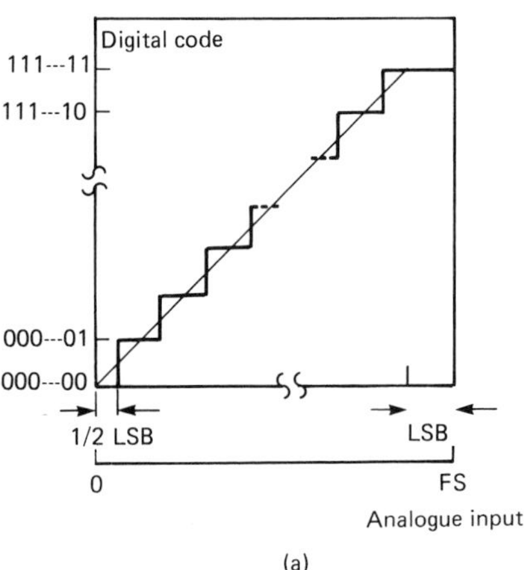

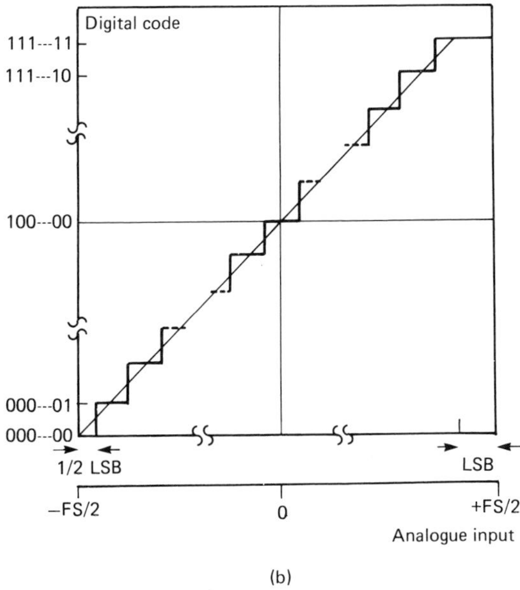

Figure 4.36 (a) Unipolar and (b) bipolar ADCs.

In such a case the data are transferred serially in two bytes, a high-order byte, which contains the more significant bits of the digital representation, and a low-order byte containing the remaining bits to complete the digital representation. For microprocessor applications it is necessary for the digital output of the converter to be tri-stated to provide the necessary isolation.

The control section is typically specified by the signals which are required by the ADC for such functions as start conversion, output the high-order byte, output the low-order byte and the control signals which the ADC gives to indicate the end of conversion.

The resolution provided by an ADC is fixed by the number of bits in the conversion.

The accuracy of the ADC is measured by its absolute and relative accuracies. The absolute error is the difference between the specified and actual values required to produce a given code. Since a range of analogue values will produce a given code, the analogue value is specified as the mid-range value. The error is caused by gain, zero and non-linearity errors together with noise. The relative accuracy is the error once the full-scale range has been calibrated.

The linearity of the converter is measured by its differential and integral non-linearity. Differential non-linearity, as shown in Figure 4.37, measures the difference in the range of values of the analogue input to produce a given code from the range equivalent to 1 LSB. A non-linearity of greater than 1 LSB in an ADC implies a missed code. This can occur particularly when a non-monotonic DAC is used in a feedback network to produce an ADC. If an ADC is specified as having no missed codes then its differential non-linearity is less than 1 LSB. Dual-slope ADCs do not exhibit missed codes. However, they are likely to exhibit integral non-linearity, which is concerned with the overall shape of the converter characteristic.

The conversion time of an ADC is the time required for a complete measurement to be made. The conversion rate for most ADCs is the inverse of the conversion time. In high-speed converters pipelining may, however, allow one conversion to commence before the previous one is completed.

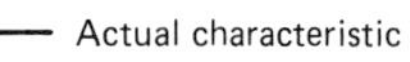

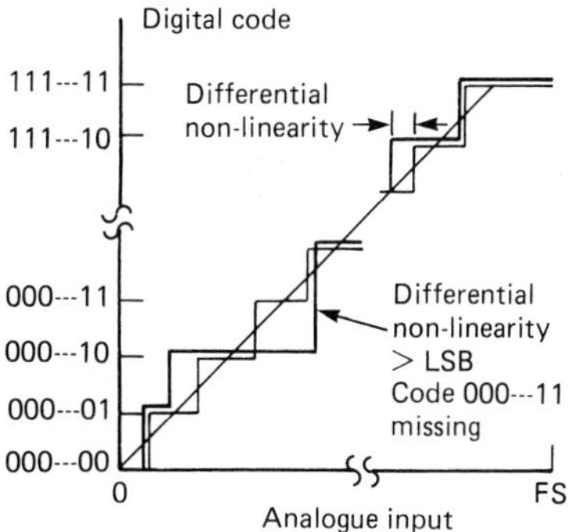

Figure 4.37 Differential non-linearity for ADC

Table 4.5 Specification of three ADCs

Device	AD571J	ICL7109	AD5010KD
Technique employed	Successive approximation	Dual ramp	Flash conversion
Number of bits	10	12	6
Linearity	Differential non-linearity ≤1LSB	Non-linearity w.r.t. straight-line fit ≤1LSB	Linearity error ±¼LSB
Analogue input ranges	Unipolar 0 V to +10 V Bipolar −5 to +5 V	+6.2 V to −9 V	±2.5 V
Output coding	Unipolar: positive true binary Bipolar: positive true offset binary	12-bit binary + polarity and over range bits	6 binary + over range bit
Format	Parallel output	Two-byte parallel output UART compatible	Parallel output
Digital inputs/outputs	TTL/CMOS	TTL/CMOS	ECL
Conversion time/rate	25 μs	30 conversion/s	10 ns

Thus the conversion rate can exceed the rate determined from the conversion time.

Other specifications which are given for an ADC include gain, linearity and offset temperature coefficients. Table 4.5 compares typical characteristics of three commonly used converters.

4.5 Spectrum analysers and related equipment

Signal analysis in the frequency domain is used extensively in the testing of mechanical systems and in electronics and telecommunications. In mechanical systems it is used with suitable vibration transducers to analyse the modes of vibration of mechanical structures and to investigate vibrations in rotating machinery brought about by mechanical unbalance or worn bearings or gears.

In electronics and telecommunications, frequency domain analysis is applied to the analysis of both random and periodic signals. Signal analysers can provide measurements of the frequency stability and spectral purity of signal sources. When used in conjunction with a tracking frequency generator or a source of white or pseudo-random noise they can be used to measure the frequency response of amplifiers, filters and other networks. The operational characteristics of transceivers and communications systems are assessed by the measurement of such parameters as the spectral purity of the carrier wave, the spectral power distribution of the amplitude or frequency modulated wave, signal distortion and system signal-to-noise ratios.

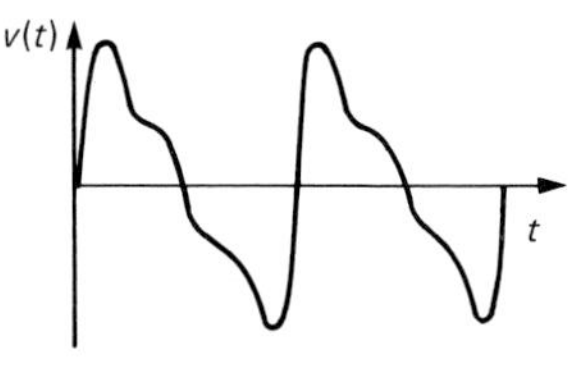

$v(t) = \sin \omega t + 0.4 \sin 2\omega t + 0.25 \sin 3\omega t$

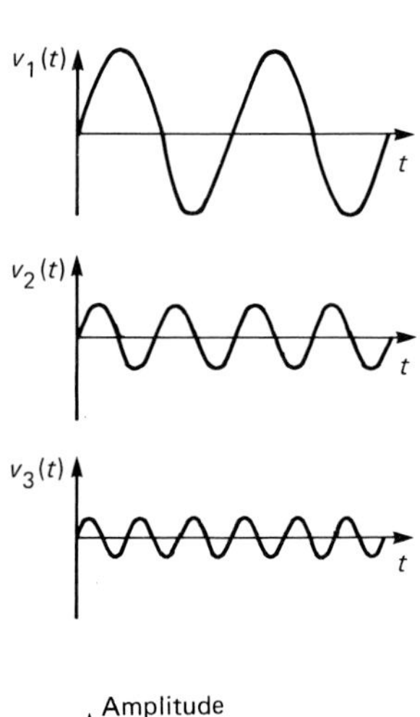

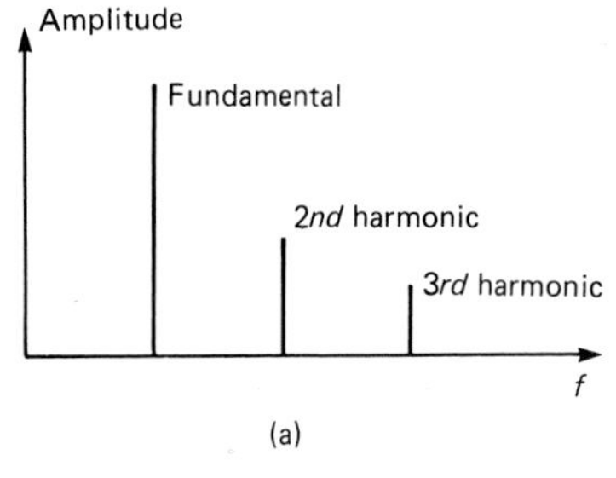

(a)

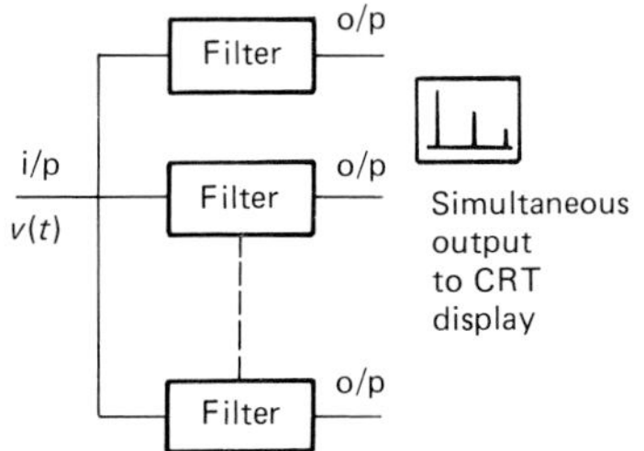

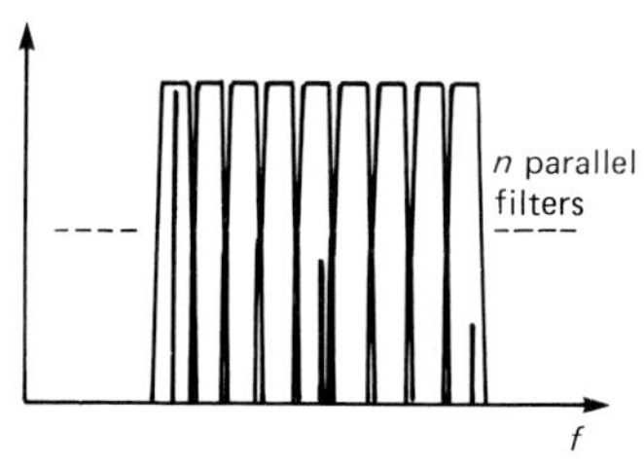

(i) Overlapping filter bank parallel filter bank analyser

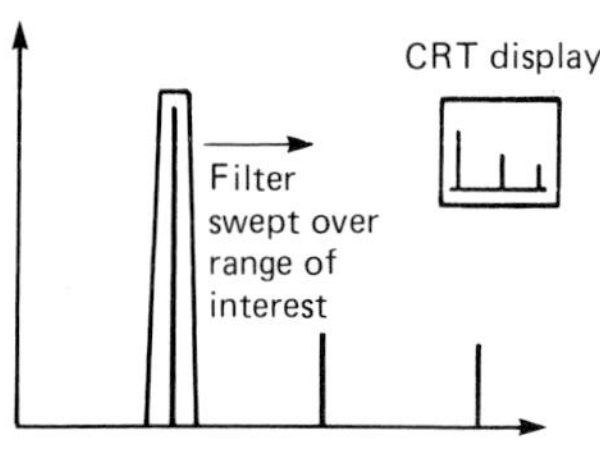

(ii) Swept-frequency analyser

(b)

Such analysis is provided by spectrum analysers, digital Fourier analysers, wave analysers and distortion analysers. Figure 4.38 shows how these different devices measure the various frequency parameters of a deterministic waveform whose time response $v(t)$ is composed of three frequency components $v_1(t)$, $v_2(t)$ and $v_3(t)$.

4.5.1 Spectrum analysers

These instruments provide displays of the frequency spectrum over a given frequency band. Spectrum analysers use either a parallel filter bank or a swept frequency technique. In the parallel filter bank analyser the frequency range is covered by a series of filters whose central frequencies and bandwidths are chosen so that they overlap. Typically, an audio analyser will have 32 of these filters, each covering one third of an octave. For wide band–narrow resolution analysis, particularly of r.f. or microwave signals, the preferred method of measurement is by means of the swept-frequency technique. In such analysers a narrow-band filter is centred around a frequency which is swept over the range for which the display is required. At a particular frequency the absolute value of the signal within that band is measured. The swept-frequency aspect of the spectrum analyser is usually achieved by heterodyning the input signal with the output of a local swept-frequency oscillator. A low-pass filter on the output of the mixer stage fixes the bandwidth of the narrow-band filter whilst the frequency of the local oscillator fixes its central frequency. By the use of a long-persistence CRT or a digital display it is

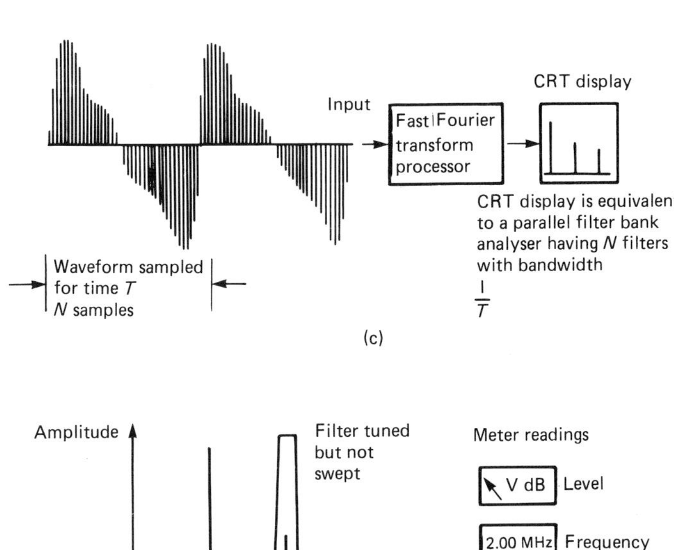

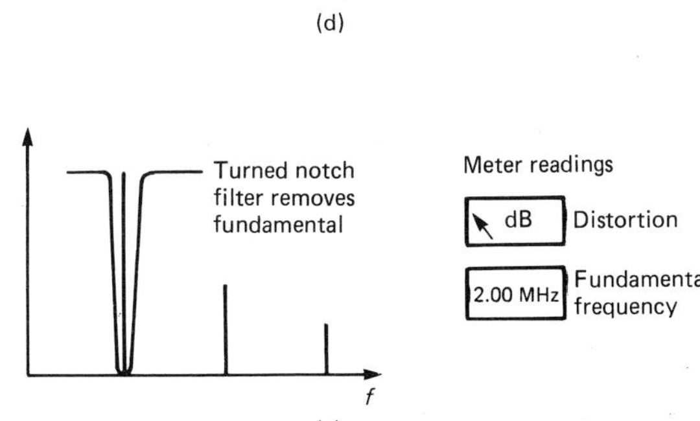

Figure 4.38 (a) Input waveform; (b) spectrum analyser; (c) digital Fourier analyser; (d) wave analyser; (e) distortion analyser.

possible to display the frequency spectrum as the swept-frequency oscillator sweeps over the required range. Figure 4.39 shows a schematic diagram of such an analyser suitable for analysing signals up to 1.25 GHz. The swept frequency is provided by sweeping either the 2–3.3 GHz local oscillator or the 500 MHz local oscillator, depending on the required range, which can be from 100 kHz to 1.25 GHz. The bandwidth of the filter is fixed by the band pass filters centred around 3 MHz at the output of the 3 MHz i.f. amplifier. This can be varied from 100 Hz to 300 kHz.

Typically, swept-frequency analysers are capable of operating with signals in the range from 5 Hz to 220 GHz with power levels in the range of −140 to +30 dBm. The bandwidth of the narrow-band filter varies with the frequency range over which the spectrum is being measured, and can vary from 1 Hz to 3 MHz.

4.5.2 Fourier analysers

Digital Fourier analysers convert the analogue waveform over a time period T into N samples. The discrete spectral response, $S_x(k\Delta f)$; $k = 1,2,\ldots,N$, which is equivalent to simultaneously obtaining the output from N filters having a bandwidth given by $\Delta f = 1/T$, is obtained by applying a discrete Fourier transform (DFT) to the sampled version of the signal. The spectral response is thus given by:

$$S_x(k.\Delta F) = \frac{T}{N}\sum_{n=1}^{N} x(n.\Delta t)\exp\left(\frac{-j.2\pi kn}{N}\right);\ k = 1,2,\ldots,N \quad (4.41)$$

$S_x(k\Delta f)$ is a complex quantity, which is obtained by operating on all the samples $x(n\Delta t)$; $n = 1,2,\ldots,N$ by the complex factor $\exp[-j(2\pi kn/N)]$. The discrete inverse transform is given by:

$$x(n\Delta t) = \frac{N}{T}\sum_{k=1}^{N} S_x(k.\Delta f)\exp\left(\frac{j.2\pi kn}{N}\right);\ n = 1,2,\ldots,N \quad (4.42)$$

Since $S_x(k\Delta f)$; $k = 1,2,\ldots,N$ is a complex quantity the DFT provides both amplitude and phase information at a particular point in the spectrum.

The discrete transforms are usually implemented by means of the fast Fourier transform (FFT) (Cooley and Tukey, 1965), which is particularly

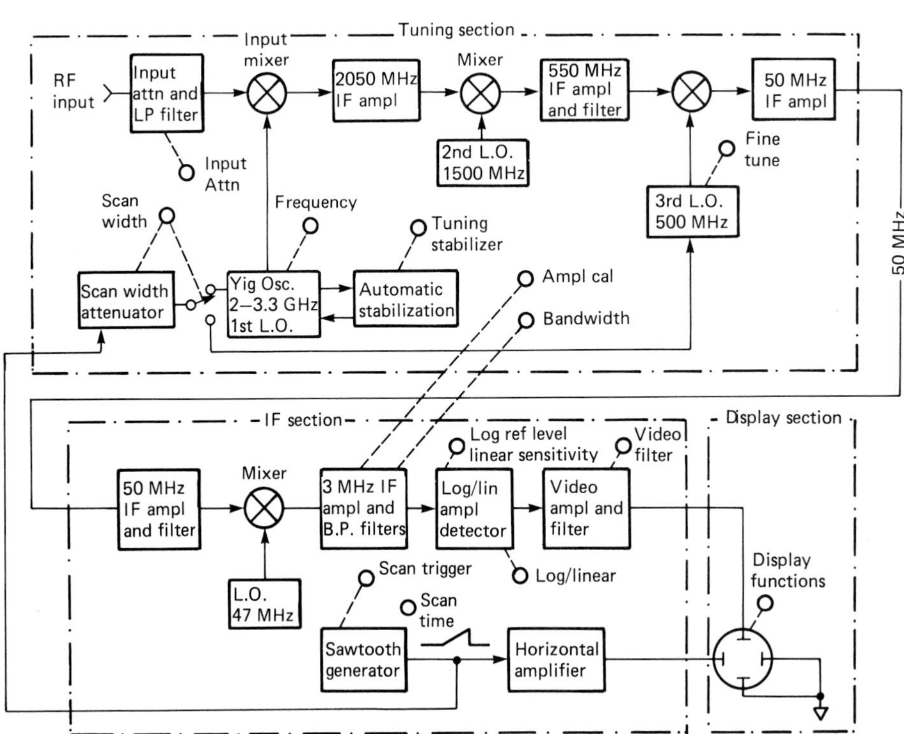

Figure 4.39 Swept-frequency analyser.

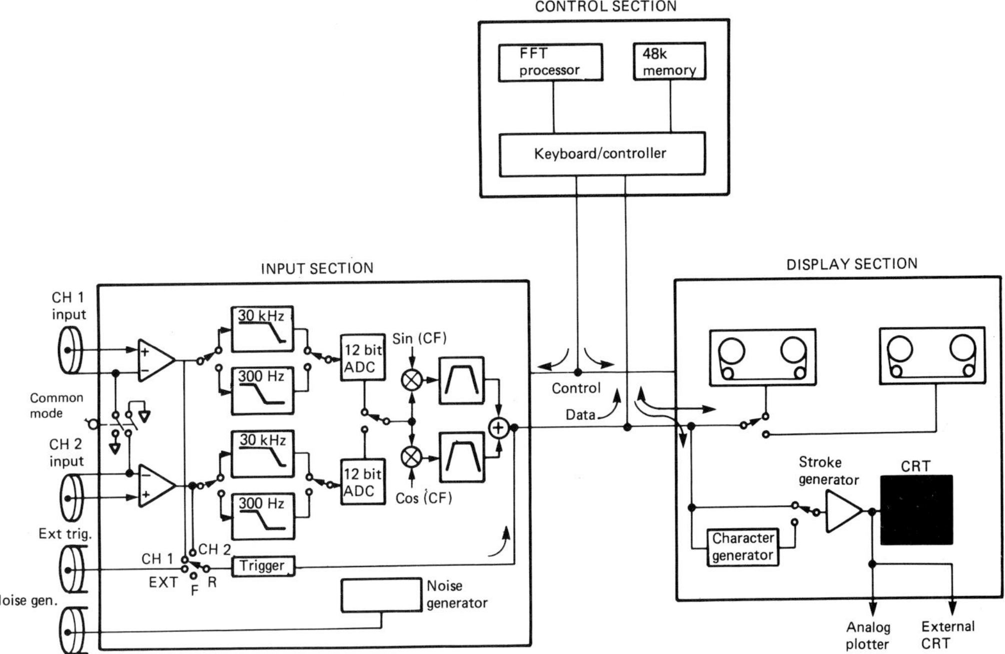

Figure 4.40 Digital signal analyser.

suitable for implementation in a digital computer since N is constrained to powers of 2 (e.g. 1024).

Figure 4.40 shows the block diagram representation of the HP5420 Digital Signal Analyser which employs a FFT algorithm. The input section consists of two identical channels. In each channel after the signal has been conditioned by the input amplifier the signal is passed through one of two anti-aliasing filters (see section 4.2.7.1). The cut-off frequency of these filters is chosen with respect to which of the sampling frequencies is being employed. The 30 kHz filter is used with a sampling rate of 102.4 kHz and the 300 kHz filter with a sampling rate of 1.024 MHz. The signal is then converted to a digital form using a 12-bit ADC. The multiplier and digital filter which follow allow the analyser to be used in either a baseband mode, in which the spectrum is displayed from d.c. to an upper frequency within the bandwidth of the analyser, or in a band-selectable mode, which allows the full resolution of the analyser to be focused in a narrow frequency band. The processing section of the analyser provides FFT processing on the input signal.

For one channel this can provide the real and imaginary or magnitude and phase components of the linear spectrum $S_x(f)$ of a time domain signal:

$$S_x(f) = F(x(t)) \tag{4.43}$$

where $F(x(t))$ is the Fourier transform of $x(t)$. The autospectrum, $G_{xx}(f)$, which contains no phase information is obtained from $S_x(f)$ by:

$$G_{xx}(f) = S_x(f).S_x(f)^* \tag{4.44}$$

where $S_x(f)^*$ indicates the complex conjugate of $S_x(f)$. $G_{xx}(f)$ normalized to a bandwidth of 1 Hz is the power spectral density (PSD), and represents the power in a bandwidth of 1 Hz centred around the frequency f.

In terms of the time domain characteristics of the signal $x(t)$ its autocorrelation function defined as:

$$R_{xx}(\tau) = \lim_{T\to\infty} \frac{1}{T} \int_0^T x(t)x(t+\tau).dt \tag{4.45}$$

is obtained by using the fact that the autocorrelation function is the inverse Fourier transform of $G_{xx}(f)$, i.e.:

$$R_{xx}(\tau) = F^{-1}(G_{xx}(f)) \tag{4.46}$$

and thus

$$R_{xx}(\tau) = F^{-1}(S_x(f).S_x(f)^*) \tag{4.47}$$

The inverse transform is obtained by use of equation (4.42).

Joint properties of two signals can be obtained by the use of the two channels. The cross power spectrum of two signals $x(t)$ and $y(t)$ can be computed as:

$$G_{yx}(f) = S_y(f).S_x(f)^* \tag{4.48}$$

where $S_y(f)$ is the linear spectrum of $y(t)$ and $S_x(f)^*$ is the complex conjugate linear spectrum of $x(t)$.

If $x(t)$ represents the input to a system and $y(t)$ the output of the system, then its transfer function, $H(f)$, which contains both amplitude and phase information, can be obtained by computing:

$$H(f) = \frac{\overline{G_{yx}(f)}}{\overline{G_{xx}(f)}} \tag{4.49}$$

where the bars indicate the time-averaged values. The input signal used for such measurements is often the internal random noise generator.

Coherence, given as:

$$\gamma^2 = \frac{\overline{G_{yx}(f) \,.\, G_{yx}(f)^*}}{\overline{G_{xx}(f)} \,.\, \overline{G_{yy}(f)}} \;; 0 \leqslant \gamma^2 \leqslant 1 \tag{4.50}$$

measures the degree of causality between the input to a system and its output. If $\gamma < 1$ this indicates that the system output is caused by sources in addition to the system input or caused by system non-linearity.

The cross-correlation function between the two signals $x(t)$ and $y(t)$, $R_{xy}(\tau)$, defined as:

$$R_{xy}(\tau) = \lim_{T\to\infty} \frac{1}{T} \int_0^T y(t).x(t+\tau).\mathrm{d}t \tag{4.51}$$

is also calculated within the analyser by means of the relationship which exists between the cross-correlation function in the time domain and the cross-spectral density in the frequency domain, namely:

$$R_{xy}(\tau) = F^{-1}(S_y(f).S_x(f)^*) \tag{4.52}$$

The HP 5420 Signal Analyser operates either in a base-band mode with a bandwidth from 0.8 Hz to 25.5 KHz, or in a passband mode, in which the central frequency of the frequency spectrum can be set between 0.016 Hz to 25.5 kHz, with bandwidths of between 0.008 Hz to 25.5 kHz. The input amplifiers have full-scale inputs variable between ±0.1 V and ±10 V.

For further details of the application of frequency analysis techniques in engineering the reader is directed to the work by Bendat and Piersol (1980). The series of applications notes on spectrum analysis produced by Hewlett Packard and referred to in the References provides an excellent introduction to the subject and to techniques for obtaining the best results from spectrum analysis equipment.

4.5.3 Wave and distortion analysers

Wave analysers (which are also known as frequency selective voltmeters, carrier frequency voltmeters or selective level meters) provide a finite bandwidth window filter which can be tuned over a frequency range. As the frequency range is swept, the analyser gives a visual indication of its central frequency and the amplitude at that frequency. Such analysers are used to provide amplitude measurements of a single component of a complex frequency signal, amplitude measurements in the presence of noise or interfering signals and measurement of energy in a well-defined bandwidth. Figure 4.38(d) shows the wave analyser measuring the amplitude of the $v_2(t)$ component in the waveform $v(t)$. Wave analysers typically operate from 15 Hz to above 32 MHz, with a selective band of between 3 Hz and 3.1 kHz, on signals having an absolute dynamic range from 0.1 μV to 300 V.

Distortion analysers provide band rejection around the central frequency to which it has been tuned and measure the energy in the rest of the spectrum. They are used to measure total harmonic distortion (THD), given by:

$$\text{THD} = \frac{\sqrt{[\Sigma(\text{harmonic amplitude})^2]}}{\text{fundamental amplitude}} \tag{4.53}$$

First, the energy in the total spectrum is measured and then a narrow-band filter is applied and the energy in the harmonics and noise is measured. THD is thus measured by:

$$\text{THD} = \frac{\sqrt{(\Sigma(\text{harmonics})^2 + \text{noise}^2)}}{\sqrt{((\text{fundamental})^2 + (\text{harmonics})^2 + (\text{noise})^2)}} \tag{4.54}$$

For harmonic content below 10 per cent this approximation will be within 0.5 per cent of the value given by the original definition.

Distortion analysers cover a frequency range from 5 Hz to 600 kHz and can measure distortion as low as 0.0018 per cent (−95 dB).

4.6 Lock-in amplifiers and phase-sensitive detection

Lock-in amplifiers provide a technique for the recovery of a coherent signal in the presence of noise. They can provide a very high degree of signal-to-noise ratio improvement without the drift associated with the production of high-Q bandpass filters. Their extensive range of applications includes signal processing from capacitive and inductive displacement transducers, radiometry, nuclear magnetic resonance and fringe position monitors (Blair and Sydenham, 1975).

The central element in the lock-in amplifier is the phase-sensitive detector (PSD), the operation of which is shown in Figure 4.41. The PSD consists of two channels having gain +1 and −1, the signal being synchronously switched between the two. The switching waveform can be represented by the Fourier series:

$$v_s(t) = \frac{4}{\pi}\left[\sin \omega t + \frac{1}{3}\sin 3\omega t + \frac{1}{5}\sin 5\omega t + \ldots\right] \quad (4.55)$$

If the input signal is:

$$v_{in}(t) + v \sin(\omega t + \phi) \quad (4.56)$$

then the output signal:

$$v_{out}(t) = v_{in}(t).v_s(t) \quad (4.57)$$

is given by:

$$v_{out}(t) = \frac{4v}{\pi}\sin(\omega t+\phi)\left[\sin \omega t + \frac{1}{3}\sin 3\omega t + \frac{1}{5}\sin 5\omega t \ldots\right] \quad (4.58)$$

and thus:

$$v_{out}(t) = 2v\left[\cos \phi - \frac{2}{3}\cos(2\,\omega t + \phi) + \ldots\right] \quad (4.59)$$

The low-pass filter on the output of the PSD provides a pass band for d.c. to f_{LPF} and attenuates the outputs at harmonics of the input frequency. Thus the d.c. output of the filter is given by:

$$v_{out}\text{ d.c.} = \frac{2v}{\pi}\cdot\cos\phi \quad (4.60)$$

For input signals at frequencies other than the fundamental of the switching waveform the response of the PSD is as shown in Figure 4.42, where the effect of the bandwidth of the low-pass filter is

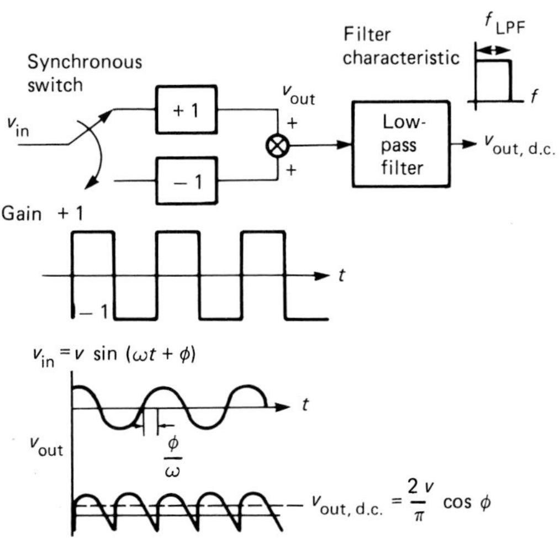

Figure 4.41 Phase-sensitive detector.

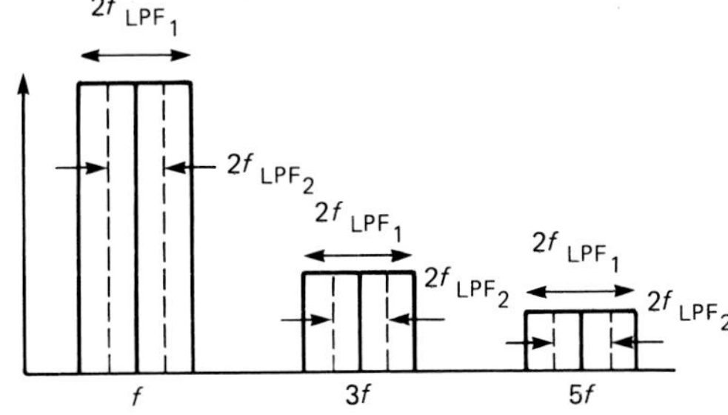

Figure 4.42 Frequency response of PSD.

shown. The PSD responds to signals in frequency bands centred around the fundamental and odd harmonics of the switching waveform. Signals whose frequencies correspond to the harmonic components of the switching waveform will give rise to d.c. signals. Those within the frequency bands centred around the harmonic frequencies will give rise to a.c. output signals whose frequency corresponds to a beat between the input signal and the harmonic of the switching waveform within that band. The amplitude response in each of these bands falls off as the number of the harmonic. By reducing the bandwidth of the low-pass filter it is thus possible to provide narrow-band filtering of the input signal. Figure 4.43 shows the block diagram representation of the Brookdeal Ortholoc SC 9505 two channel lock-in amplifier. The lock-in amplifier consists of a variable gain a.c. amplifier, a reference channel, two phase-sensitive detectors followed by d.c. amplification and filtering, and a vector computer. The input amplifier provides for either single-ended or differential voltage inputs or current input. These amplifiers are capable of providing an input sensitivity for full-scale output of between 10 nV and 500 mV or a current sensitivity as low as 10^{-14} A. The a.c. amplifier provides variable gain in order that the correct level of signal is presented to the PSDs together with high-pass and low-pass filtering. The reference channel generates two orthogonal reference waveforms for the two PSDs from a wide variety of input signal types and levels. Internal to the reference channel is a phase shifter which allows the phase of these two signals to be adjusted relative to the input signal. The lock-in amplifier has several modes of operation. These different modes adjust the distribution of gain between the a.c. gain prior to the PSD and the d.c. gain after the PSD.

In its HI-STAB mode the d.c. gain is minimized, and in such a mode the instrument has the best baseline stability. In its HI-RES mode the d.c. gain

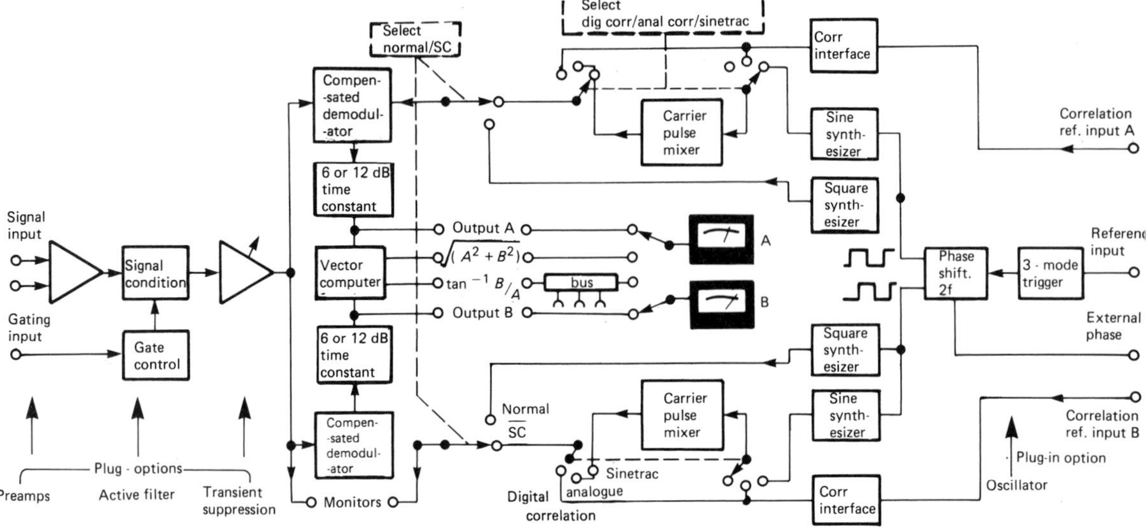

Figure 4.43 Two-channel lock-in amplifier.

is switched to its maximum value and consequently the PSD has its maximum overload capability and this allows the lock-in amplifier to extract the signal from a high level of noise. The lock-in amplifier output can be switched to indicate the magnitudes of the two orthogonal components A and B of the incoming signal or, by using the vector computer, the amplitude $\sqrt{(A^2 + B^2)}$ or the phase $\phi = \tan^{-1}(B/A)$ of the incoming signal.

By switching the reference channel with a variable mark to space ratio square wave whose mark-to-space ratio is determined by the input signal, the lock-in amplifier can be used in a SINETRAC mode, in which the response is to the fundamental only or as an analogue or digital correlator. The Brookdeal Ortholoc has a frequency range from 0.2 Hz to 200 kHz, a maximum broadband non-coherent input voltage for full-scale output of 10 000 × full scale and an input dynamic range of up to 160 dB.

For further details of the design of lock-in amplifiers and of their applications the reader is directed to the two works by Meade (1983a,b).

4.7 Box-car integrators

In the averaging of noisy repetitive signals which arise as a consequence of some external stimulus, as in the measurement of the signals within the neurological system, or which can be time referenced to some external triggering signal, the box-car

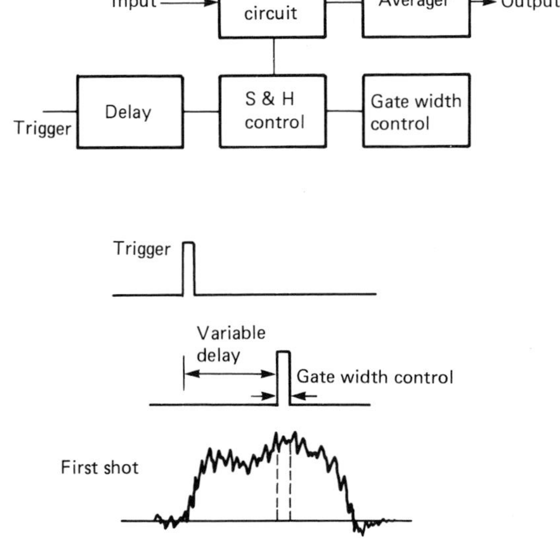

Figure 4.44 Box-car integrator.

integrator provides a method of averaging out the noise signals and of thus improving the signal-to-noise ratio (Arbel, 1980).

The operation of a box-car integrator is shown in Figure 4.44. The system employs a triggering signal which is time referenced to the signal being averaged. This, in neurological systems, may be the applied stimulus. The variable delay allows a particular section of the response signal to be selected. The sample and hold circuit is opened for a short aperture period and the signal within the gate width of the sample and hold circuit is stored. Repetition of the signal allows the portion of the signal at exactly the same time relative to the trigger to be selected. The system then averages the signal in this portion of the waveform. As the number of repetitions increases, the signal-to-noise ratio of the averaged signal improves. The improvement is proportional to the root of the number of repetitions. Automatic systems are available which scan the whole of the waveform, with an internally selected gate width to ensure that over a series of repetitions of the signal each section is averaged several times.

4.8 Correlators

Correlation is used in control and instrumentation for system identification, signal recovery and for the measurement of transport delays (for example, in the measurement of two-phase flows and steel strip and paper strip velocity measurement). Details of such applications can be found in Lange (1967) and Beck (1983).

The application of correlation techniques to flow velocity measurements is shown in Figure 4.45. These techniques depend upon measuring a random disturbance at one point in the process and then the length of time taken for the disturbance to pass the second measurement point. The transit time is estimated by cross correlating some signal generated by the disturbance which may be detected using optical, ultrasonic, thermal or impedance measurement techniques.

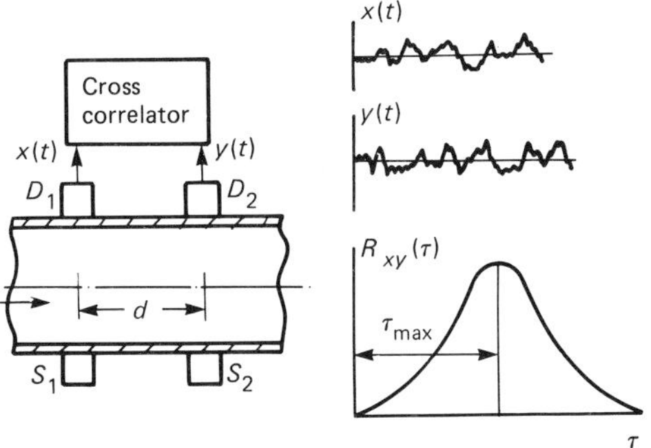

Figure 4.45 Flow velocity measurement using cross correlation.

The cross-correlation function of the two signals is given by:

$$R_{xy}(\tau) = \lim_{T\to\infty} \frac{1}{T} \int_0^T x(t-\tau) \,.\, y(t) \,.\, dt \qquad (4.61)$$

$R_{xy}(\tau)$ has a maximum value at a time τ_{max} corresponding to the transit time. If the separation of the two measuring stations is d then the transport velocity is given by:

$$v = \frac{d}{\tau_{max}} \qquad (4.62)$$

As shown in section 4.5, the cross-correlation function between two signals can be obtained by performing a Fourier transform on their cross-power spectrum, and thus a Fourier analyser can be used. Computation of the cross-correlation function can be provided by direct digital computation as:

$$R_{xy}(n.\Delta t) = \frac{1}{N} \sum_{k=1}^{N} x((k-n)\Delta t).y.(k.\Delta t) \qquad (4.63)$$

However, quantizing the data into a large number of bits, providing the necessary delayed version of the x signal, and the digital computation of the cross-correlation function require systems which hitherto have been expensive. The problem can be somewhat simplified, and yields itself to solutions using VLSI technology or microprocessor-based systems by either quantizing the signal into only two levels (depending on whether the signal is positive or negative) or by correlating zero crossings of the two signals. Examples of such approaches have been given by Jordan (1979), Henry (1979) and Keech (1982).

Quantizing the signal into two levels is known as 'parity bit quantization', and the estimate of the correlation function in such a scheme is given by:

$$R_{xyp}(n.\Delta t) = \frac{1}{N} \sum_{k=1}^{N} \mathrm{sgn}[x(k-n)\Delta t]\mathrm{sgn}[y(k\Delta t)] \qquad (4.64)$$

Thus multiplication is reduced to the logical exclusive OR between the bit representing sgn $x((k-n)\Delta t)$ and the bit representing sgn $y(k\Delta t)$.

Figure 4.46 shows the block diagram representation of a commercially available parity bit correlator designed for two-phase flow measurement. The correlator provides either a 256-, 512- or 1024-point correlation function with sampling intervals of 100,

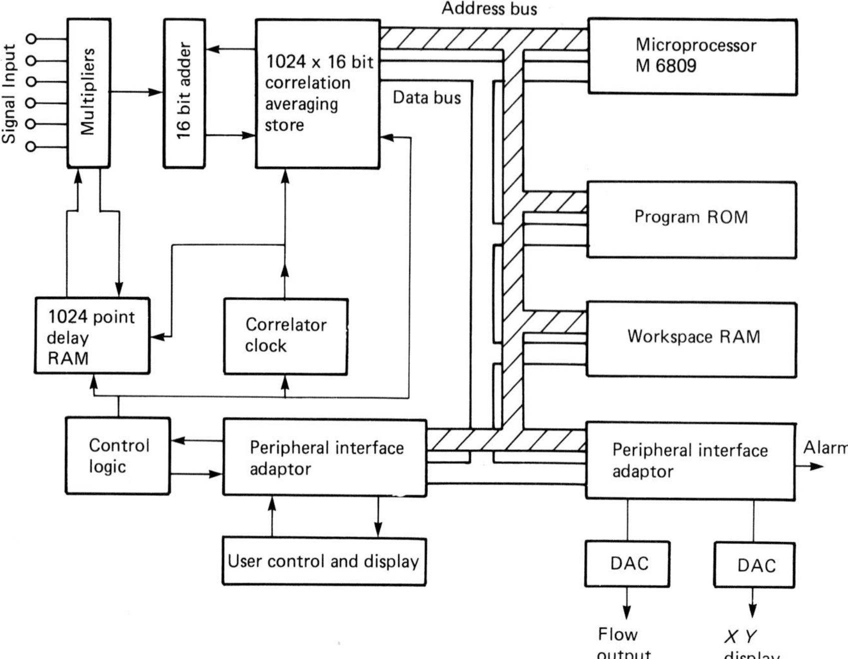

Figure 4.46 Parity-bit correlator (courtesy Kent Industrial Measurements).

200 or 400 μs, respectively. The correlation function, which can be represented by 1024 × 16 bits, is provided by means of a hard-wired logic. Computation on the correlation function is provided by the microprocessor, which provides adaptive filtering of the correlation function to improve the performance of the instrument under transient conditions; estimates the peak of the correlation function; and provides validation of the results by sensing such conditions as zero flow, shock waves, intense pressure waves and oscillating flow components.

4.9 Multichannel analysers

Multichannel analysers (MCAs) are used to measure the statistical properties of random signals. They can be used in the analysis of the energies of α, β and γ particles, or X-rays; for the measurement of the time intervals between events; or for obtaining count information of the number of occurrences of a particular event in sequential time intervals. They are used extensively in nuclear, chemical, medical and materials analysis.

The MCA operates in two modes, known as the pulse height analysis (PHA) mode and the multichannel scaling (MCS) mode. Both of these are shown in Figure 4.47.

In the PHA mode the MCA measures the amplitude frequency distribution of a series of input pulses. The MCA consists of a series of addressable memory locations which are referred to as channels. Initially, the contents of all the memory locations are zero. The ADC converts the amplitude of the input signal into a digital form. This in turn is used

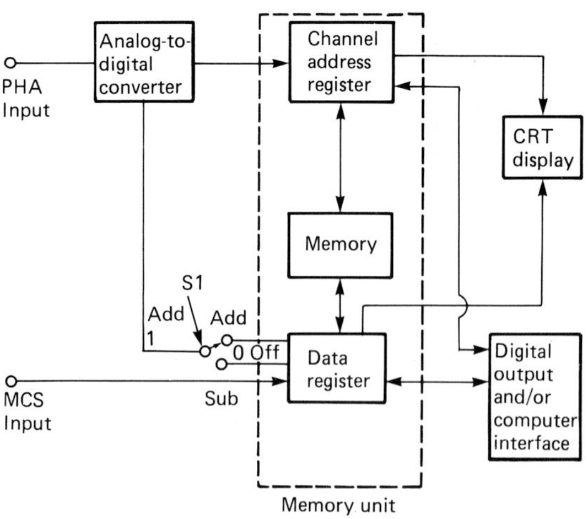

Figure 4.47 Multichannel analyser.

to address the memory. The value in the memory location corresponding to this address is loaded into the data register. A count of 1 is added to the contents of the data register and the data are then returned to the memory location from which it came. The count value in each channel or memory location at the end of the processing period is equal to the total number of pulses processed having amplitudes corresponding to that channel address.

In its MCS mode the channels act as a sequence of counters, with each channel counting events for a predetermined 'dwell time'. After this predetermined dwell time the counting is automatically passed to the next channel. The MCS thus provides a histogram of count-rate data, each channel representing a sequential time interval.

4.10 Computer systems

Much signal processing is now undertaken using a digital computer, with a wide variety of computing systems being used for the processing, ranging in size from embedded single-chip microprocessor-based systems up to large mainframe computers. It is not possible here to give more than an overview of the subject. There are a large number of specialist texts available dealing with digital computer systems and their applications, and for further details the reader should consult, for example, Bartree (1981), Lewin (1980) and Boyce (1977) for general system considerations; Paker (1980) for minicomputer systems and their application in instrumentation and control; and Aspinall (1980) and Barney (1985) for microcomputer systems and their applications.

There are two prime considerations in the specification of a digital computer system, the hardware and the software. The hardware of the system is the collection of electronic, electrical and mechanical devices making up the computer and its peripherals, which for a given system is fixed. The software is the set of stored programs which enable it to perform its prescribed tasks. The software is not fixed and within certain constraints (some of which are imposed by the particular language in which the programs are written and others which are imposed by the hardware of the computer) it is possible to modify the tasks performed by the computer. It is the stored-program aspect of the digital computer, giving the operator the ability to modify the tasks performed by the computer, which gives such a system its flexibility and power. The hardware aspects of the digital computer are dealt with in section 4.10.1 and the software is dealt with in section 4.10.2. Typical tasks undertaken by digital computers are considered in section 4.10.3. Section 4.10.4 gives examples of a single-chip microcomputer system suitable for use in an embedded microcomputer system, a control and data-logging subsystem based on a microcomputer and a measurement and control processor hosted by a minicomputer.

4.10.1 Hardware

Despite the wide variety of digital computer systems available, most systems use central processing units (CPUs) with the architecture shown in Figure 4.48(a) in computer systems with the overall structure as shown in Figure 4.48(b).

The digital computer system consists of a CPU, memory and input/output to peripheral devices. The CPU consists of three units. The arithmetic/logic unit (ALU), the control unit and the internal registers. The ALU performs both arithmetic operations such as addition, subtraction and possibly multiplication and division, together with logical operations on data brought from the memory. The control unit generates the timing and signals required for fetching, decoding and executing instructions stored in the memory and for input–output. As such, it provides the internal and external control signals required for correct operation of the complete system. In a microprocessor

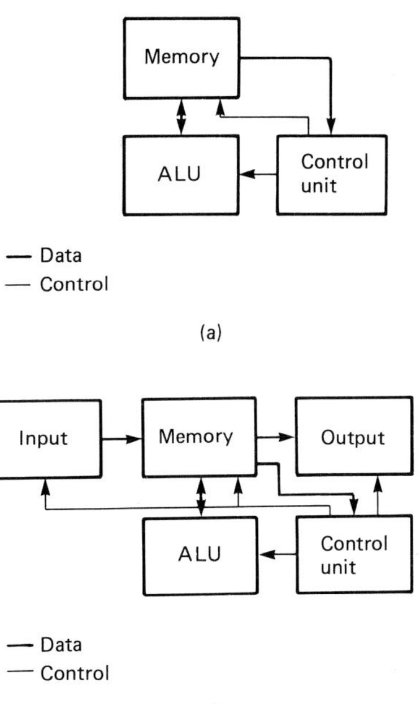

Figure 4.48 (a) Central processing unit; (b) schematic diagram of complete computer system.

such as the Rockwell 6502 (whose internal architecture is shown in Figure 4.49), the arithmetic/logic unit and the control unit consist of a single large-scale integrated (LSI) circuit. (The 6502 is used in the Apple, BBC Acorn and Commodore PET microcomputers.) Microcomputers in general use metal oxide semiconductor (MOS) technology for their CPUs, whereas minicomputers and mainframe machines have CPUs which are fabricated using the faster bipolar technologies such as TTL, or integrated injection logic (I^2L) or emitter coupled logic (ECL).

4.10.1.1 Memory

The memory or store consists of a series of storage locations which contain the program which the computer is executing and the data which are being operated on, together with the results of those operations. Each storage location is identified by having a unique address. The instructions and data in each of these addresses is stored as the bits of a binary number. The word length of the computer is the largest possible collection of binary bits the computer can manipulate, and in a microcomputer

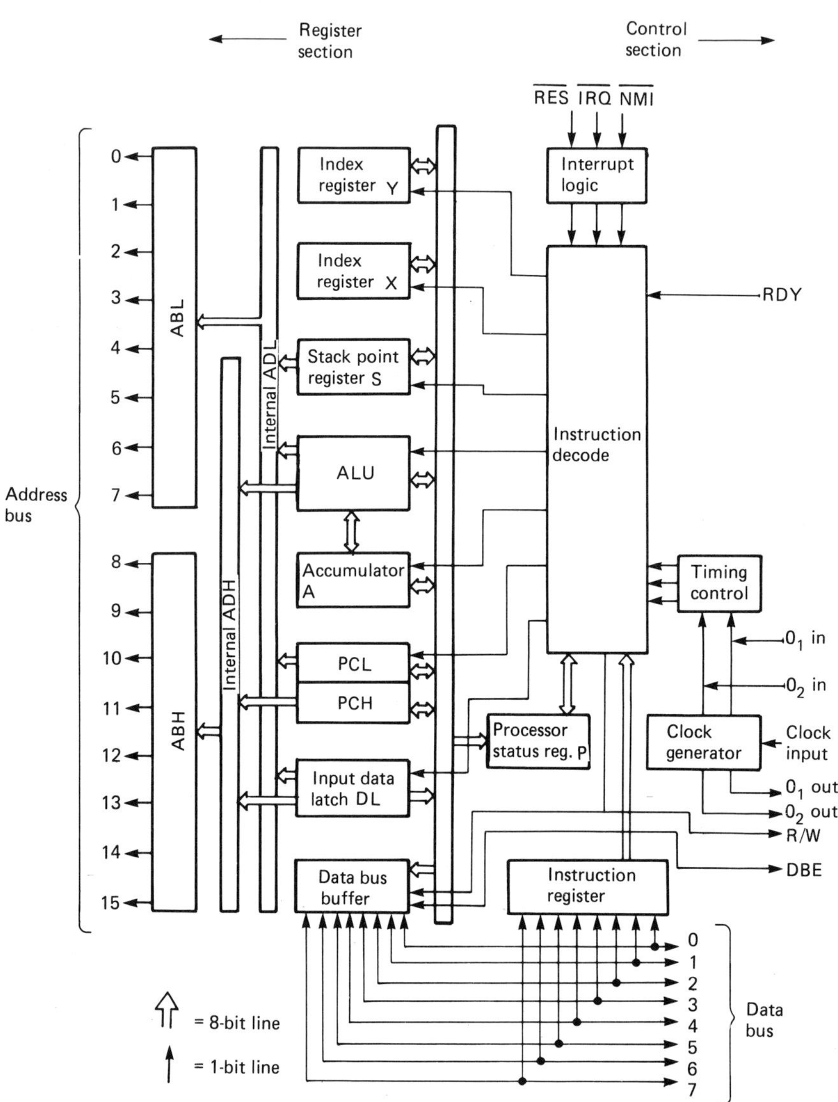

Figure 4.49 Internal architecture of 6502 microprocessor.

is typically either 8 or 16 bits. In larger machines the length is likely to be 16, 24, 32 or even 64 bits. The words in larger machines are often split down into smaller units called 'bytes'. Typically, a byte will consist of 8 bits.

There are a number of distinguishing features of different memory systems. The characteristic time associated with the memory is its access time, which is the time required to write into or read from a particular location in the store. The access time has two components: the time required for addressing and locating the required word in the store; and the switching or operation time for the storage element. Random access memory (RAM) is memory in which all the words are equally accessible, as opposed to a cyclic memory, in which the words are available only on a cyclic basis and for which the average access time is half the cycle period. The main memory of a computer system usually consists of RAM in the form of semiconductor LSI arrays.

Memory is either volatile, in which case its contents will be lost in the case of a power failure, or it is non-volatile or permanent. If reading of the memory destroys its contents then it is said to be destructive, otherwise it is said to be non-destructive. Static memories retain their information as long as the power is maintained, whereas dynamic memories are required to be constantly refreshed in order to retain their information. If it is only possible to read from the memory and not to write into it then the memory is said to be read-only memory (ROM). This is often used for permanent program storage. EPROM, Electrically Programmable ROM is a memory which can be electrically programmed but which under normal operating conditions behaves as ROM. The data are erased by the application of ultra-violet light. EAPROM is an alternative form of PROM, which is Electrically Alterable, hence its name. Both EPROM and EAPROM are used for program storage in development situations where it may be necessary to modify the program before committing it to ROM. Table 4.6 compares the characteristics of different storage media used in computer systems.

4.10.1.2 Peripheral devices

A complete computer system as shown in Figure 4.50 consists of a CPU together with a range of peripheral devices (Wilkinson and Horrocks, 1980).

Input devices The most common form of computer input terminal is the VDU, which consists of an alphanumeric keyboard together with a cathode ray tube (CRT) display which can provide either alphanumeric or graphical display. The alphanumeric input from the keyboard is usually converted to a 7-bit ASCII code and bi-directional data communication between the VDU and the computer is by means of two asynchronous serial lines at a

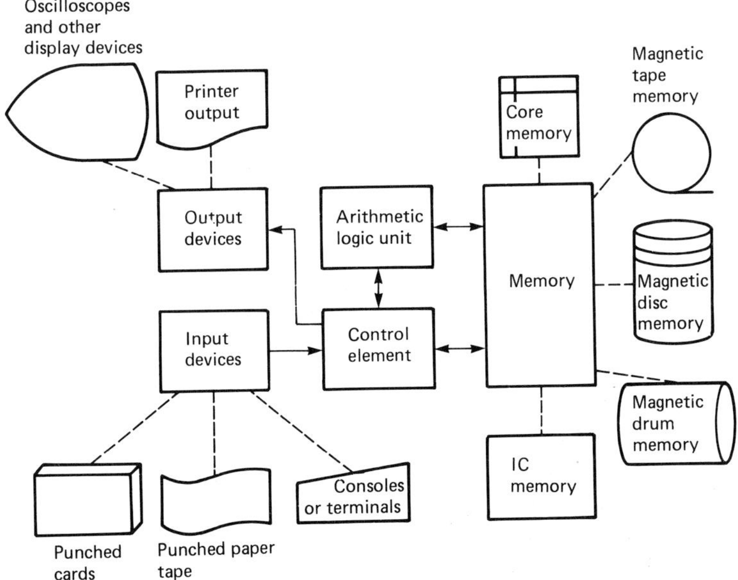

Figure 4.50 Computer system and its peripheral devices.

Table 4.6 Characteristics of memory systems

Storage device	*Access time and type*	*Capacity*	*Recording density*	*Data rate*	*Physical characteristics*	*Main application*
Magnetic drum	8.5–17 ms cyclic access	200 k–200 M bits	1600 BPI	2–8 M bits/s	Permanent storage	Backing storage
Magnetic disc	25–70 ms cyclic access	800 k–500 M bits	1000–6000 BPI	800 k–8 M bits/s	Permanent storage Rigid disc Fixed or moving heads	Backing and file storage
Floppy disc	100–400 ms cyclic access	2–5 M bits	3000 BPI	250 k bits/s	Permanent storage flexible disc	Cheap form of disc store; transportable packs
Magnetic tape	Several minutes serial access	30–800 M bits	1600–6250 BPI	10^7 bits/s	Permanent storage	Mass storage, on-line and archival
Cassette tape	50–500 s serial access	1–5 M bits	800 BPI	8–20 k bits/s	Permanent storage	Cheap high-capacity store; transportable packs
Magnetic cartridge	10–50 s serial access	20–22 M bits	1600 BPI	48–160 k bits/s	Permanent storage	Cheap high-capacity store; transportable packs
Magnetic core	250–750 ns (cycle times 650 ns–1 μs) random access	4 k–1 M bytes	—	—	Volatile unless protected; destructive read-out	Main store and backing store extension
Semiconductor						
Bipolar RAM	45–60 ns (cycle times 60–100 ns random access	256–1 k bits	—	—	Volatile	Registers, accumulators, buffers, push-down stores. Cache stores
CMOS RAM	50–100 ns (cycle times 500–600 ns random access	1–4 k bytes	—	—	Volatile	Cache stores Fast main memory
PMOS/NMOS RAM	150–400 ns (cycle times 350–800 ns) random access	1–16 k bytes	—	—	Volatile	Main memory Buffer stores
MOS/Bipolar ROM/PROM	55–500 ns random access	1–64 k bytes	—	—	Permanent/volatile	Read Only Memory Micro-program control stores, control programs, table-look-up
CCD	50–500 ns serial access	4–64 k bits	—	5–20 M bits/s	Volatile	Backing store
Magnetic bubbles	Several milliseconds serial access	16 k–64 k bits	—	100–300 k bits/s	Volatile	Backing store Mass memory

bit rate between 75 and 9600 bits/s. The VDU provides facilities for transmitting characters, lines or pages together with editing facilities for inserting or deleting characters or lines. Many VDUs are now intelligent terminals including a microprocessor and a local backing store in the form of a cassette or floppy disc. They can be programmed to perform specific tasks and may provide such facilities as a BASIC interpreter, utility programs for creating, deleting and editing files, and also communication packages.

Teletypes provide a keyboard and printer and can thus provide hard copy, but this is restricted to alphanumeric output. Additionally, teletypes provide a paper tape punch and reader. Paper tape input is usually by an 8-hole tape with 7-bit ASCII coding, the eighth bit being used as a parity check. Reading of the tape is by means of photoelectric sensing at rates of up to 500 characters/s (c/s). The punch is generally capable of operating at 300 c/s.

Larger mainframe machines may also provide means of input using card readers/punches. The data for these are usually formatted as 80 characters/card with each character using a 12-bit Hollerith code. The cards are read using optical techniques. Card readers are capable of reading at rates of between 100 and 2000 cards/min and punching cards at between 100 and 300 cards/min. Newer forms of data input to computer systems employ such techniques as light pens, graphics tablets and voice input.

Output devices In addition to output by means of VDUs or teletypes or other visual display systems employing light-emitting diodes (LEDs), liquid crystal displays (LCDs) and plasma displays, computer systems use both serial and line printers and digital plotters. Serial printers for alphanumeric output employ print head types such as a daisywheel printer or a dot matrix printer, which can also be programmed to provide graphical hard copy. Typically, such printers are capable of printing at rates of up to 200 c/s with up to 80 characters/line.

A line printer is used in applications where it is required to output a large amount of printed material. Line printers use such techniques as impact drum or dot printing, electrosensitive paper, electrostatic or electrophotographic printing, or laser printing. Such devices are capable of printing at up to 2000 lines/min.

Digital plotters provide hard copy of graphical and alphanumeric data from the computer. Such plotters, which are either flat-bed plotters or drum plotters, can have a step size as small as 0.05 mm and are capable of plotting at up to 10 000 steps/s. Display and recording devices are covered in Chapter 6.

Analogue and digital interfaces In measurement and control applications the input and output peripherals will also include analogue and digital interface units. The analogue input interface typically provides several analogue channels with signal conditioning and sample and hold amplifiers multiplexed to a single ADC. The analogue output interface may be either a single DAC whose output is connected to a series of sample and hold amplifiers or a bank of DACs. Input to a digital interface may be at TTL levels or higher voltages. The digital output may be required to drive TTL circuitry, lamps, relays or provide switching of a.c. power. Often both the analogue and digital interfaces provide electrical isolation between the computer and the external world by employing isolation amplifiers or optical couplers.

Mass data storage The peripheral back-up memory provides low-speed mass storage. Conventionally, this has been produced by either magnetic tape or disc systems, although newer forms of mass storage such as magnetic bubble memories and optical memories are now beginning to appear. The methods of digital information storage using magnetic surface storage are dealt with in Lewin, 1980.

Magnetic tape storage systems span a range from the large tape systems used on mainframe computers, which can provide up to 350 Mbytes of memory with recording densities of up to 12 500 bits per inch (bpi) and transfer rates of 1250 kbytes/s to audiocassette systems. Standard audiocassette recorders, used mainly with microprocessor systems, provide up to 1 Mbyte of memory storage on a 90-min cassette at a typical recording density of 800 bpi and transfer rates of 150 bytes/s. Access in magnetic tape storage systems is serial, with average access times in both large tape systems and cassette systems being of the order of minutes.

There are two varieties of magnetic discs, known as 'hard' and 'soft' discs. Hard discs are made of aluminium and coated with ferric oxide. Winchester disc drives, common on small and medium-size computer systems, are a form of hard disc having a high storage density and data-reading rate. The capacity of an 8 in Winchester drive lies between 10 and 50 Mbytes. Such systems typically have a density of 6000 bpi with 500 tracks/in (tpi) and data transfer rate of 800 kbytes/s. The average access time for such a system is between 40 and 50 ms.

Soft or 'floppy' discs derive their name from the fact that they are fabricated from Mylar with a ferric oxide coating, and hence are floppy. Floppy discs come in a range of sizes 8 in, 5.25 in and 3.5 in. 5.25 in discs, which are widely used with microcomputer systems and which are referred to as minidiscs, can provide storage of 800 kbytes of data with data transfer rates of up to 250 kbits/s. The average access time in a floppy disc system is between 100 and 400 ms.

4.10.2 Software

4.10.2.1 Machine code

Both data and instructions are stored in the memory of the CPU as binary numbers. Within the control unit of the CPU there is a decoding unit which takes the words in sequence from the memory, decodes them as to whether they are data or instructions and, if they are instructions, then provides the necessary control signals for the rest of the system for that operation to be executed. At this level in the memory the instructions are stored in a form that they can be executed by the CPU. This most fundamental level of language is called 'machine code'. In writing programs in machine code there can be difficulties in remembering the machine code instructions in binary or hexadecimal (to the base 16) form; in remembering the addresses to which branch, jump or loop instructions go; and in keeping track of these when altering the program. Mnemonic assemblers have therefore been devised in which each machine code instruction has a mnemonic such as ADD, SUB and INX and in which store locations are identified by labels. Table 4.7 lists the machine code instructions and mnemonic codes for the 6502 microprocessor system. Such assemblers ease the problems of programming in machine code since the assembler automatically takes care of the changes necessary in the addresses to which jump, loop and branch instructions refer. There is still, however, a one-to-one correspondence between assembly language instructions and the machine code instructions, and thus such a language is called a low-level language (LLL).

4.10.2.2 High-level languages

High-level languages (HLLs), which resemble English and employ mathematical notation, require no knowledge on the part of the programmer of the internal workings of the computer on which it is running but only of the syntax and semantics of the

Table 4.7 Machine code instructions and mnemonics for 6502 microprocessor

ADC	Add Memory to Accumulator with Carry	JSR	Jump to New Location Saving Return Address
AND	'AND' Memory with Accumulator		
ASL	Shift Left One Bit (Memory or Accumulator)	LDA	Load Accumulator with Memory
		LDX	Load index X with Memory
BCC	Branch on Carry Clear	LDY	Load Index Y with Memory
BCS	Branch on Carry Set	LSR	Shift Right One Bit (Memory or Accumulator)
BEQ	Branch on Result Zero		
BIT	Test Bits in Memory with Accumulator	NOP	No Operation
BMI	Branch on Result Minus	ORA	'OR' Memory with Accumulator
BNE	Branch on Result not Zero		
BPL	Branch on Result Plus	PHA	Push Accumulator on Stack
BRK	Force Break	PHP	Push Processor Status on Stack
BVC	Branch on Overflow Clear	PLA	Pull Accumulator from Stack
BVS	Branch on Overflow Set	PLP	Pull Processor Status from Stack
CLC	Clear Carry Flag	ROL	Rotate One Bit Left (Memory or Accumulator)
CLD	Clear Decimal Mode	ROR	Rotate One Bit Right (Memory or Accumulator)
CLI	Clear Interrupt Disable Bit	RTI	Return from Interrupt
CLV	Clear Overflow Flag	RTS	Return from Subroutine
CMP	Compare Memory and Accumulator		
CPX	Compare Memory and Index X	SBC	Subtract Memory from Accumulator with Borrow
CPY	Compare Memory and Index Y	SEC	Set Carry Flag
		SED	Set Decimal Mode
DEC	Decrement Memory by One	SEI	Set Interrupt Disable Status
DEX	Decrement Index X by One	STA	Store Accumulator in Memory
DEY	Decrement Index Y by One	STX	Store Index X in Memory
		STY	Store Index Y in Memory
EOR	'Exclusive-Or' Memory with Accumulator		
		TAX	Transfer Accumulator to Index X
INC	Increment Memory by One	TAY	Transfer Accumulator to Index Y
INX	Increment Index X by One	TXS	Transfer Stack Pointer to Index X
INY	Increment Index Y by One	TXA	Transfer Index X to Accumulator
		TXS	Transfer Index X to Stack Pointer
JMP	Jump to New Location	TYA	Transfer Index Y to Accumulator

HLL. HLLs are used for economy and convenience in program development, but this is achieved at the expense of compactness and efficiency of the programming. The compilers and interpreters of HLLs generate several machine code instructions for each statement of the HLL. Compiled languages differ from interpreted languages in that in a compiled language the source code is compiled into a binary code and at run time it is this code which is executed, whereas in an interpreted language at run time each instruction of the HLL is interpreted and executed. Consequently, interpreted languages are generally slower in execution than compiled languages.

In microcomputer systems HLLs are used either as a development tool (in which case the compiled code is installed on the microcomputer) or as the language of a system which has its own compiler for that particular language, either resident in ROM or available on disc.

There are at present a large number of HLLs suitable for running on micro- and minicomputers employed in real-time instrumentation and control applications. They are compared in some detail in the book by Bibbero and Stern (1982).

Although BASIC (Beginners All Purpose Symbolic Instruction Code) is to be found on a large number of micro- and minicomputers, it is a poor language for real-time applications. It is generally implemented as an interpreted language and therefore slow. As a language it is not internally structured and consequently concurrent task programming is difficult; also its input–output routines are awkward.

FORTRAN (FORmula TRANslation), which is a compiled language, has more highly developed input–output routines than BASIC but its large compiler requires disc storage. Real Time FORTRAN (RTF) is used extensively for control and military applications and cross compilers are available which will allow the compiled object code from a FORTRAN program to be installed in ROM or PROM on a microcomputer.

CORAL is based on ALGOL 60 (ALGOrithmic Language) and is commonly used industrially for online systems. CORAL provides a COMMON communicator facility which allows programs to be written as a number of compiled segments which each perform their own specified function when called by a control routine, and this therefore allows for flexible programming. The language offers advantages in that it allows for both fixed and floating point variables and also in its method of storing data in memory.

FORTH, which employs a technique known as 'indirect threaded coding', is significantly faster than BASIC and is suitable for multitask operations such as process control. A typical FORTH compiler requires 6k of memory. It has a lower program memory requirement than most other high-level languages.

C-CODE is a language which requires a large compiler but produces a compiled object code which requires typically only between 10 and 30 per cent more memory space than an efficient machine code program. As such, it is used extensively as a high-level development language for machine code programs for microcomputers. Suitable cross compilers allow the C-CODE programs to be targeted to a particular microcomputer system.

PASCAL, which is a derivative of ALGOL, is a structured language with a block structure capable of providing concurrent program support for the most complex real-time applications programs. P-CODE is an intermediate interpreted language between PASCAL and machine code, and thus PASCAL can be implemented by either compiling to P-CODE and interpreting the P-CODE with a small resident onboard interpreter, or by cross compiling to the machine code of the processor.

4.10.2.3 The operating system

The program which controls the overall operation of the computer is referred to as the operating system (OS), executive or monitor. In instrumentation and control systems the operating system has to be a real-time operating system which must keep in step with the external world. Events in the external world generate interrupt signals for the computer by causing contacts to close or signals to change levels. The events in the external world may be, for example, that one of the monitored variables has gone out of its permitted range or that there is a requirement for input to the system via the VDU or teletype. On receipt of the interrupt signal, after the present instruction has been executed, the sequence of instructions being executed is suspended in order to respond to the external event. This is usually done by means of an interrupt service routine. When the service routine has been executed control will return to the interrupted program. In large systems there may be several levels of interrupt priority with time-critical external events having the highest priority. The interrupt service routine has to detect the level of the interrupt which has been raised and in the presence of more than one interrupt has to respond to the interrupt having the highest priority level.

The operating system schedules and controls the handling of different input/output activities, including the processing of interrupts, and includes input–output organization, storage allocation, communication with the operator, interrupt control, queue control and display handling. The design of the operating system is fundamental to the efficient operation of the whole computer system.

4.10.3 Typical tasks performed by digital computers

In instruments which employ embedded computer systems the presence of the microcomputer may be transparent to the user, who will not have access to the programs resident in the microcomputer system and will therefore be unable to modify them. In such systems the program is generally written in machine code and stored in ROM or PROM.

The tasks which an embedded computer system provide depend largely on the individual application, but may include:

(1) Replacement of discrete digital circuitry for logic or sequence control of the overall system.
(2) Provision of dedicated computational facilities such as scaling, linearization and filtering.
(3) Improved system performance by the provision of auto-zeroing, auto-ranging and self-calibration facilities.
(4) Self diagnosis of its own operation and the operation of the total system.
(5) Control of the user interface, including keyboards, displays and printers.
(6) Communications with other systems and computers.

General-purpose computer systems for use in instrumentation and control are based on micro- or minicomputers and are programmed in a HLL. It is therefore open to the user to modify the tasks undertaken by the system.

The tasks performed by such systems are wide ranging (Sanderson, 1976; Paker, 1980) but may include:

(1) Data acquisition and logging of analogue and digital signals from instruments or processes together with the provision of alarm signals.
(2) Data reduction for recording or display.
(3) Computational facilities under user control to provide statistical analysis, digital filtering, spectral analysis or correlation measurements on the logged data.
(4) Sequence control of batch and continuous processes including start-up and emergency shutdown procedures.
(5) Direct digital control (DDC), in which analogue three-term controllers are replaced by discrete three-term controllers provided by software in the computer.
(6) Supervisory control, in which the set points of conventional analogue controllers are monitored and adjusted by the computer system.
(7) Optimization of system-operating parameters.
(8) Control of data communications, which may be either between the system and a supervisory main computer or intersystem communications in a distributed computer system.

For the theoretical basis of signal analysis the reader is referred to Papoulis (1977). Owens (1983) provides a large bibliography on the application of digital processing techniques. Digital control systems are covered in the book by Kuo (1980).

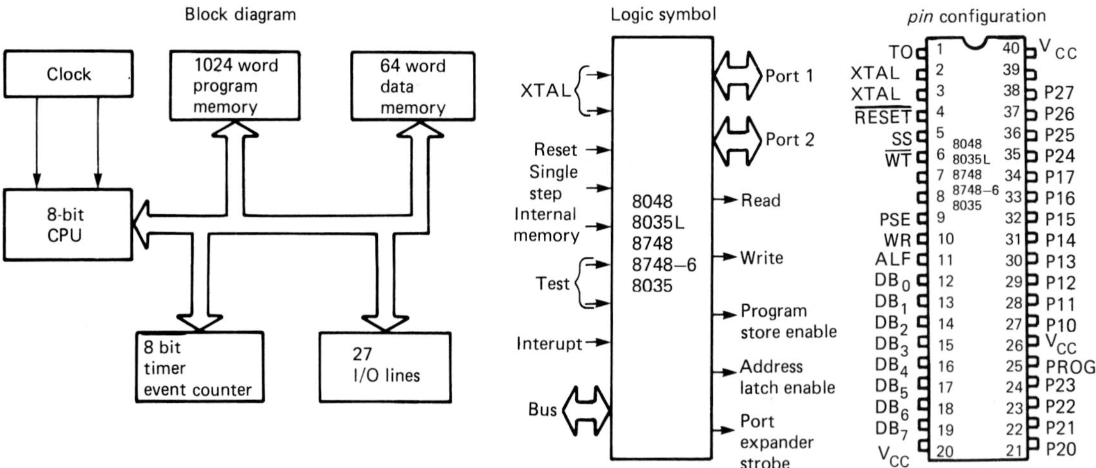

Figure 4.51 Block diagram, logic symbol and pin configuration of 8048 single-chip microcomputer.

4.10.4 A single-chip microcomputer for use in an imbedded computer system

A minimal computer system consists of an ALU, a control unit, memory for program and data storage, and input–output. A range of such systems using single-chip LSI circuits is available. Figure 4.51 shows the block diagram, logic symbol and pin configuration of the Intel 8048 single-chip microcomputer. Table 4.8 gives the key design parameters of this device which is packaged as a 40-pin dual in-line integrated circuit (Intel, 1980).

The 8048 is fabricated using an N channel MOS process and contains 1 K × 8 bit of ROM memory,

Table 4.8 Specification of 8085 single-chip microcomputer system

8-bit CPU, ROM, RAM, I/O in single package
Interchangeable ROM and EPROM versions
Single 5 V supply
2.5 μs and 5.0 μs cycle versions:
all instructions 1 or 2 cycles
Over 90 instructions: 70% single byte
1 k × 8 ROM/EPROM
64 × 8 RAM
27 I/O lines
Interval timer/event counter
Easily expandable memory and I/O
Compatible with 8080/8085 series peripherals
Single-level interrupt

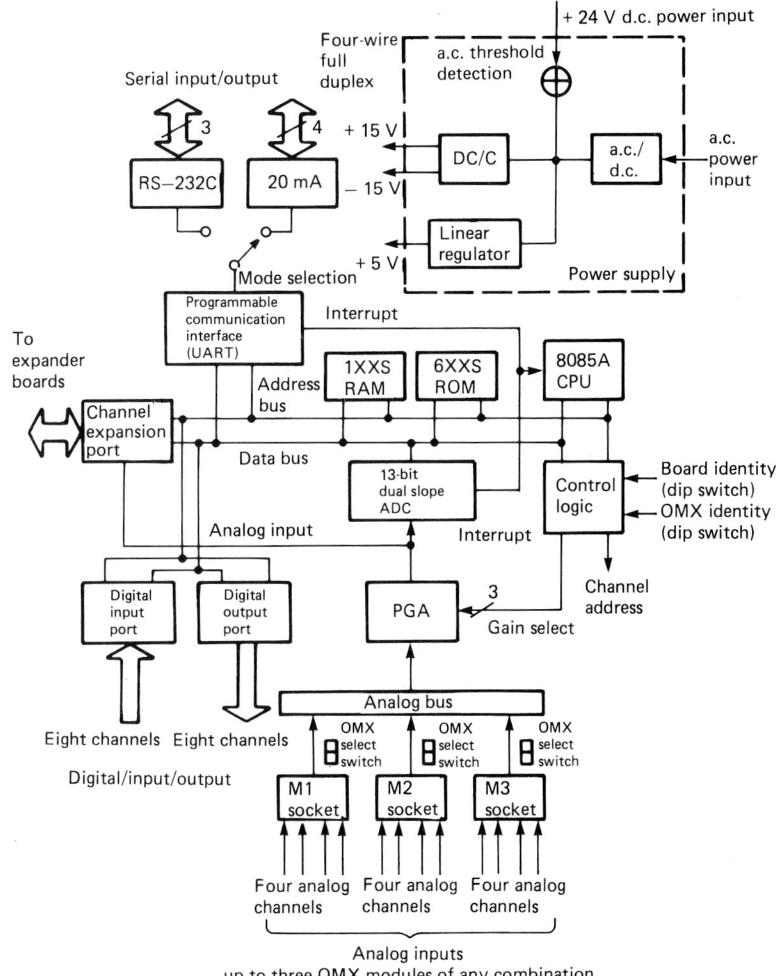

Figure 4.52 Master board for μMAC-4000 system.

Table 4.9 Input variables for μMAC-4000 system

Input	*Resolution*	*Accuracy*
Thermocouples Type J, K, T, S	0.1 K	±1.3 K
RTDs 100 Ω platinum	0.05 K	±0.3 K
Solid state temperature sensors		
AD590 or AC2626	0.1 K	±0.2 K
Strain gauge transducers		
±30 mV, ± 100 mV spans	0.025% of span	±0.01% of span
Low-level d.c. voltages		
±25 mV, ±50 mV, ±100 mV	6 μV	±0.005% of FS
High-level d.c. voltages		
±1 V, ±5 V, ±10 V	250 μV	±0.1% of FS
D.C.. Currents		
0 to ±1 mA, 0 to ±20 mA, 4–20 mA	0.031% of span	±0.025% of span

64 × 8 bit of RAM memory, 27 input–output lines and an 8-bit timer/counter. The 8048 is meant for use in high-volume production using factory programmed mask ROM. Development of such systems is undertaken using either the 8748, which uses EPROM instead of ROM, or the 8035, which can be used with external ROM or RAM. Both the 8748 and the 8035 are pin-for-pin compatible with the 8048. This family of microprocessors has been designed for efficient operation as either a controller or an arithmetic processor. Analogue signals can be processed by employing an ADC interfaced to one of the input ports of the 8048. Alternatively, single-chip microcomputers such as the 8022 provide an onboard 8-bit ADC.

4.10.4.1 A microprocessor-based measurement and control subsystem

The μMAC-4000, produced by Analog Devices (Analog Devices, 1984), is a modular measurement and control system based on an Intel 8085 microcomputer. It is designed to operate with any host computer having an RS-232-C or 20 mA serial communication port.

The basic building block of this modular system is the μMAC-4000 master board shown in Figure 4.52, which provides four, eight or 12 analogue input channels having a common mode voltage capability of ±1000 V and a common mode rejection ratio of 160 dB. Analogue-to-digital conversion is provided by means of a 13-bit ADC. A series of standard signal processing modules is available which allows the range of analogue input variables shown in Table 4.9. The eight channels of digital input provide isolation of up to ±300 V and are directly compatible with TTL signals or contact closures. The eight channels of digital output are compatible with TTL levels.

A cluster can be constructed consisting of a μMAC-4000 master board and up to six expander boards. The expansion boards can be the μMAC-4010, which has the same analogue and digital capability as the μMAC-4000 and acts as its slave; the μMAC-4030, which provides an eight-channel, 12-bit DAC capability with either voltage or current output; the μMAC-4020, which is a 16-channel digital input–output subsystem suitable for interfacing to high-level a.c. or d.c. signals and with 2500 V a.c. optical isolation; and the μMAC-4040, which provides 32 digital input channels and 32 digital output channels. A cluster can provide a maximum of 48 analogue input channels, 32 analogue output channels, 136 digital input channels and 136 digital output channels. It is possible to further expand the system by having a party line connection to up to eight clusters, as shown in Figure 4.53. In this configuration the system can have up to 384 analogue inputs, 256 analogue outputs, 1088 digital inputs and 1088 digital outputs.

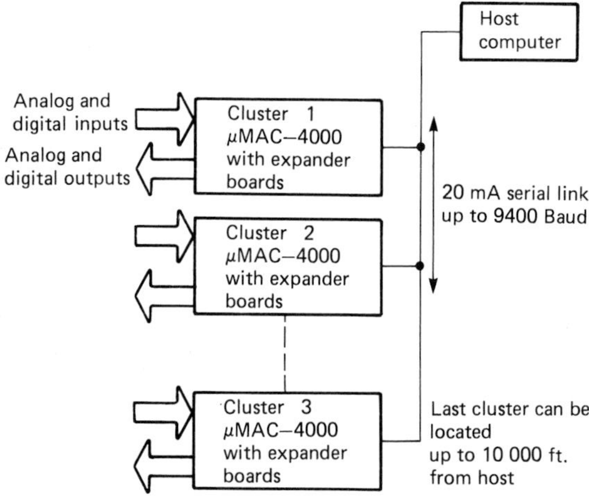

Figure 4.53 Cluster configuration for μMAC-4000 system.

The μMAC-4000 scales, linearizes and converts the input data to engineering units. It scans the analogue inputs fifteen or thirty times per second and stores the results in RAM. Communication between the subsystem and the host computer is by means of a full duplex UART which allows transmission rates of between 110 and 9600 Baud at distances of up to 10 000 ft. A powerful command set is resident in the firmware of the μMAC-4000 which allows simple communication between the subsystem and the host computer. Table 4.10 gives examples of these commands together with the T and C protocols which can be used with the system.

Table 4.10 μMAC-4000 commands and protocols

Command set

Command	Function
CHANNELn	Transmit channel n data
SCANn,m	Transmit channel n through channel m data
SETp.b.	Set digital output bit of port p
LIMITn,LL,HL	Sets 'HI' and 'LOW' limits of channel n
SCACn,v	Set channel n to analog value v

Protocols

Two serial protocols can be used with the μMAC-4000. The 'T' protocol is designed for use with CRT and TTY terminals where familiarization, debugging, system calibration and manual control is required. Simple 'English-like' commands are used with this protocol. The 'C' protocol is designed for use with computers and controllers where communication efficiency, reliability and adaptability to a wide variety of hosts is required

'T' protocol command

SCAN 0,2

This command requests the μMAC to transmit the latest data for channel 0 through 2

'T' protocol reply

CH0 = +0025.4 CH1 = +0653.5 CH2 = +0085.2

If thermocouples were connected to these channels, the data are in terms of °C or °F

4.10.4.2 A measurement and control processor hosted by a minicomputer

A more powerful data acquisition and control system is provided by a system such as the HP 2250, the components of which are shown in Figure 4.54 (Hewlett Packard, 1983). The HP 2250 derives its intelligence from the onboard HP 1000 computer with its custom-designed operating system. The system consists of two sections: the processor unit and the measurement and control unit (MCU). The processor unit consists of five cards: Battery Back-up, ROM/RAM, CPU, Measurement and Control Interface (MCI), and HP–IB Interface. The

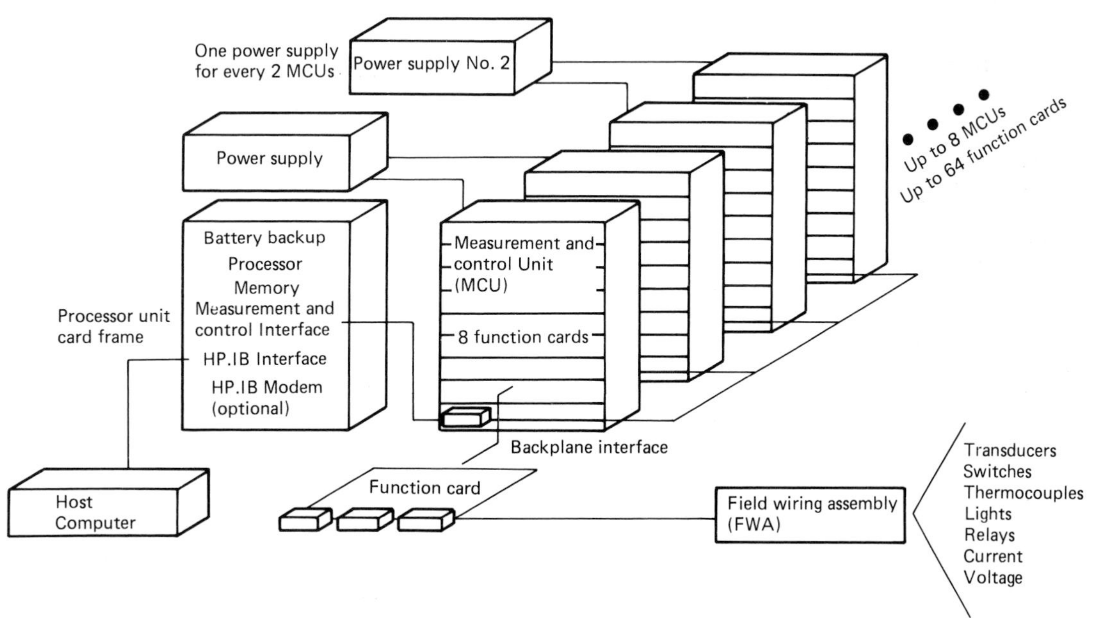

Figure 4.54 Components of HP 2250 measurement and control processor.

Battery Back-up card sustains the memory for up to 30 min in the case of a power failure. The memory card contains both the operating system for the HP 2250 in firmware and Read/Write memory for holding HP 2250 programs. The system has 28 kbytes of user memory. The CPU card employs an HP 1000 L series computer. The Measurement and Control Interface (MCI) provides control of the MCU. The MCI receives groups of control words from the CPU memory and causes signals to be output to the MCU. Data are written to the MCU or retrieved from the MCU through the MCI card.

The fifth card in the processor unit is the HP-IB Interface card. This provides the communication link between the HP 2250 and the host computer, which is typically either one of the HP 1000 or HP 200 series computers. This card allows communication between the HP 2250 and the host computer at distances up to 20 m. The separation can be increased to up to 1000 m using HP-IB extenders and fibre-optic cables.

The MCU is a cage into which eight function cards can be inserted. Each HP 2250 system may have up to eight MCUs. Table 4.11 shows the analogue and digital function cards provided for the system. Each function card is provided with slots to take signal-conditioning modules which filter, attenuate and isolate incoming and outgoing a.c. and d.c.

Table 4.11 Analogue and digital function cards for HP2250 system

Analog function cards

Function card	*No. of channels*	*Resolutions*	*Purpose of card*
High-speed analog input (HP 25501)	16	156 μV max. ±10 V	Convert analog input signal to digital representation
High-level FET multiplexer (HP 25502)	32	156 μV max. ±10 V	Extend HP 25501 ADC by 32 input channels
Low-level FET multiplexer (HP 25503)	32	1.56 μV max. ±10 V	Extend HP 25501 ADC by 32 input channels and provide gain
Relay multiplexer (HP25504)	16	1.56 μV max. ±100 V	Extend HP 25501 ADC by 16 input channels, provide gain and electrical isolation
Voltage/current output HP (25510)	4	5 mV or 5 μA max. ±10.24 V or 20 mA at 20 V	Provide analog voltage and current output

Digital function cards

Function card	*No. of channels*	*Purpose of card*
Digital input (HP25511)	32	Provide digital inputs for monitoring a.c. or d.c. signals (0–120 V d.c., 0–230 V a.c.) through required signal conditioning modules (SCMs). Inputs can be monitored individually or collectively and can generate interrupts upon transitions
Counter input (HP 25512)	4	Provide independently programmable counters which totalize, count up or down and measure periods, time intervals and frequencies. Interrupts can be generated upon overflow or completion of counting
Digital output (HP 25513)	32	Provides solid-state switching of a.c. and d.c. loads of up to 60 V (peak) at 300 mA and zero-voltage switching up to 120 V a.c. at 800 mA through required Signal Conditioning Modules (SCMs). Outputs can be programmed individually or as two 16-bit fields
Relay output (HP 25514)	16	Provides switching of high-current loads (up to 2 A at 30 V d.c. or 3 A at 125 V a.c.). SCMs suppress transients to protect the relays and prevent noise. The 16 channels can be programmed individually or collectively
Output pulse (HP 25515)	4	Provides digital pulses of programmable frequency, width and acceleration for controlling stepper motors. Limit switch inputs on this card can be programmed to abort pulse trains
Digital multifunction (HP 25516)	16-input, 16-output	Provides independently programmable digital inputs and outputs, counting and interrupt capabilities. SCMs provide a wide range of interfacing for monitoring and controlling transducers, instruments and switches

signals, enabling the cards to operate in the most electrically noisy environments. Forty-two different signal-conditioning modules are available. The system is capable of monitoring up to 1920 analogue points and 2048 digital points. The ADC provides a 14-bit conversion at a rate of 50 000 measurements/s.

The HP 2250 employs a measurement and control language called MCL/50, which provides the user with over 100 commands for high-level programming of all the analogue and digital function cards together with features found in FORTRAN and BASIC. These MCL/50 instructions can be embedded in applications programs written in FORTRAN or BASIC on the host computer. All MCL/50 commands sent to the HP 2250 pass through the HP-IB interface card and are placed in the ROM/RAM card. The CPU card then compiles and executes the commands and returns the results back to the host computer. The HP 2250 can also store the sampled data locally in its memory and operate on the data without reference back to the host computer.

Because the HP 2250 has on board a HP 1000 L series computer it is possible to download subroutines which have been written in HP 1000 FORTRAN or Assembly Language. This provides the system with increased flexibility and power and allows the manipulations provided by the HP 2250 to extend beyond the capabilities provided by the MCL/50 language.

An Automation Software Package is available for the HP 1000 host computer which contains the following programs: the External Subroutine Loader Routine, LINKR, which suitably formats files written in FORTRAN or Assembly Language for downloading from the host computer to the HP 2250; Continuous Data Acquisition (CDA) software, which allows for the collection of a large amount of data at high sampling rates; and the Measurement and Control Language Exerciser (MCX), which enables the programmer to have an interactive dialogue with the HP 2250.

The CDA software operates either in a History Mode or a Normal Mode. In the History Mode the HP 2250 samples the data and stores them locally in its memory. The storage available in this mode is limited to about 6500 readings. In the Normal Mode the software causes the data to be sent directly to the host computer where they are stored either in its memory or on high-speed, high-capacity disc drives. In such a mode it is possible to capture several minutes of data sampled at 50 kHz.

The MCX software enables the programmer to test the tasks performed by the MCL/50 software without having to write FORTRAN or BASIC programs. The software includes provision for the reporting of status information, downloading of user subroutines, providing access HP 2250 to buffers or variables, and the reporting of syntax, run time and communication errors.

References

ANALOG DEVICES INC. *Databook*, Volumes 1 and 2, Analog Devices Inc., Norwood, Massachusetts (1984)

ARBEL, A. F. *Analog Signal Processing and Instrumentation*, Cambridge University Press, Cambridge (1980)

ASPINALL, D. *The Microprocessor and its Application*, Cambridge University Press, Cambridge (1980)

BARNEY, G. C. *Intelligent Instrumentation: Microprocessor Applications in Measurement and Control*, Prentice-Hall, London (1985)

BARTREE, T. C. *Digital Computer Fundamentals* (5th edn), McGraw-Hill, London (1981)

BECK, M. S. 'Correlation instruments: cross correlation flowmeters', in *Instrument Science and Technology*, Volume 2, ed. B. E. Jones, Adam Hilger, Bristol (1983)

BENDAT, J. S. and PIERSOL, A. G. *Engineering Applications of Correlation and Spectral Analysis*, Wiley-Interscience, New York (1980)

BIBBERO, D. P. and STERN, D. M. *Microprocessor Systems: Interfacing and Applications*, Wiley-Interscience, New York (1982)

BLAIR, D. P. and SYDENHAM, P. H. 'Phase sensitive detection as a means to recover signals buried in noise, *Journal of Physics E, Scientific Instruments*, **5**, 621–627 (1975)

BOWRON, P. and STEPHENSON, F. W. *Active Filters for Communication and Instrumentation*, McGraw-Hill, Maidenhead (1979)

BOYCE, J. C. *Digital Computer Fundamentals*, Prentice-Hall, Englewood Cliffs, New Jersey (1977)

CLAYTON, G. B. *Operational Amplifiers*, 2nd edn, Newnes–Butterworths, London (1979)

COOLEY, J. W. and TUKEY, J. W. 'An algorithm for the machine calculation of complex Fourier series', *Mathematics of Computation*, **19**, No. 90, 297–313 (1965)

GIACOLLETTO, L. J. *Electronic Designers Handbook*, McGraw-Hill, New York (1977), pp. 13-140–13-146

GRAEME, J. G. *Applications of Operational Amplifiers: Third Generation Techniques*, McGraw-Hill, New York (1973)

GULD, C. 'Microelectrodes and input amplifiers', in *IEE Medical Electronics Monographs*, Nos 7–12, eds D. W. Hill and B. W. Watson, Peter Peregrinus, London,(1974), pp. 1–27

HENRY, R. M. 'An improved algorithm allowing fast on-line polarity correlation by microprocessor or minicomputer', *IEE Conference Digest, No. 1979/32*, 3/1-4 (1979)

HEWLETT PACKARD. 150 Series: *Spectrum Analyser Series Applications Notes*, Palo Alto, California (1971 onwards)

HEWLETT PACKARD. *An Introduction to Programming the HP 2250*, Product Note 2250-1, Palo Alto, California (1983)

INTEL CORPORATION. *Component Data Catalog*, Santa Clara (1980)

INTERSIL INC. *Data Book*, Intersil Inc., Cupertino, California (1979)

JONES, B. E. *Instrumentation, Measurement and Feedback*, McGraw-Hill, Maidenhead (1977)

JORDAN, J. 'Correlation circuits for measurement systems', *IEE Conference Digest No. 1979/32*, 1/1-4 (1979)
KEECH, R. P. 'The KPC multichannel correlation signal processor for velocity measurement', *Transactions of the Institute of Measurement and Control*, **4**, No. 1, 43–52 (1982)
KUO, B. C. *Digital Control Systems*, 2nd edn, Holt, Rinehart and Winton, New York (1980)
LANGE, F. H. *Correlation Techniques*, Iliffe Books, London (1967)
LEWIN, D. *Theory and Design of Digital Computer Systems*, Nelson, Walton-on-Thames (1980)
MEADE, M. L. 'Advances in lock-in amplifiers', in *Instrument Science and Technology*, Volume 2, ed. B. E. Jones, Adam Hilger, Bristol (1983a)
MEADE, M. L. *Lock-in Amplifiers: Principles and Applications*, Peter Peregrinus, London (1983b)
OWENS, A. R. 'Digital signal conditioning and conversion', in *Instrument Science and Technology*, ed. B. E. Jones, Adam Hilger, Bristol (1983), pp. 57–78
PAKER, Y. *Minicomputers: A Reference Book for Engineers and Managers*, Abacus Press, Tunbridge Wells (1981)
PAPOULIS, A. *Signal Analysis*, McGraw-Hill, London (1977)
SANDERSON, P. C. *Minicomputers*, Newnes–Butterworth, London (1976)
SHEINGOLD, D. H. *Analog/digital Conversion Notes*, Analog Devices, Norwood, Massachusetts (1977)
STEELE, R. *Delta Modulation Systems*, Pentech Press, London (1975)
TOBEY, G. E., GRAEME, J. G. and HUELSMAN, L. P. *Operational Amplifiers*, McGraw-Hill, New York (1971)
WILKINSON, B. and HORROCKS, D. *Computer Peripherals*, Hodder, London (1980)

5 Telemetry

M.L. SANDERSON

5.1 Introduction

Within instrumentation there is often a need for telemetry in order to transmit data or information between two geographical locations. The transmission may be required to enable centralized supervisory data logging, signal processing or control to be exercised in large-scale systems which employ distributed data logging or control subsystems. In a chemical plant or power station these subsystems may be spread over a wide area. Telemetry may also be required for systems which are remote or inaccessible such as a spacecraft, a satellite, or an unmanned buoy in the middle of the ocean. It can be used to transmit information from the rotating sections of an electrical machine without the need for slip rings. By using telemetry-sensitive signal processing and recording, apparatus can be physically remote from hazardous and aggressive environments and can be operated in more closely monitored and controlled conditions.

Telemetry has traditionally been provided by either pneumatic or electrical transmission. Pneumatic transmission, as shown in Figure 5.1, has been used extensively in process instrumentation and control. The measured quantity (pressure, level, temperature, etc.) is converted to a pneumatic pressure, the standard signal ranges being 20–100 kPa gauge pressure (3–15 lb/in^2/g) and 20–180 kPa (3–27 lb/in^2/g). The lower limit of pressure provides a live zero for the instrument which enables line breaks to be detected, eases instrument calibration and checking, and provides for improved dynamic response since, when venting to atmospheric pressure, there is still sufficient driving pressure at 20 kPa. The pneumatic signals can be transmitted over distances up to 300 m in 6.35 mm or 9.5 mm OD plastic or metal tubing to a pneumatic indicator, recorder or controller. Return signals for control purposes are transmitted from the control element. The distance is limited by the speed of response, which quadruples with doubling the

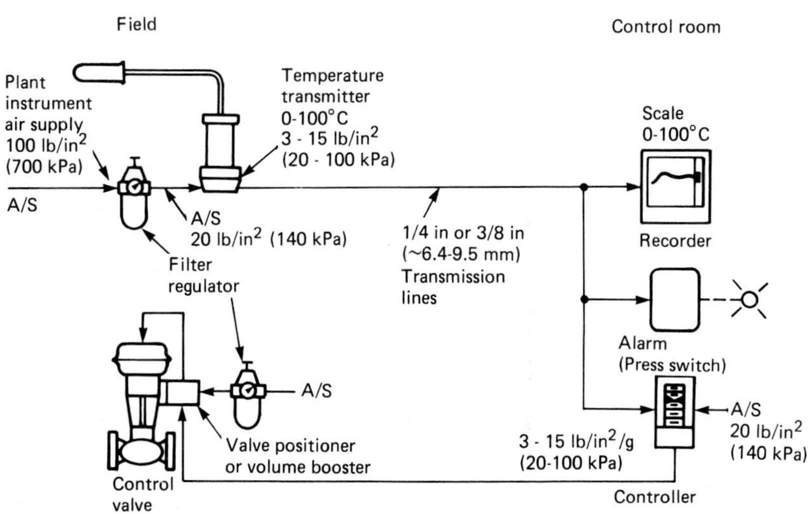

Figure 5.1 Pneumatic transmission.

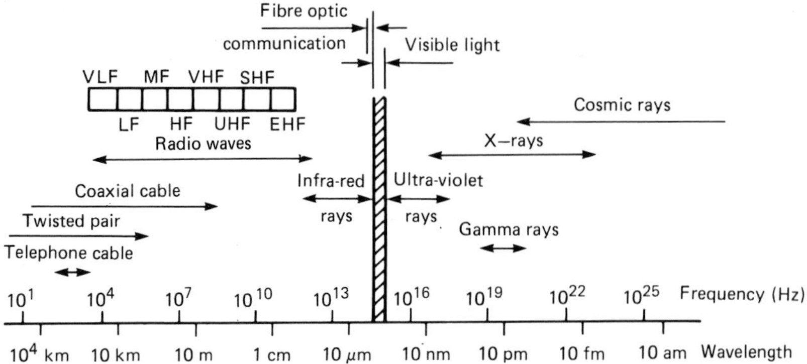

Figure 5.2 Electromagnetic spectrum.

distance. Pneumatic instrumentation generally is covered at greater length in Chapter 7.

Pneumatic instruments are intrinsically safe, and can therefore be used in hazardous areas. They provide protection against electrical power failure since systems employing air storage or turbine-driven compressors can continue to provide measurement and control during power failure. Pneumatic signals also directly interface with control valves which are pneumatically operated and thus do not require the electrical/pneumatic converters required by electrical telemetry systems, although they do suffer from the difficulty of being difficult to interface to data loggers. Pneumatic transmission systems require a dry, regulated air supply. Condensed moisture in the pipework at subzero temperatures or small solid contaminants can block the small passages within pneumatic instruments and cause loss of accuracy and failure. Further details of pneumatic transmission and instrumentation can be found in Bentley (1983) and Warnock (1985).

Increasingly telemetry in instrumentation is being undertaken using electrical, radio frequency, microwave or optical fibre techniques. The communication channels used include transmission lines employing two or more conductors which may be a twisted pair, a coaxial cable or a telephone line physically connecting the two sites; radio frequency (r.f.) or microwave links which allow the communication of data by modulation of an r.f. or microwave carrier; and optical links in which the data are transmitted as a modulation of light down a fibre-optic cable. All of these techniques employ some portion of the electromagnetic spectrum, as shown in Figure 5.2.

Figure 5.3 shows a complete telemetry system. Signal conditioning in the form of amplification and filtering normalizes the outputs from different transducers and restricts their bandwidths to those available on the communication channel. Transmission systems can employ voltage, current, position, pulse or frequency techniques in order to transmit analogue or digital data. Direct transmission of analogue signals as voltage, current or position

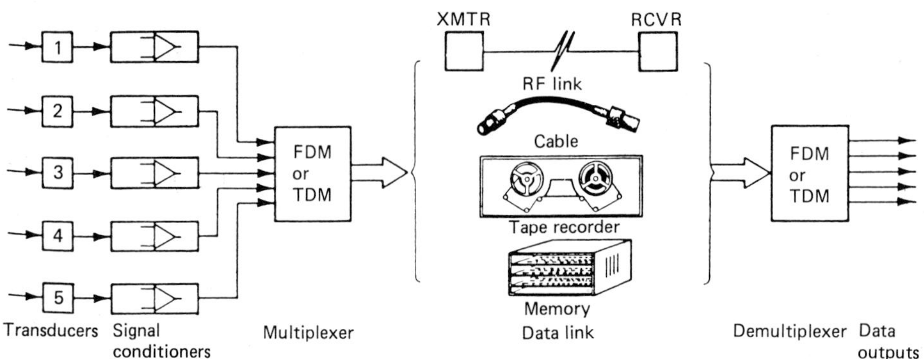

Figure 5.3 Telemetry system.

requires a physical connection between the two points in the form of two or more wires and cannot be used over the telephone network. Pulse and frequency telemetry can be used for transmission over both direct links and also for telephone, r.f., microwave and optical links. Multiplexing either on a time or frequency basis enables more than one signal to be transmitted over the same channel. In pulse operation the data are encoded as the amplitude, duration or position of the pulse or in a digital form. Transmission may be as a baseband signal or as an amplitude, frequency or phase modulation of a carrier wave.

In the transmission of digital signals the information capacity of the channel is limited by the available bandwidth, the power level and the noise present on the channel. The Shannon–Hartley theorem states that the information capacity, C, in bits/s (bps) for a channel having a bandwidth B Hz and additative Gaussian band-limited white noise is given by

$$C = B.\log_2\left(1 + \frac{S}{N}\right)$$

where S is the average signal power at the output of the channel and N is the noise power at the output of the channel.

This capacity represents the upper limit at which data can be reliably transmitted over a particular channel. In general, because the channel does not have the ideal gain and phase characteristics required by the theorem and also because it would not be practical to construct the elaborate coding and decoding arrangements necessary to come close to the ideal, the capacity of the channel is significantly below the theoretical limit.

Channel bandwidth limitations also give rise to bit rate limitations in digital data transmission because of intersymbol interference (ISI), in which the response of the channel to one digital signal interferes with the response to the next. The impulse response of a channel having a limited bandwidth of B Hz is shown in Figure 5.4(a). The response has zeros separated by $1/2B$ s. Thus for a second impulse transmitted across the channel at a time $1/2B$ s later there will be no ISI from the first impulse. This is shown in Figure 5.4(b). The maximum data rate for the channel such that no ISI occurs is thus $2B$ bps. This is known as the Nyquist rate. Figure 5.4(c) shows the effect of transmitting data at a rate in excess of the Nyquist rate.

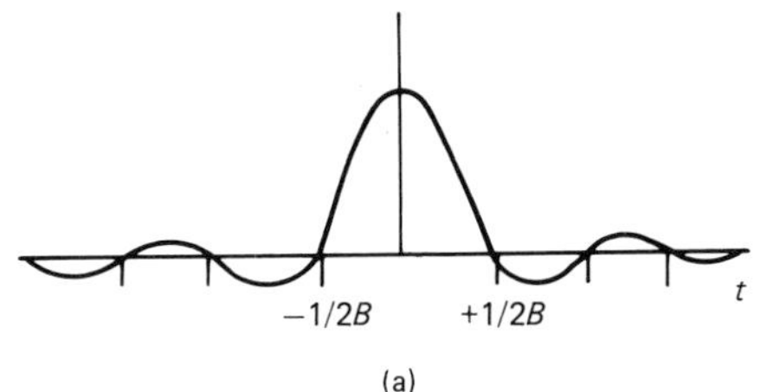

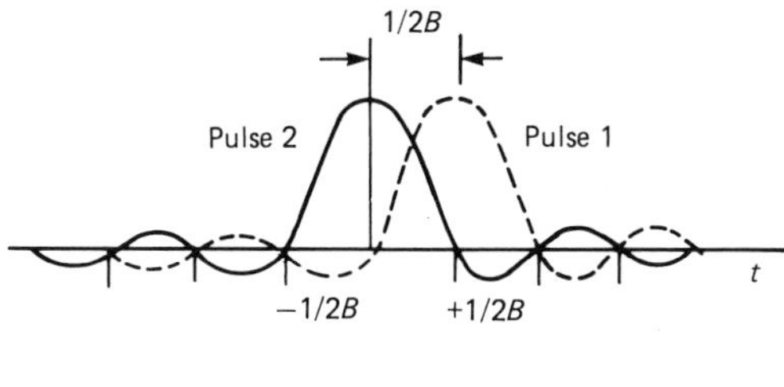

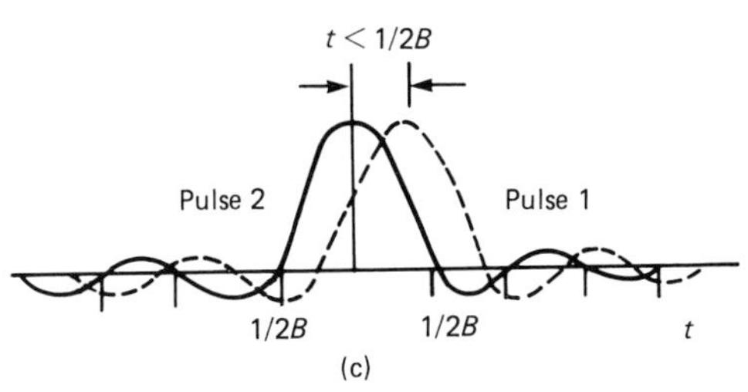

Figure 5.4 (a) Impulse response of a bandlimited channel; (b) impulse responses delayed by $1/2B$ s; (c) impulse responses delayed by less than $1/2B$ **s.**

5.2 Communication channels

5.2.1 Transmission lines

Transmission lines are used to guide electromagnetic waves, and in instrumentation these commonly take the form of a twisted pair, a coaxial cable or a telephone line. The primary constants of such lines in terms of their resistance, leakage conductance, inductance and capacitance are distributed as shown in Figure 5.5. At low frequencies, generally below 100 kHz, a medium-length line may be represented by the circuit shown in Figure 5.6, where R_L is the resistance of the wire and C_L is the lumped capacitance of the line. The line thus acts as a low-pass filter. The frequency response can be extended by loading the line with regularly placed lumped inductances.

Transmission lines are characterized by three secondary constants. These are the characteristic impedance, Z_0; the attenuation, α, per unit length of line which is usually expressed in dB/unit length; and the phase shift, β, which is measured in

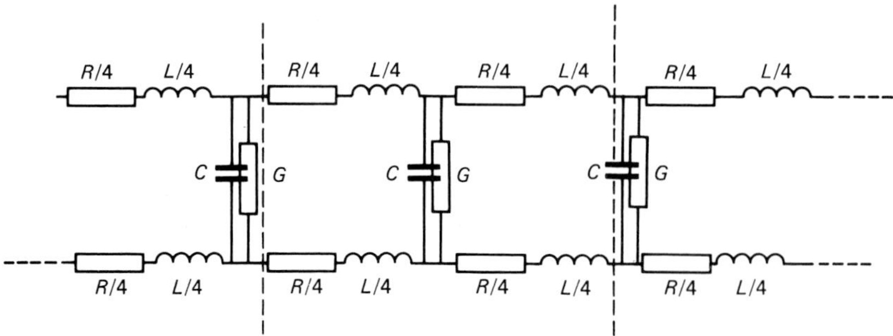

Figure 5.5 Distributed primary constants of a transmission line.

radians/unit length. The values of Z_0, α, β, are related to the primary line constants by:

$$Z_0 = \sqrt{\left(\frac{R + j\omega L}{G + j\omega C}\right)}\ \Omega$$

$$\alpha = 8.68.[0.5(\{(R^2 + \omega^2L^2)(G^2 + \omega^2C^2)\}^{1/2} + (RG - \omega^2LC))]^{1/2}\ \text{dB/unit length}$$

$$\beta = [0.5(\{(R^2 + \omega^2L^2)(G^2 + \omega^2C^2)\}^{1/2} - (RG - \omega^2LC))]^{1/2}\ \text{radians/unit length}$$

where R is the resistance per unit length, G is the leakage conductance per unit length, C is the capacitance per unit length and L is the inductance per unit length.

It is necessary to terminate transmission lines with their characteristic impedance if reflection or signal echo is to be avoided. The magnitude of the reflection for a line of characteristic impedance Z_0 terminated with an impedance Z_T is measured by the reflection coefficient, ρ, given by:

$$\rho = \frac{Z_T - Z_0}{Z_T + Z_0}$$

Twisted pairs are precisely what they say they are, namely two insulated conductors twisted together. The conductors are generally copper or aluminium and plastic is often used as the insulating material. The twisting reduces the effect of inductively coupled interference. Typical values of the primary constants for a 22 gauge copper twisted pair are $R = 100\ \Omega$/km, $L = 1$ mH/km, $G = 10^{-5}$ S/km and $C = 0.05\ \mu$F/km. At high frequencies the characteristic impedance of the line is approximately 140 Ω. Typical values for the attenuation of a twisted pair are 3.4 dB/km at 100 kHz, 14 dB/km at 1 MHz and 39 dB/km at 10 MHz. The high-frequency limitation for the use of twisted pairs at approximately 1 MHz occurs not so much as a consequence of attenuation but because of crosstalk caused by capacitive coupling between adjacent twisted pairs in a cable.

Coaxial cables which are used for data transmission at higher frequencies consist of a central core conductor surrounded by a dielectric material which may be either polythene or air. The construction of such cables is shown in Figure 5.7. The outer conductor consists of a solid or braided sheath around the dielectric. In the case of the air dielectric the central core is supported on polythene spacers placed uniformly along the line. The outer conductor is usually covered by an insulating coating. The loss at high frequencies in coaxial cable is due to the 'skin effect', which forces the current in the central core to flow near to its surface and thus increases the resistance of the conductor. Such cables have a characteristic impedance of between 50 and 75 Ω. The typical attenuation of a 0.61 cm diameter coaxial cable is 8 dB/100 m at 100 MHz and 25 dB/100 m at 1 GHz.

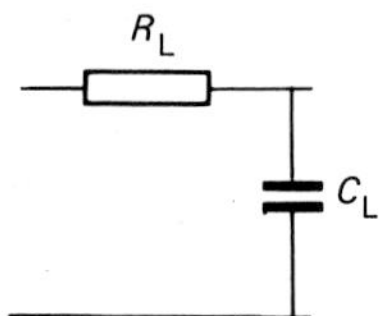

Figure 5.6 Low-frequency lumped approximation for a transmission line.

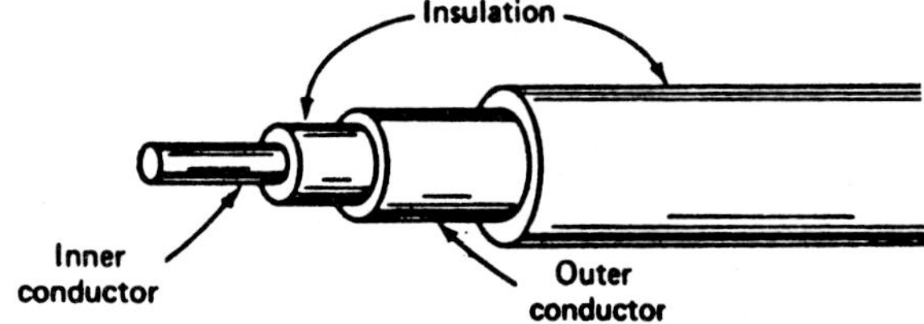

Figure 5.7 Coaxial cable.

Trunk telephone cables connecting exchanges consist of bunched twisted conductor pairs. The conductors are insulated with paper or polyethylene, the twisting being used to reduce the crosstalk between adjacent conductor pairs. A bunch of twisted cables is sheathed in plastic and the whole cable is given mechanical strength by binding with steel wire or tape which is itself sheathed in plastic. At audiofrequencies the impedance of the cable is dominated by its capacitance and resistance. This results in an attenuation which is frequency dependent and also phase delay distortion, since signals of different frequencies are not transmitted down the cable with the same velocity. Thus a pulse propagated down a cable results in a signal which is not only attenuated (of importance in voice and analogue communication) but which is also phase distorted (of importance in digital signal transmission). The degree of phase delay distortion is measured by the group delay $d\beta/d\omega$. The bandwidth of telephone cables is restricted at low frequencies by the use of a.c. amplification in the repeater stations used to boost the signal along the line. Loading is used to improve the high-frequency amplitude response of the line. This takes the form of lumped inductances which correct the attenuation characteristics of the line. These leave the line with a significant amount of phase delay distortion and also give the line attenuation at high frequencies. The useable frequency band of the telephone line is between 300 Hz and 3 kHz. Figure 5.8 shows typical amplitude and phase or group delay distortions relative to 800 Hz for a typical leased line and a line to which equalization or conditioning has been applied.

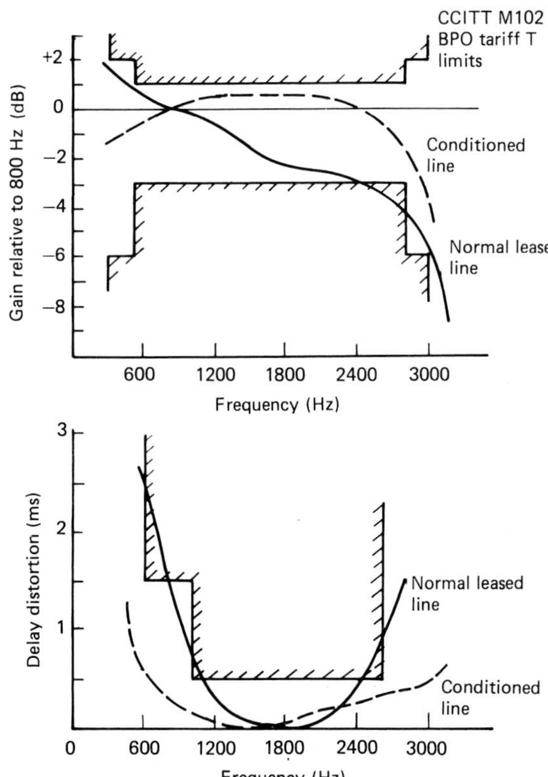

Figure 5.8 Gain and delay distortion on telephone lines.

In order to transmit digital information reliably the transmission equipment has to contend with a transmission loss which may be as high as 30 dB; a limited bandwidth caused by a transmission loss which varies with frequency; group delay variations with frequency; echoes caused by impedance mismatching and hybrid crosstalk; and noise which may be either Gaussian or impulsive noise caused by dial pulses, switching equipment or lightning strikes. Thus it can be seen that the nature of the telephone line causes particular problems in the transmission of digital data. Devices known as modems (MOdulators/DEModulators) are used to transmit digital data along telephone lines. These are considered in section 5.9.1.

5.2.2 Radiofrequency transmission

Radiofrequency (r.f.) transmission is widely used in both civilian and military telemetry and can occur from 3 Hz (which is referred to as very low frequency (VLF)) up as high as 300 GHz (which is referred to as extremely high frequency (EHF)). The transmission of the signal is by means of line-of-sight propagation, ground or surface wave diffraction, ionospheric reflection or forward scattering (Coates, 1982). The transmission of telemetry or data signals is usually undertaken as the amplitude, phase or frequency modulation of some r.f. carrier wave. These modulation techniques are described in section 5.5. The elements of an r.f. telemetry system are shown in Figure 5.9.

The allocation of frequency bands has been internationally agreed under the Radio Regulations of the International Telecommunication Union based in Geneva. These regulations were agreed in 1959 and revised in 1979 (HMSO, 1980). In the UK the Radio Regulatory Division of the Department of Trade approves equipment and issues licences for the users of radio telemetry links. For general-purpose low-power telemetry and telecontrol there are four bands which can be used. These are 0–185 kHz and 240–315 kHz, 173.2–173.35 MHz and 458.5–458.8 MHz. For high-power private point systems the allocated frequencies are in the UHF band 450–470 MHz.

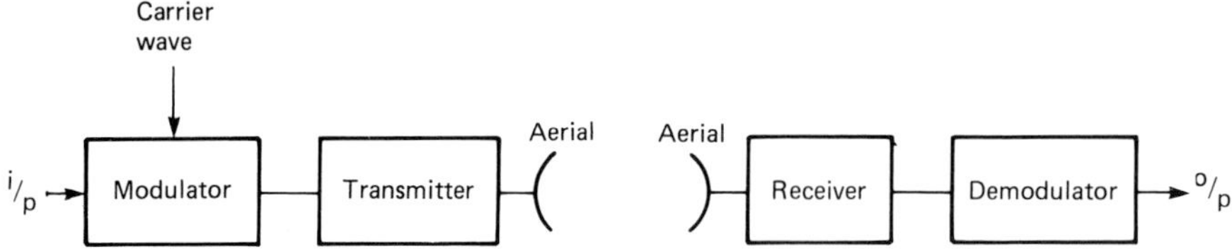

Figure 5.9 R.F. telemetry system.

For medical and biological telemetry there are three classes of equipment. Class I are low-power devices operating between 300 kHz and 30 MHz wholly contained within the body of an animal or man. Class II is broad-band equipment operating in the band 104.6–105 MHz. Class III equipment is narrow-band equipment operating in the same frequency band as the Class II equipment. Details of the requirements for r.f. equipment can be found in the relevant documents cited in the References (HMSO, 1963, 1978, 1979).

5.2.3 Fibre-optic communication

Increasingly, in data-communication systems there is a move towards the use of optical fibres for the transmission of data. Detailed design considerations for such systems can be found in Keiser (1983). Wilson and Hawkes (1983) and Senior (1985). As a transmission medium fibre-optic cables offer the following advantages:

(1) They are immune to electromagnetic interference.
(2) Data can be transmitted at much higher frequencies and with lower losses than twisted pairs or coaxial cables. Fibre optics can therefore be used for the multiplexing of a large number of signals along one cable with greater distances required between repeater stations.
(3) They can provide enhanced safety when operating in hazardous areas.
(4) Earth loop problems can be reduced.
(5) Since the signal is confined within the fibre by total internal reflection at the interface between the fibre and the cladding fibre-optic links provide a high degree of data security and little fibre-to-fibre crosstalk.
(6) The material of the fibre is very much less likely to be attacked chemically than copper-based systems and it can be provided with mechanical properties which will make such cables need less maintenance than the equivalent twisted pair or coaxial cable.
(7) Fibre-optic cables can offer both weight and size advantages over copper systems.

5.2.3.1 Optical fibres

The elements of an optical fibre as shown in Figure 5.10 are the core material, the cladding and the buffer coating. The core material is either plastic or glass. The cladding is a material whose refractive index is less than that of the core. Total internal reflection at the core/cladding interface confines the light to travel within the core. Fibres with plastic cores also have plastic cladding. Such fibres exhibit high losses but are widely used for short distance transmission. Multicomponent glasses containing a number of oxides are used for all but the lowest loss fibres which are usually made from pure silica. In low- and medium-loss fibres the glass core is surrounded by a glass or plastic cladding. The buffer coating is an elastic, abrasion-resistant plastic material which increases the mechanical strength of the fibre and provides it with mechanical isolation from geometrical irregularities, distortions or roughness of adjacent surfaces which could otherwise cause scattering losses when the fibre is incorporated into cables or supported by other structures.

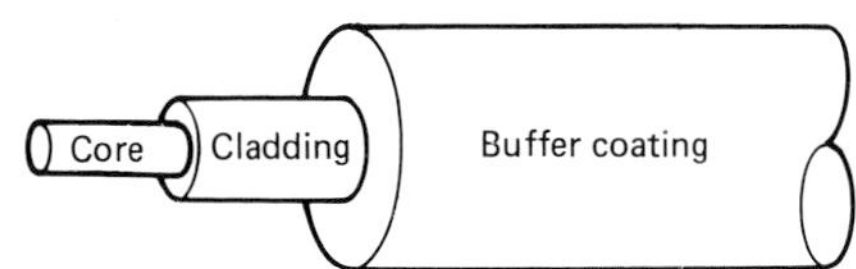

Figure 5.10 Elements of an optical fibre.

The numerical aperture (*NA*) of a fibre is a measure of the maximum core angle for light rays to be reflected down the fibre by total internal reflection.

By Snell's Law:

$$NA = \sin\theta = \sqrt{(\mu_1^2 - \mu_2^2)}$$

where μ_1 is the refractive index of the core material and μ_2 is the refractive index of the cladding material.

Fibres have *NA*s in the region of 0.15–0.4, corresponding to total acceptance angles of between 16 and 46 degrees. Fibres with higher *NA* values

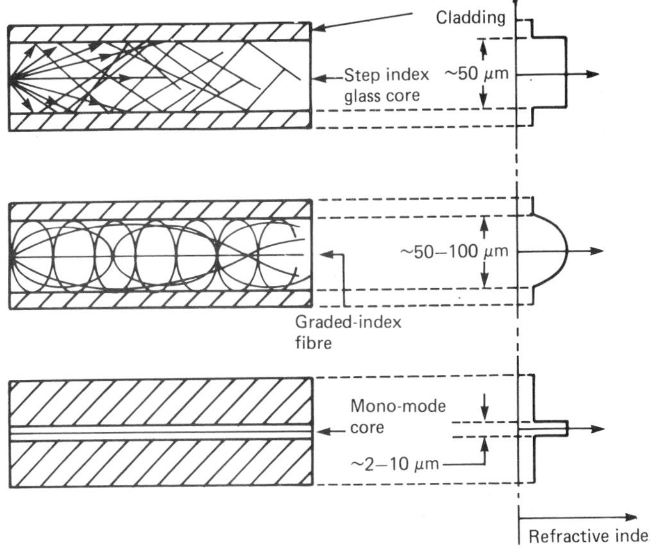

Figure 5.11 Propagation down fibres.

generally exhibit greater losses and low bandwidth capabilities.

The propagation of light down the fibres is described by Maxwell's equations, the solution of which gives rise to a set of bounded electromagnetic waves called the 'modes' of the fibre. Only a discrete number of modes can propagate down the fibre, determined by the particular solution of Maxwell's equation obtained when boundary conditions appropriate to the particular fibre are applied. Figure 5.11 shows the propagation down three types of fibre. The larger-core radius multimode fibres are either step index or graded index fibres. In the step index fibres there is a step change in the refractive index at the core/cladding interface. The refractive index of the graded index fibre varies across the core of the fibre. Monomode fibres have a small-core radius, which permits the light to travel along only one path in the fibre.

The larger-core radii of multimode fibres make it much easier to launch optical power into the fibre and facilitate the connecting of similar fibres. Power can be launched into such a fibre using light-emitting diodes (LEDs), whereas single-mode fibres must be excited with a laser diode.

Intermodal dispersion occurs in multimode fibres because each of the modes in the fibres travels at a slightly different velocity. An optical pulse launched into a fibre has its energy distributed amongst all its possible modes, and therefore as it travels down the fibre the dispersion has the effect of spreading the pulse out. Dispersion thus provides a bandwidth limitation on the fibre. This is specified in MHz.km. In graded index fibres the effect of intermodal dispersion is reduced over that in step index fibres because the grading bends the various possible light rays along paths of nominal equal delay. There is no intermodal dispersion in a single-mode fibre, and therefore these are used for the highest-capacity systems. The bandwidth limitation for a plastic clad step index fibre is typically 6–25 MHz.km. Employing graded index plastic-clad fibres this can be increased to the range of 200–400 MHz.km. For monomode fibres the bandwidth limitation is typically 500–1500 MHz.km.

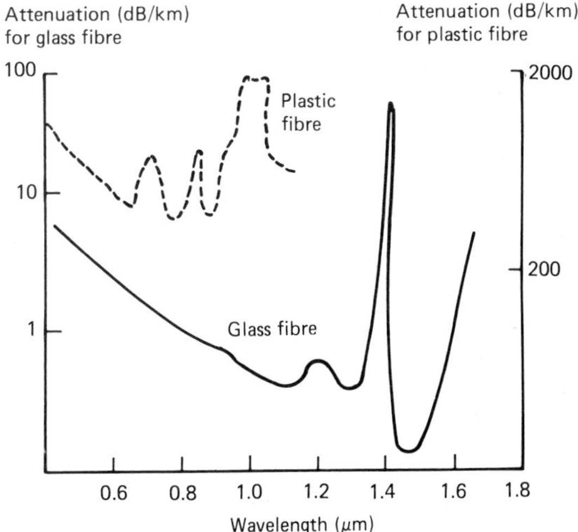

Figure 5.12 Attenuation characteristics of optical fibres.

Attenuation within a fibre, which is measured in dB/km, occurs as a consequence of absorption, scattering and radiative losses of optical energy. Absorption is caused by extrinsic absorption by impurity atoms in the core and intrinsic absorption by the basic constituents of the core material. One impurity which is of particular importance is the OH (water) ion, and for low-loss materials this is controlled to a concentration of less than 1 ppb. Scattering losses occur as a consequence of microscopic variations in material density or composition, and from structural irregularities or defects introduced during manufacture. Radiative losses occur whenever an optical fibre undergoes a bend having a finite radius of curvature.

Attenuation is a function of optical wavelength. Figure 5.12 shows the typical attenuation versus wavelength characteristics of a plastic and a monomode glass fibre. At 0.8 μm the attenuation of the plastic fibre is 350 dB/km and that of the glass fibre is approximately 1 dB/km. The minimum attenuation of the glass fibre is 0.2 dB/km at 1.55 μm. Figure 5.13 shows the construction of the light- and medium-duty optical cables.

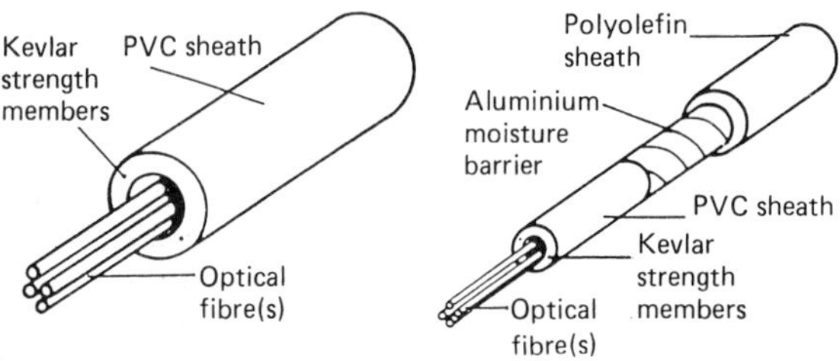

Figure 5.13 Light- and medium-duty optical cables.

5.2.3.2 Sources and detectors

The sources used in optical fibre transmission are LEDs and semiconductor laser diodes. LEDs are capable of launching a power of between 0.1 and 10 mW into the fibre. Such devices have a peak emission frequency in the near infra-red, typically between 0.8 and 1.0 μm. Figure 5.14 shows the typical spectral output from a LED. Limitations on the transmission rates using LEDs occur as a consequence of its rise time, typically between 2 and 10 ns, and chromatic dispersion. This occurs because the refractive index of the core material varies with optical wavelength, and therefore the various spectral components of a given mode will travel at different speeds.

Semiconductor laser diodes can provide significantly higher power, particularly with low-duty

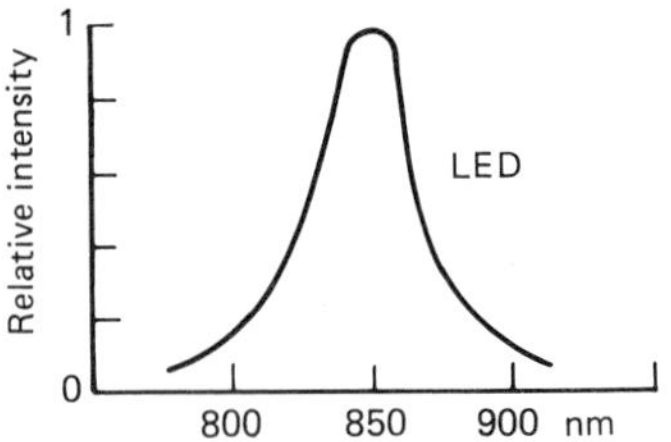

Figure 5.14 Spectral output from a LED.

cycles, with outputs typically in the region of 1 to 100 mW. Because they couple into the fibre more efficiently they offer a higher electrical to optical efficiency than do LEDs. The lasing action means that the device has a narrower spectral width compared with a LED, typically 2 nm or less, as shown in Figure 5.15. Chromatic dispersion is therefore less for laser diodes which also have a faster rise time, typically 1 ns.

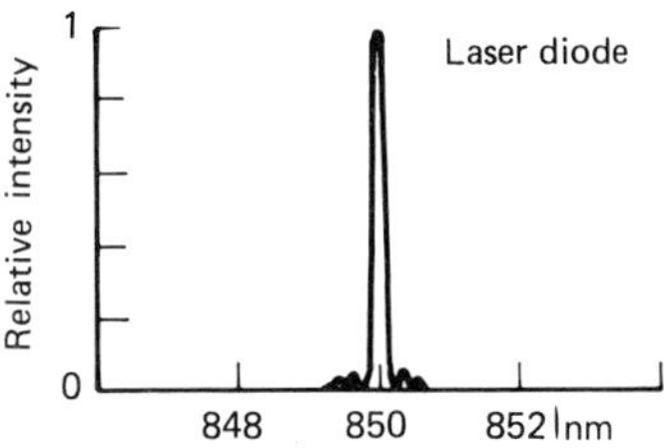

Figure 5.15 Spectral output from a laser diode.

For digital transmissions of below 50 Mbps LEDs require less complex drive circuitry than laser diodes and require no thermal or optical power stabilization.

Both p–i–n (p material–intrinsic–n material) diodes and avalanche photodiodes are used in the detection of the optical signal at the receiver. In the region 0.8–0.9 μm silicon is the main material used in the fabrication of these devices. The p–i–n diode has a typical responsivity of 0.65 A/W at 0.8 μm. The avalanche photodiode employs avalanche action to provide current gain and therefore higher detector responsivity. The avalanche gain can be 100, although the gain produces additional noise. The sensitivity of the photodetector and receiver system is determined by photodetector noise which occurs as a consequence of the statistical nature of the production of photoelectrons, and bulk and dark surface current, together with the thermal noise in the detector resistor and amplifier. For p–i–n diodes the thermal noise of the resistor and amplifier dominates, whereas with avalanche photodiodes the detector noise dominates.

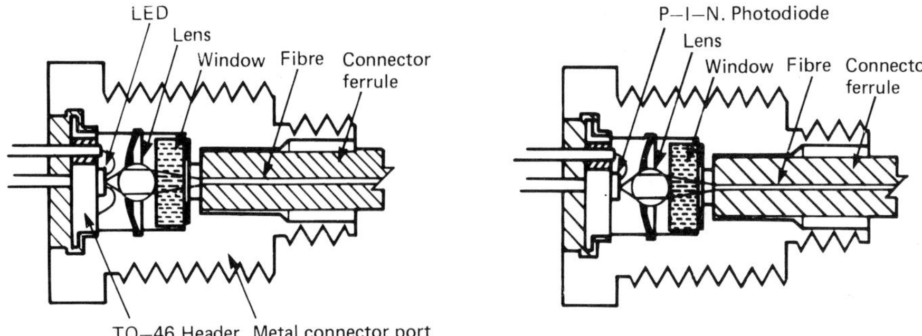

Figure 5.16 LED and p–i–n diode detector for use in a fibre-optic system.

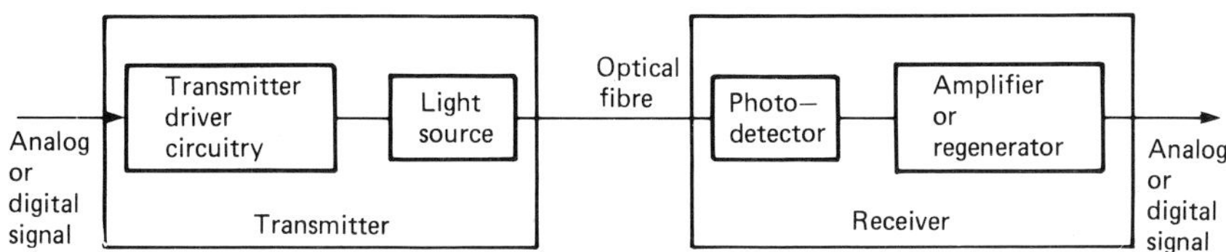

Figure 5.17 Fibre-optic communication system.

Figure 5.16 shows a LED and p–i–n diode detector for use in a fibre-optic system.

5.2.3.3 Fibre-optic communication systems

Figure 5.17 shows a complete fibre-optic communications system. In the design of such systems it is necessary to compute the system insertion loss in order that the system can be operated using the minimum transmitter output flux and minimum receiver input sensitivity. In addition to the loss in the cable itself, other sources of insertion loss occur at the connections between the transmitter and the cable and the cable and the receiver; at connectors joining cables; and at points where the cable has been spliced. The losses at these interfaces occur as a consequence of reflections, differences in fibre diameter, *NA* and fibre alignment. Directional couplers and star connectors also increase the insertion loss.

5.3 Signal multiplexing

In order to enable several signals to be transmitted over the same medium it is necessary to multiplex the signals. There are two forms of multiplexing—frequency-division multiplexing (FDM) and time-division multiplexing (TDM). FDM splits the available bandwidth of the transmission medium into a series of frequency bands and uses each of the frequency bands to transmit one of the signals. TDM splits the transmission into a series of time slots and allocates certain time slots, usually on a cyclical basis, for the transmission of one signal.

The basis of FDM is shown in Figure 5.18(a). The bandwidth of the transmission medium f_m is split into a series of frequency bands, having a bandwidth f_{ch}, each one of which is used to transmit one signal. Between these channels there are frequency bands, having bandwidth f_g, called 'guard bands' which are used to ensure that there is adequate separation and minimum crosstalk between any two adjacent channels. Figure 5.18(b) shows the transmission of three band-limited signals having spectral characteristics as shown, the low-pass filters at the input to the modulators being used to bandlimit the signals. Each of the signals then modulates a carrier. Any form of carrier modulation can be used, although it is desirable to use a modulation which requires minimum bandwidth. The modulation shown in Figure 5.18(b) is amplitude modulation (see section 5.5). The individually modulated signals are then summed and transmitted. Bandpass filters after reception are used to separate the channels, by providing attenuation which starts in the guard bands. The signals are then demodulated and smoothed.

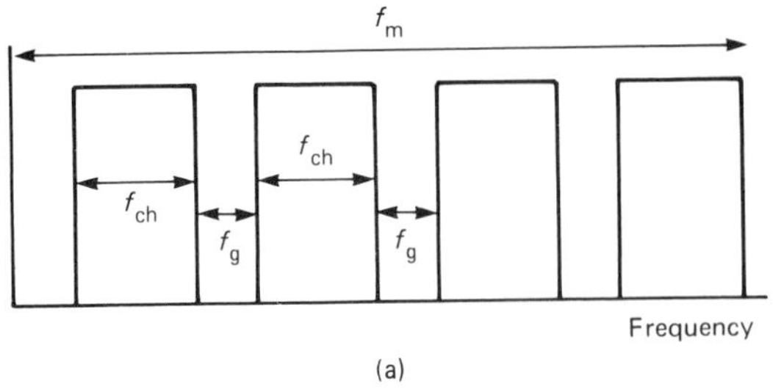

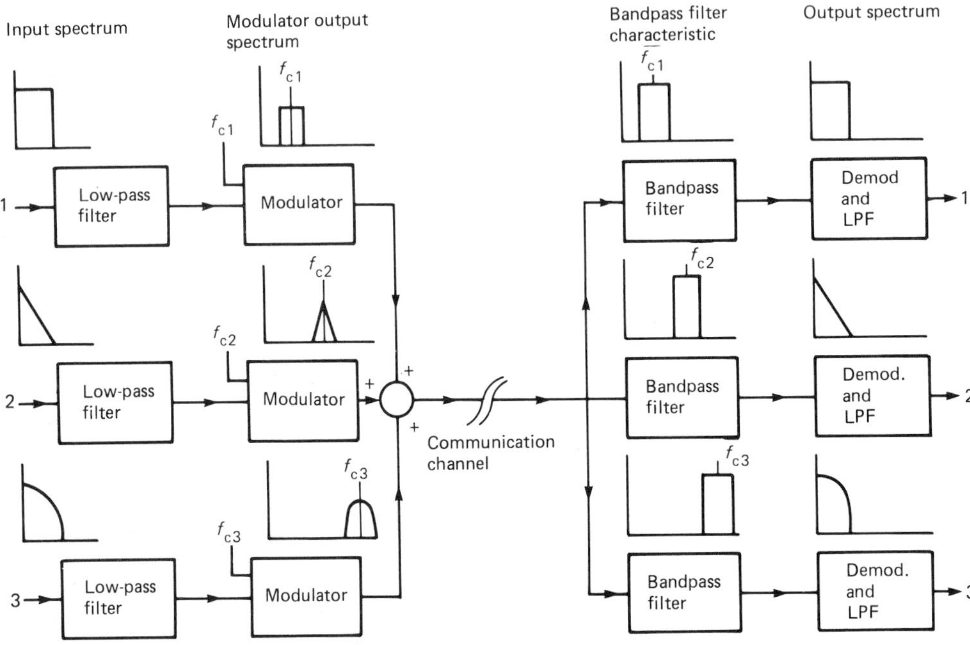

Figure 5.18 (a) Frequency-division multiplexing; (b) transmission of three signals using FDM.

TDM is shown schematically in Figure 5.19. The multiplexer acts as a switch connecting each of the signals in turn to the transmission channel for a given time. In order to recover the signals in the correct sequence it is necessary to employ a demultiplexer at the receiver or to have some means inherent within the transmitted signal to identify its source. If N signals are continuously multiplexed then each one of them is sampled at a rate of $1/N$ Hz. They must therefore be bandlimited to a frequency of $1/2N$ Hz if the Shannon sampling theorem is not to be violated.

The multiplexer acts as a multi-input–single output switch, and for electrical signals this can be done by mechanical or electronic switching. For high frequencies electronic multiplexing is employed, with integrated circuit multiplexers which use CMOS or BIFET technologies.

TDM circuitry is much simpler to implement than FDM circuitry, which requires modulators, bandpass filters and demodulators for each channel. In TDM only small errors occur as a consequence of circuit non-linearities, whereas phase and amplitude non-linearities have to be kept small in order to limit intermodulation and harmonic distortion in FDM systems. TDM achieves its low channel crosstalk by using a wideband system. At high transmission rates errors occur in TDM systems due to timing jitter, pulse accuracy and synchronization problems. Further details of FDM and TDM systems can be found in Johnson (1976) and Shanmugan (1979).

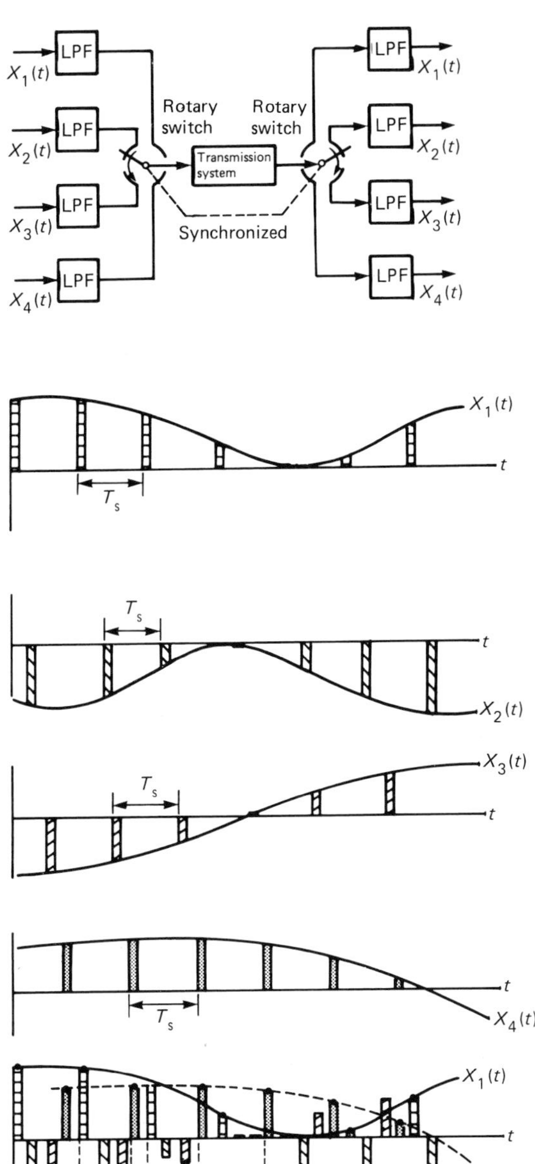

Figure 5.19 Time-division multiplexing.

5.4 Pulse encoding

Pulse code modulation (PCM) is one of the most commonly used methods of encoding analogue data for transmission in instrumentation systems. In PCM the analogue signal is sampled and converted into binary form by means of an ADC, and these data are then transmitted in serial form. This is shown in Figure 5.20. The bandwidth required for the transmission of a signal using PCM is considerably in excess of the bandwidth of the original signal. If a signal having a bandwidth f_d is encoded into an N-bit binary code the minimum bandwidth required to transmit the PCM encoded signal is $f_d.N$ Hz, i.e. N times the original signal bandwidth.

Several forms of PCM are shown in Figure 5.21. The non-return to zero (NRZ-L) is a common code that is easily interfaced to a computer. In the non-return to zero mark (NRZ-M) and the non-return to zero space (NRZ-S) codes level transitions represent bit changes. In bi-phase level (BIΦ-L) a bit transition occurs at the centre of every period. One is represented by a '1' level changing to a '0' level at the centre transition point, and zero is represented by a '0' level changing to a '1' level. In bi-phase mark and space code (BIΦ-M) and (BIΦ-S) a level change occurs at the beginning of each bit period. In BIΦ-M one is represented by a mid-bit transition; a zero has no transition. BIΦ-S is the converse of BIΦ-M. Delay modulation code DM-M and DM-S have transitions at mid-bit and at the end of the bit time. In DM-M a one is represented by a level change at mid-bit; a zero followed by a zero is represented by a level change after the first zero. No level change occurs if a zero precedes a one. DM-S is the converse of DM-M. Bi-phase codes have a transition at least every bit time which can be used for synchronization, but they require twice the bandwidth of the NRZ-L code. The delay modulation codes offer the greatest bandwidth saving but are more susceptible to error, and are used if bandwidth compression is needed or high signal-to-noise ratio is expected.

Alternative forms of encoding are shown in Figure 5.22. In pulse amplitude modulation (PAM) the amplitude of the signal transmitted is proportional to the magnitude of the signal being transmitted, and it can be used for the transmission of both analogue and digital signals. The channel bandwidth required for the transmission of PAM is less than that required for PCM, although the effects of ISI are more marked. PAM as a means of transmitting digital data requires more complex decoding schemes, in that it is necessary to discriminate between an increased number of levels.

Other forms of encoding which can be used include pulse-width modulation (PWM), otherwise referred to as pulse-duration modulation (PDM), which employs a constant height variable width pulse with the information being contained in the width of the pulse. In pulse-position modulation (PPM) the position of the pulses corresponds to the width of the pulse in PWM. Delta modulation and

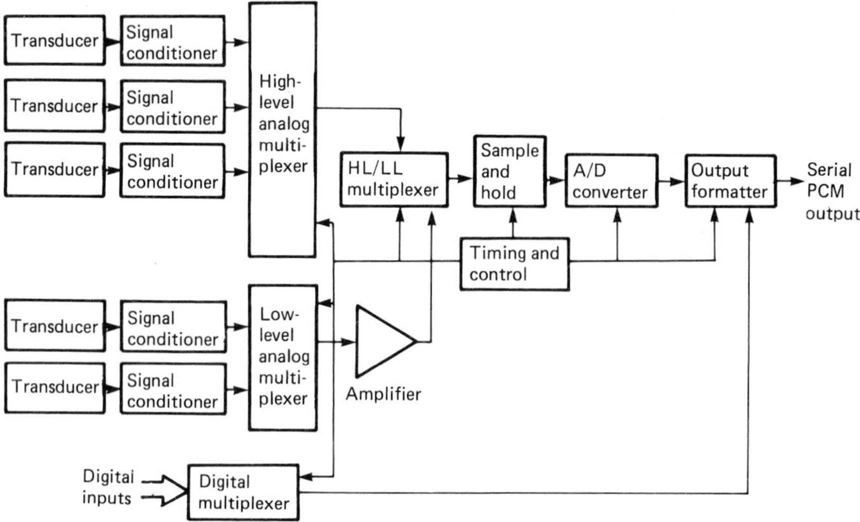

Figure 5.20 Pulse code modulation.

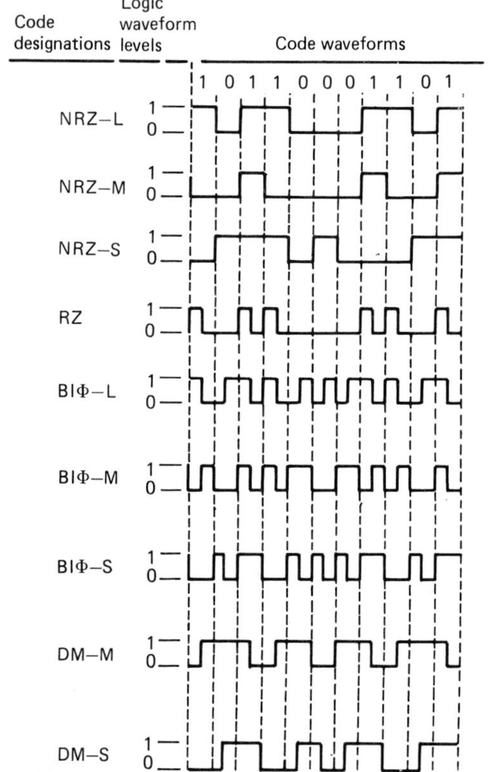

Figure 5.21 Types of pulse code modulation.

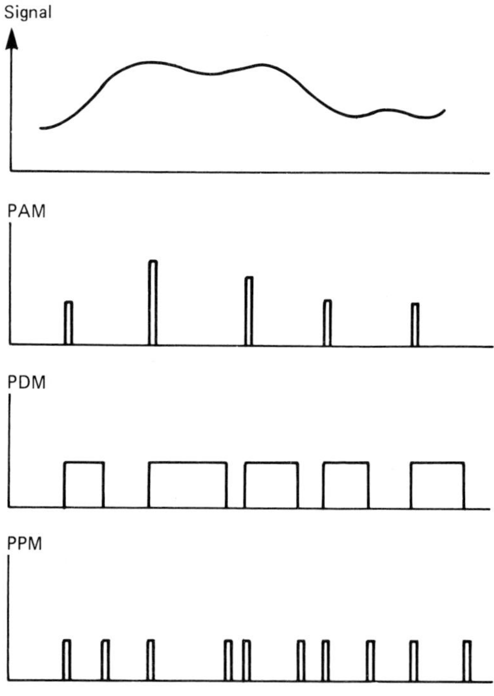

Figure 5.22 Other forms of pulse encoding.

sigma–delta modulation use pulse trains, the frequencies of which are proportional to either the rate of change of the signal or the amplitude of the signal itself. For analyses of the above systems in terms of the bandwidth required for transmission, signal-to-noise ratios and error rate, together with practical details the reader is directed to Hartley *et al.* (1967), Cattermole (1969), Steele (1975) and Shanmugan (1979).

5.5 Carrier wave modulation

Modulation is used to match the frequency characteristics of the data to be transmitted to those of the transmission channel, to reduce the effects of unwanted noise and interference and to facilitate the efficient radiation of the signal. These are all effected by shifting the frequency of the data into some frequency band centred around a carrier frequency. Modulation also allows the allocation of specific frequency bands for specific purposes such as in a FDM system or in r.f. transmission systems, where certain frequency bands are assigned for broadcasting, telemetry, etc. Modulation can also be used to overcome the limitations of signal-processing equipment in that the frequency of the signal can be shifted into frequency bands where the design of filters or amplifiers is somewhat easier, or into a frequency band that the processing equipment will accept. Modulation can be used to provide the bandwidth against signal-to-noise trade-offs which are indicated by the Hartley–Shannon theorem.

Carrier-wave modulation uses the modulation of one of its three parameters, namely amplitude, frequency or phase, and these are all shown in Figure 5.23. The techniques can be used for the transmission of both analogue and digital signals.

In amplitude modulation the amplitude of the carrier varies linearly with the amplitude of the signal to be transmitted. If the data signal $d(t)$ is represented by a sinusoid $d(t) = \cos 2\pi f_d t$ then in amplitude modulation the carrier wave $c(t)$ is given by:

$$c(t) = C(1 + m.\cos 2\pi f_d t)\cos 2\pi f_c t$$

where C is the amplitude of the unmodulated wave, f_c its frequency and m is the depth of modulation which has a value lying between 0 and 1. If $m = 1$ then the carrier is said to have 100 per cent modulation. The above expression for $c(t)$ can be rearranged as:

$$c(t) = C.\cos 2\pi f_c t + \frac{Cm}{2}[\cos 2\pi(f_c + f_d)t + \cos 2\pi(f_c - f_d)t]$$

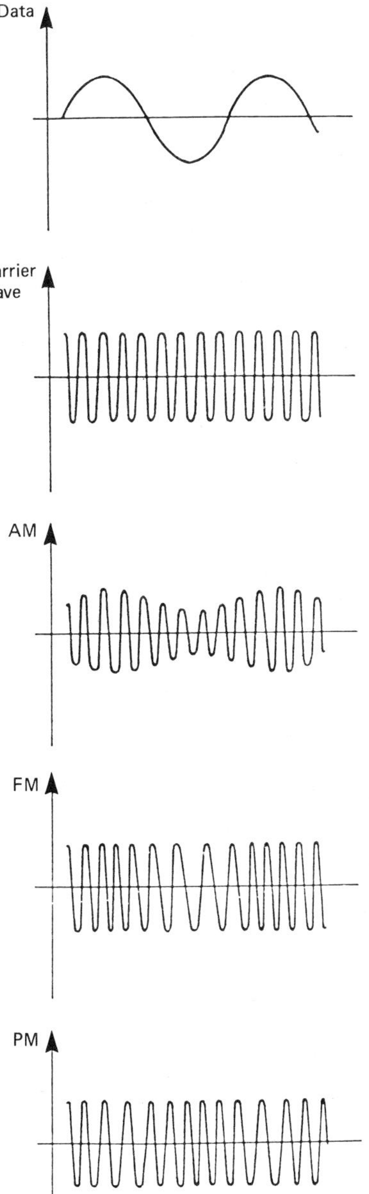

Figure 5.23 Amplitude, frequency and phase modulation of a carrier wave.

showing that the spectrum of the transmitted signal has three frequency components at the carrier frequency f_c and at the sum and difference frequencies $(f_c + f_d)$ and $(f_c - f_d)$. If the signal is represented by a spectrum having frequencies up to f_d then the transmitted spectrum has a bandwidth of $2f_d$ centred around f_c. Thus in order to transmit data using AM a bandwidth equal to twice that of the data is required. As can be seen, the envelope of the AM signal contains the information, and thus demodulation can be effected simply by rectifying and smoothing the signal.

Both the upper and lower sidebands of AM contain sufficient amplitude and phase information to reconstruct the data, and thus it is possible to reduce the bandwidth requirements of the system. Single side-band modulation (SSB) and vestigial side-band modulation (VSM) both transmit the data using amplitude modulation with smaller bandwidths than straight AM. SSB has half the bandwidth of a simple AM system; the low-frequency response is generally poor. VSM transmits one side band almost completely and only a trace of the other. It is very often used in high-speed data transmission, since it offers the best compromise between bandwidth requirements, low-frequency response and improved power efficiency.

In frequency modulation consider the carrier signal $c(t)$ given by:

$$c(t) = C\cos(2\pi f_c t + \phi(t))$$

Then the instantaneous frequency of this signal is given by:

$$f_i(t) = f_c + \frac{1}{2\pi}\cdot\frac{d\phi}{dt}$$

The frequency deviation

$$\frac{1}{2\pi}\cdot\frac{d\phi}{dt}$$

of the signal from the carrier frequency is made to be proportional to the data signal. If the data signal is represented by a single sinusoid of the form:

$$d(t) = \cos 2\pi f_d t$$

then:

$$\frac{d\phi(t)}{dt} = 2\pi k_f.\cos 2\pi f_d t$$

where k_f is the frequency deviation constant which has units of Hz/V. Thus:

$$c(t) = C\cos\left(2\pi f_c t + 2\pi k_f \int_{-\infty}^{t} d(\tau).d\tau\right)$$

and assuming zero initial phase deviation, then the carrier wave can be represented by:

$$c(t) = C\cos(2\pi f_c t + \beta\sin 2\pi f_d t)$$

where β is the modulation index and represents the maximum phase deviation produced by the data. It is possible to show that $c(t)$ can be represented by an infinite series of frequency components $f \pm nf_d$, $n = 1,2,3,\ldots$, given by:

$$c(t) = C\sum_{n=-\infty}^{\infty} J_n(\beta)\cos(2\pi f_c + n2\pi f_d)t$$

where $J_n(\beta)$ is a Bessel function of the first kind of order n and argument β. Since the signal consists of an infinite number of frequency components, limiting the transmission bandwidth distorts the signal, and the question arises as to what is a reasonable bandwidth for the system to have in order to transmit the data with an acceptable degree of distortion. For $\beta << 1$ only J_0 and J_1 are important, and large β implies large bandwidth. It has been found in practice that if 98 per cent or more of the FM signal power is transmitted then the signal distortion is negligible. Carson's rule indicates that the bandwidth required for FM transmission of a signal having a spectrum with components up to a frequency of f_d is given by $2(f_\Delta + f_d)$, where f_Δ is the maximum frequency deviation. For narrow-band FM systems having small frequency deviations the bandwidth required is the same as that for AM. Wide-band FM systems require a bandwidth of $2f_\Delta$. Frequency modulation is used extensively in r.f. telemetry and in FDM.

In phase modulation the instantaneous phase deviation ϕ is made proportional to the data signal. Thus:

$$\phi = k_p.\cos 2\pi f_d t$$

and it can be shown that the carrier wave $c(t)$ can be represented by:

$$c(t) = C\cos(2\pi f_c + \beta\cos 2\pi f_d t)$$

where β is now given by k_p. For further details of the various modulation schemes and their realizations the reader should consult Shanmugan (1979) and Coates (1982).

5.6 Error detection and correction codes

Errors occur in digital data communications systems as a consequence of the corruption of the data by noise. Figure 5.24 shows the bit error probability as a function of signal-to-noise ratio for a PCM transmission system using NRZ-L coding.

In order to reduce the probability of an error occurring in the transmission of the data, bits are added to the transmitted message. These bits add redundancy to the transmitted data, and since only part of the transmitted message is now the actual data, the efficiency of the transmission is reduced. There are two forms of error coding, known as forward error detection and correction coding (FEC), in which the transmitted message is coded in such a way that errors can be both detected and corrected continuously, and automatic repeat request coding (ARQ), in which if an error is detected then a request is sent to repeat the transmission. In terms of data-throughput rates FEC codes are more efficient than AQR codes because of the need to retransmit the data in the case of error in an ARQ code, although the equipment required to detect errors is somewhat simpler than that required to correct the errors from the corrupted message. ARQ codes are commonly used in instrumentation systems.

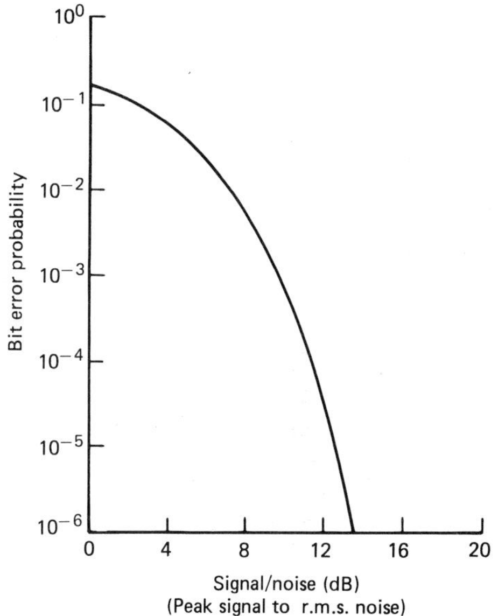

Figure 5.24 Bit-error probability for PCM transmission using a NRZ-L code.

Parity-checking coding is a form of coding used in ARQ coding in which $(n-k)$ bits are added to the k bits of the data to make an n-bit data stream. The simplest form of coding is parity-bit coding in which the number of added bits is one, and this additional bit is added to the data stream in order to make the total number of ones in the data stream either odd or even. The received data are checked for parity. This form of coding will only detect an odd number of bit errors. More complex forms of coding include linear block codes such as Hamming codes, cyclic codes such as Bose–Chanhuri–Hocquenghen codes and geometric codes. Such codes can be designed to detect multiple-burst errors, in which two or more successive bits are in error. In general the larger the number of parity bits, the less efficient the coding is, but the larger are both the maximum number of random errors and the maximum burst length that can be detected. Figure 5.25 shows examples of some of these coding techniques. Further details of coding techniques can be found in Shanmugan (1979), Bowdell (1981) and Coates (1982).

5.7 Direct analogue signal transmission

Analogue signals are rarely transmitted over transmission lines as a voltage since the method suffers from errors due to series and common mode inductively and capacitively coupled interference signals and those due to line resistance. The most common form of analogue signal transmission is as current.

Current transmission as shown in Figure 5.26 typically uses 0–20 or 4–20 mA. The analogue signal is converted to a current at the transmitter and is detected at the receiver either by measuring the potential difference developed across a fixed resistor or using the current to drive an indicating instrument or chart recorder. The length of line over which signals can be transmitted at low frequencies is primarily limited by the voltage available at the transmitter to overcome voltage drop along the line and across the receiver. With a typical voltage of 24 V the system is capable of transmitting the current over several kilometres. The percentage error in a current transmission system can be calculated as 50 × the ratio of the loop resistance in ohms to the total line insulation resistance, also expressed in ohms. The accuracy of current transmission system systems is typically ±0.5 per cent.

The advantage of using 4–20 mA instead of 0–20 mA is that the use of a live zero enables instrument or line faults to be detected. In the 4–20 mA system zero value is represented by 4 mA and failure is indicated by 0 mA. It is possible to use a 4–20 mA system as a two-wire transmission system in which both the power and the signal are transmitted along the same wire, as shown in Figure 5.27. The 4 mA standing current is used to power the remote instrumentation and the transmitter. With 24 V drive the maximum power available to the remote station is 96 mW. Integrated-circuit devices such as the Burr–Brown XTR 100 are available for providing two-wire transmission. This is capable of providing a 4–20 mA output span for an input voltage as small as 10 mV, and is capable of transmitting at frequencies up to 2 kHz over a distance of 600 m. Current transmission cannot be used over the public telephone system because it requires a d.c. transmission path, and telephone systems use a.c. amplifiers in the repeater stations.

Position telemetry transmits an analogue variable by reproducing at the receiver the positional information available at the transmitter. Such devices employ null techniques with either resistive or inductive elements to achieve the position telemetry. Figure 5.28 shows an inductive 'synchro'.

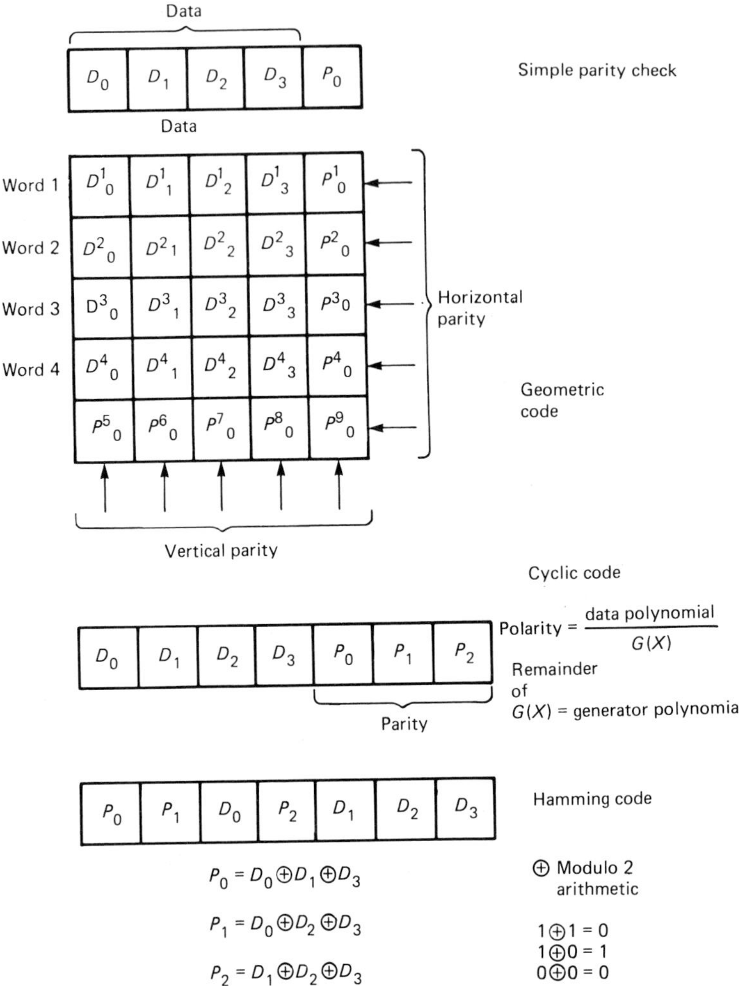

Figure 5.25 Error-detection coding.

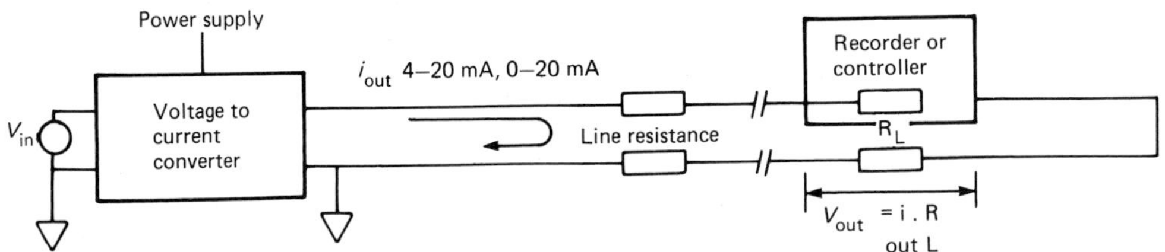

Figure 5.26 4-20 mA current transmission system.

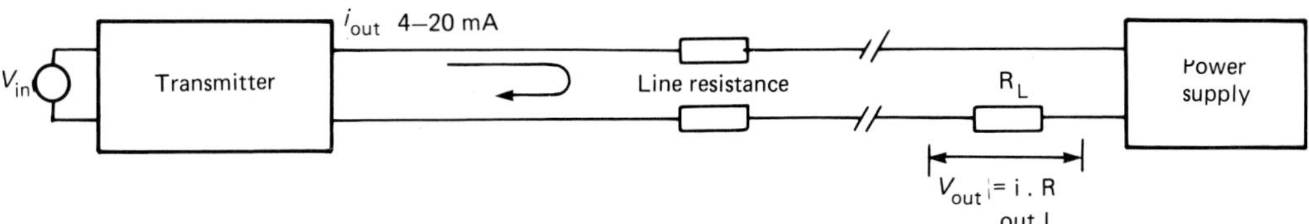

Figure 5.27 Two-wire transmission system.

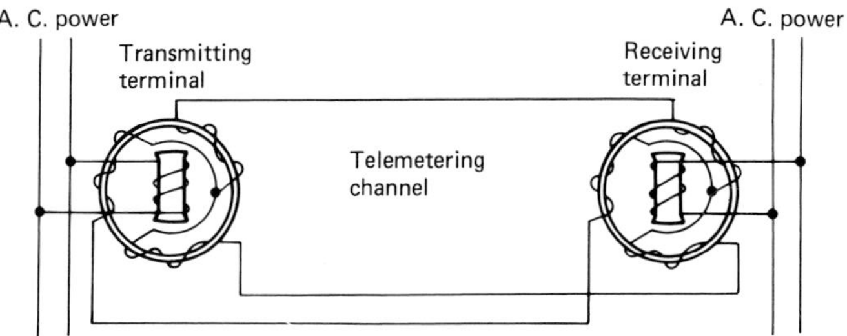

Figure 5.28 Position telemetry using an inductive 'synchro'.

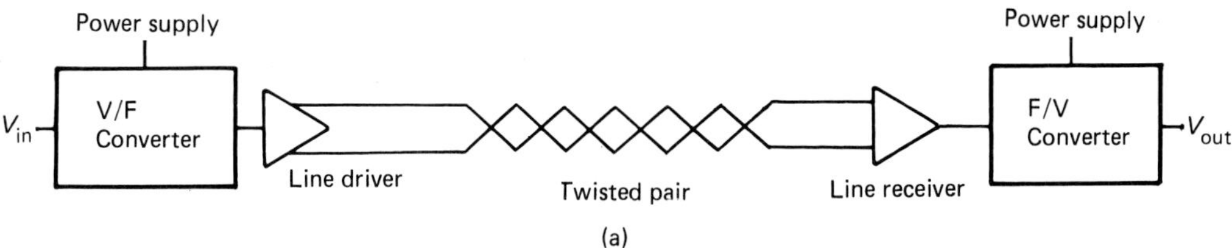

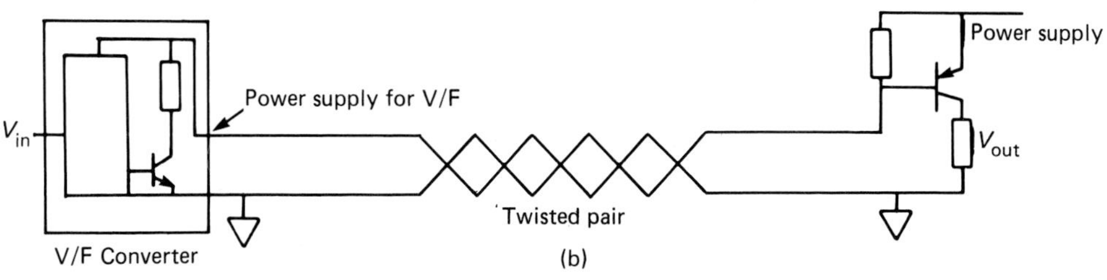

Figure 5.29 (a) Frequency-transmission system; (b) two-wire frequency-transmission system.

The a.c. power applied to the transmitter induces in the three stator windings, e.m.f.s, the magnitude of which are dependent upon the position of the transmitter rotor. If the receiver rotor is aligned in the same direction as the transmitter rotor then the e.m.f.s. induced in the stator windings of the receiver will be identical to those on the stator windings of the transmitter. There will therefore be no resultant circulating currents. If the receiver rotor is not aligned to the direction of the transmitter rotor then the circulating currents in the stator windings will be such as to generate a torque which will move the receiver rotor in such a direction as to align itself with the transmitter rotor.

5.8 Frequency transmission

By transmitting signals as frequency the characteristics of the transmission line in terms of amplitude and phase characteristics are less important. On reception the signal can be counted over a fixed period of time to provide a digital measurement. The resolution of such systems will be 1 count in the total number received. Thus for high resolution it is necessary to count the signal over a long time period, and this method of transmission is therefore unsuitable for rapidly changing or multiplexed signals but is useful for such applications as batch control, where, for example, a totalized value of a variable over a given period is required. Figure 5.29(a) shows a frequency-transmission system. Frequency-transmission systems can also be used in two-wire transmission systems, as shown in Figure 5.29(b), where the twisted pair carries both the power to the remote device and the frequency signal in the form of current modulation. The frequency range of such systems is governed by the bandwidth of the channel over which the signal is to be transmitted, but commercially available integrated circuit V to f converters such as the Analog Devices AD458 convert a 0–10 V d.c. signal to a frequency in the range 0–10 kHz or 0–100 kHz with a maximum non-linearity of ±0.01 per cent of FS output, a maximum temperature coefficient of ±5 ppm/K, a maximum input offset voltage of ±10 mV and a maximum input offset voltage temperature coefficient of 30 μV/K. The response time is two output pulses plus 2 μs. A low-cost f to V converter such as the Analog Devices AD453 has an input frequency range of 0–100 kHz with a variable threshold voltage of between 0 and ±12 V, and can be used with low-level signals as well as high-level inputs from TTL and CMOS. The converter has a full-scale output of 10 V and a non-linearity of less than ±0.008 per cent of FS with a maximum temperature coefficient of ±50 ppm/K. The maximum response time is 4 ms.

5.9 Digital signal transmission

Digital signals are transmitted over transmission lines using either serial or parallel communication.

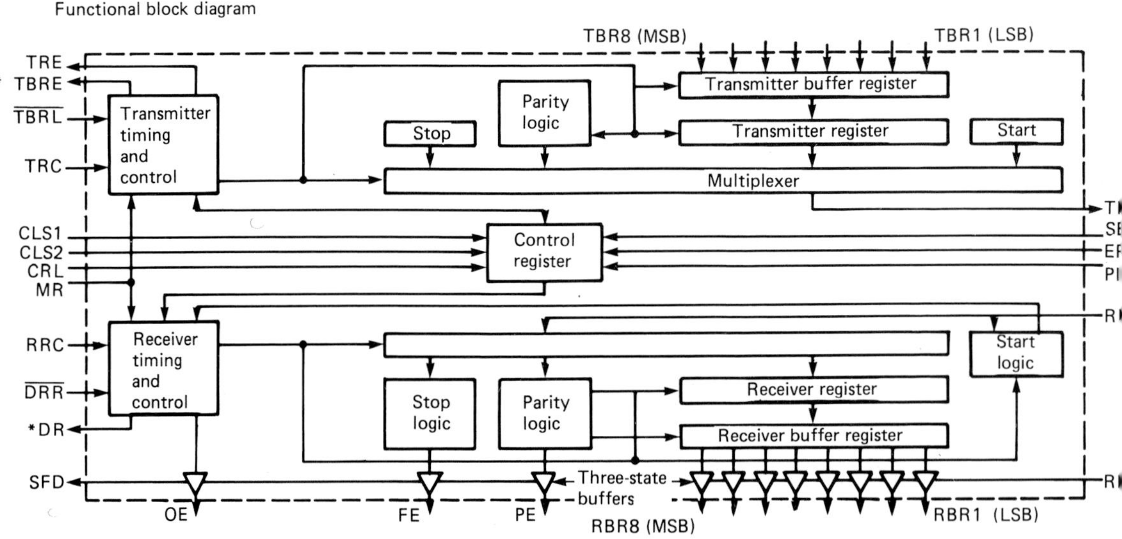

Figure 5.30(a) Universal asynchronous receiver transmitter (UART).

For long-distance communication serial communication is the preferred method. The serial communication may be either synchronous or asynchronous. In synchronous communication the data are sent in a continuous stream without stop or start information. Asynchronous communication refers to a mode of communication in which data are transmitted as individual blocks framed by start and stop bits. Bits are also added to the data stream for error detection. Integrated circuit devices known as universal asynchronous receiver transmitters (UARTS) are available for converting parallel data into a serial format suitable for transmission over a twisted pair or coaxial line and for reception of the data in serial format and reconversion to parallel format with parity-bit checking. The schematic diagram for such a device is shown in Figure 5.30.

Because of the high capacitance of twisted-pair and coaxial cables the length of line over which standard 74 series TTL can transmit digital signals is

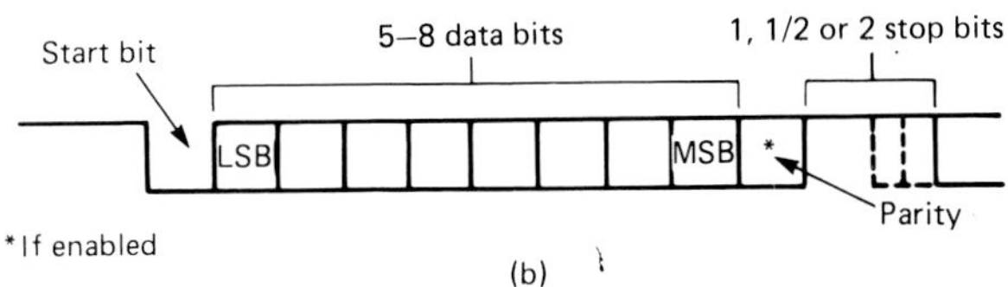

Figure 5.30(b) Serial data format.

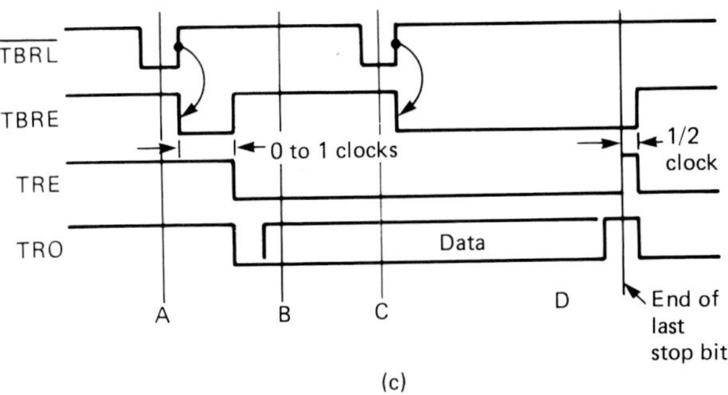

Figure 5.30(c) Transmitter timing (not to scale).

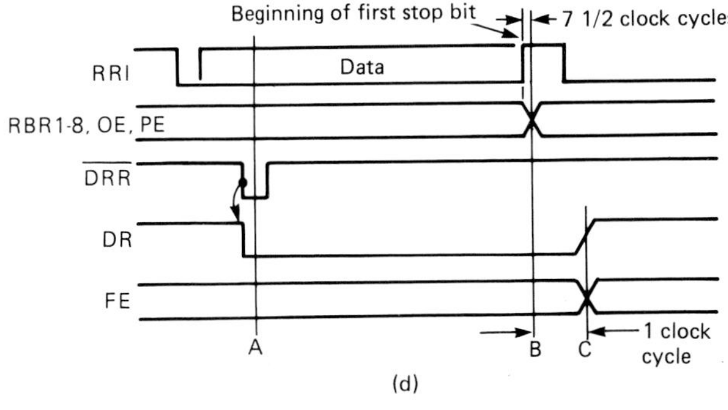

Figure 5.30(d) Receiver timing (not to scale).

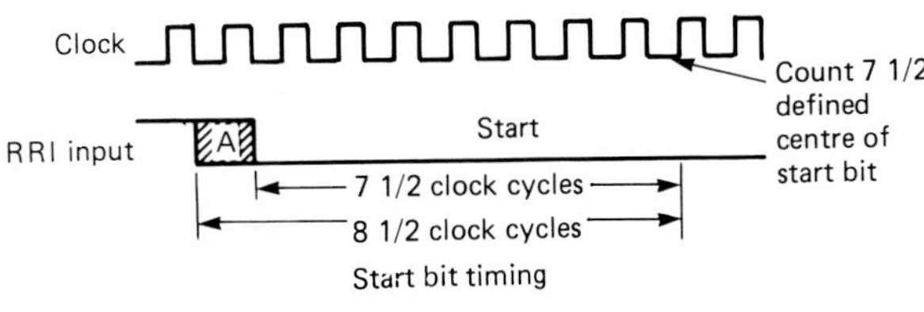

Figure 5.30(e) Start bit timing.

limited typically to a length of 3 m at 2 Mbit/s. This can be increased to 15 m by the use of open-collector TTL driving a low-impedance terminated line.

In order to drive digital signals over long lines special-purpose line driver and receiver circuits are available. Integrated circuit Driver/Receiver combinations such as the Texas Instruments SN75150/SN75152, SN75158/SN75157 and SN75156/SN75157 devices meet the internationally agreed EIA Standards RS-232C, RS-422A and RS-423A, respectively (see section 5.9.2).

5.9.1 Modems

In order to overcome the limitations of the public telephone lines digital data are transmitted down these lines by means of a modem. The two methods of modulation used by modems are frequency-shift keying (FSK) and phase-shift keying (PSK). Amplitude-modulation techniques are not used because of the unsuitable response of the line to step changes in amplitude. Modems can be used to transmit information in two directions along a telephone line.

Full-duplex operation is transmission of information in both directions simultaneously; half-duplex is the transmission of information in both directions but only in one direction at any one time; and simplex is the transmission of data in one direction only.

The principle of FSK is shown in Figure 5.31. FSK uses two different frequencies to represent a 1 and a 0, and this can be used for data transmission rates up to 1200 bits/s. The receiver uses a frequency discriminator whose threshold is set mid-way between the two frequencies. The recommended frequency shift is not less than 0.66 of the modulating frequency. Thus a modem operating at 1200 bits/s has a recommended central frequency of

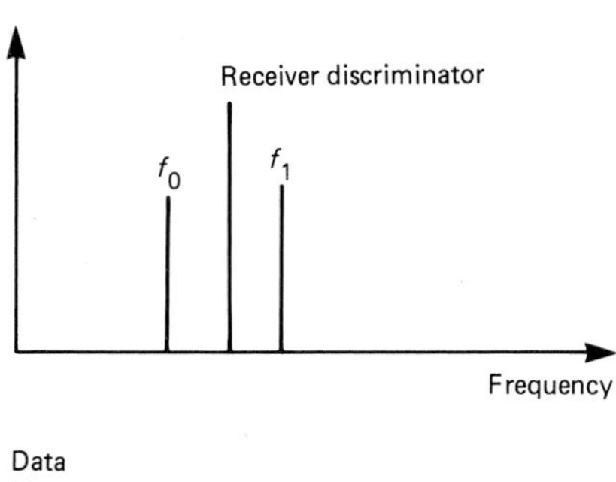

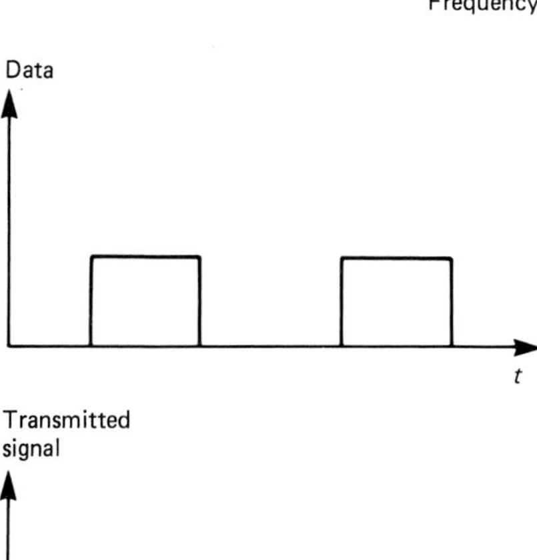

Figure 5.31 Frequency-shift keying.

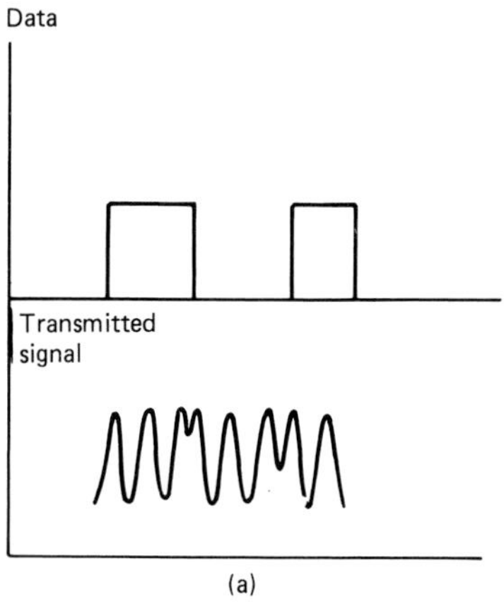

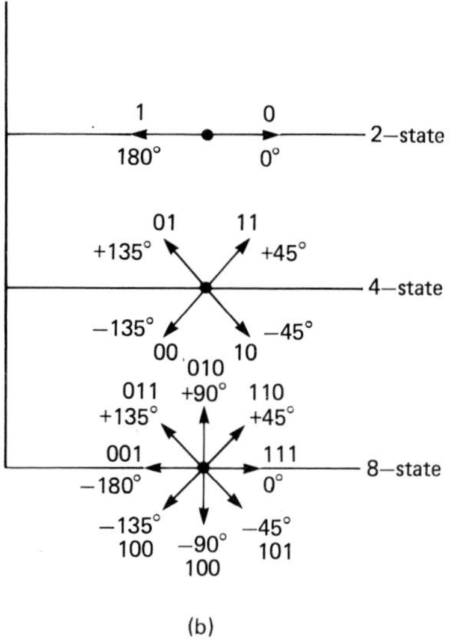

Figure 5.32 (a) Principle of phase-shift keying; (b) two-, four- and eight-state-shift keying.

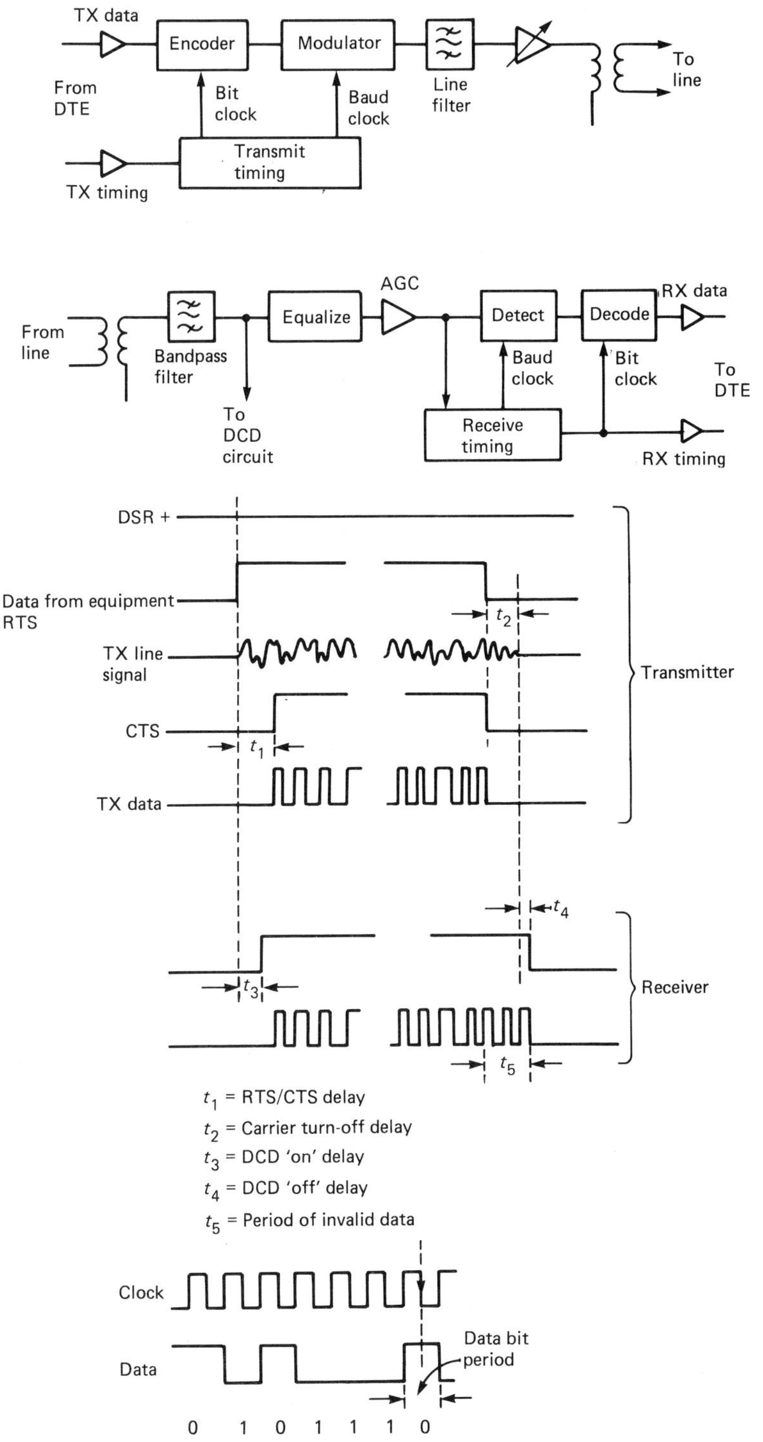

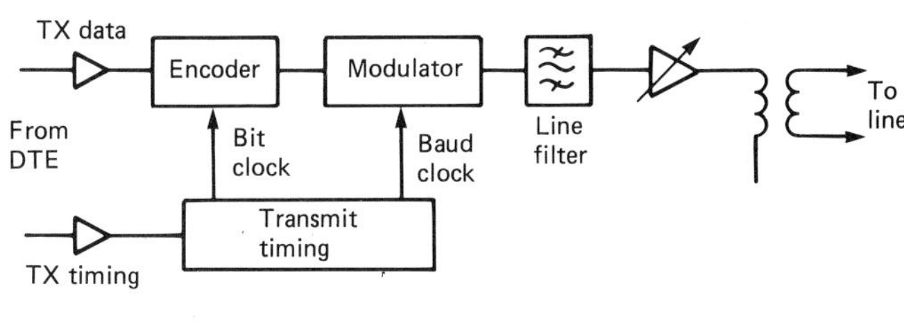

Figure 5.33 Modem operation.

1700 Hz and a frequency deviation of 800 Hz, with a 0 represented by a frequency of 1300 Hz and a 1 by a frequency of 2100 Hz. At a transmission rate of 200 bits/s it is possible to operate a full-duplex system. At 600 and 1200 bits/s half-duplex operation is used incorporating a slow-speed backward channel for supervisory control or low-speed return data.

At bit rates above 2400 bits/s the bandwidth and group delay characteristics of telephone lines make it impossible to transmit the data using FSK. It is necessary for each signal to contain more than one bit of information. This is achieved by a process known as phase shift keying (PSK), in which the phase of a constant-amplitude carrier is changed. Figure 5.32(a) shows the principle of PSK and Figure 5.32(b) shows how the information content of PSK can be increased by employing two-, four- and eight-state systems. It should now be seen that the number of signal elements/s (which is referred to as the Baud rate) has to be multiplied by the number of states to obtain the data transmission rate in bits/s. Thus an eight-state PSK operating at a Baud rate of 1200 bauds can transmit 9600 bits/s. This is the fastest transmission over telephone cables and is intended for operation over leased lines, i.e. lines which are permanently allocated to the user as opposed to switched lines. At the higher data transmission rates it is necessary to apply adaptive equalization of the line to ensure correct operation and also to have in-built error-correcting coding. Details of various schemes for modem operation are to be found in Coates (1982) and Blackwell (1981). The International Telephone and Telegraph Consultative Committee (CCITT) have made recommendations for the mode of operation of modems operating at different rates over telephone lines. These are set out in recommendations V21, V23, V26, V27 and V29. These are listed in the References.

Figure 5.33 shows the elements and operation of a typical modem. The data set ready (DSR) signal indicates to the equipment attached to the modem that it is ready to transmit data. When the equipment is ready to send the data it sends a request to send (RTS) signal. The modem then starts transmitting down the line. The first part of the transmission is to synchronize the receiving modem. Having given sufficient time for the receiver to synchronize, the transmitting modem sends a clear to send (CTS) signal to the equipment

Table 5.1 Pin assignments for RS-232

Pin number	*Signal nomenclature*	*Signal abbreviation*	*Signal description*	*Category*
1	AA	—	Protective ground	Ground
2	BA	TXD	Transmitted data	Data
3	BB	RXD	Received data	Data
4	CA	RTS	Request to send	Control
5	CB	CTS	Clear to send	Control
6	CC	DSR	Data set ready	Control
7	AB	—	Signal ground	Ground
8	CF	DCD	Received line signal detector	Control
9	—	—	—	Reserved for test
10	—	—	—	Reserved for test
11	—	—	—	Unassigned
12	SCF	—	Secondary received line signal detector	Control
13	SCB	—	Secondary clear to send	Control
14	SBA	—	Secondary transmitted data	Data
15	DB	—	Transmission signal element timing	Timing
16	SBB	—	Secondary received data	Data
17	DD	—	Received signal element timing	Timing
18	—	—	—	Unassigned
19	SCA	—	Secondary request to send	Control
20	CD	DTR	Data terminal ready	Control
21	CG	—	Signal quality detector	Control
22	CE	—	Ring indicator	Control
23	CH/CI	—	Data signal rate selector	Control
24	DA	—	Transmit signal element timing	Timing
25	—	—	—	Unassigned

and the data are then sent. At the receiver the detection of the transmitted signal sends the data carrier detected (DCD) line high and the signal transmitted is demodulated.

5.9.2 Data transmission and interfacing standards

To ease the problem of equipment interconnection various standards have been introduced for serial and parallel data transmission. For serial data transmission between data terminal equipment (DTE), such as a computer or a piece of peripheral equipment, and data communication equipment (DCE), such as a modem, the standards which are currently being used are the RS-232C standard produced in the USA by the Electronic Industries Association (EIA) in 1969 and their more recent RS-449 standard with its associated RS-422 and RS-423 standards.

The RS-232C standard defines an electromechanical interface by the designation of the pins of a 25-pin plug and socket which are used for providing electrical ground, data interchange, control and clock or timing signals between the two pieces of equipment. The standard also defines the signal levels, conditions and polarity at each interface connection. Table 5.1 gives the pin assignments for the interface and it can be seen that only pins 2 and 3 are used for data transmission. Logical 1 for the driver is an output voltage between -5 and -15 V with logical zero being between $+5$ and $+15$ V. The receiver detects logical 1 for input voltages <-3 V and logical 0 for input voltages >3 V, thus giving the system a minimum 2 V noise margin. The maximum transmission rate of data is 20 000 bits/s and the maximum length of the interconnecting cable is limited by the requirement that the receiver should not have more than 2500 pF across it. The length of cable permitted thus depends on its capacitance/unit length.

Table 5.2 Pin assignments for RS-449

Circuit mnemonic	*Circuit name*	*Circuit direction*	*Circuit type*
SG	Signal ground	—	Common
SC	Send common	To DCE	
RC	Receive common	From DCE	
IS	Terminal in service	To DCE	Control
IC	Incoming call	From DCE	
TR	Terminal ready	To DCE	
DM	Data mode	From DCE	
SD	Send data	To DCE	Primary channel data
RD	Receive data	From DCE	
TT	Terminal timing	To DCE	Primary channel timing
ST	Send timing	From DCE	
RT	Receive timing	From DCE	
RS	Request to send	To DCE	Primary channel control
CS	Clear to send	From DCE	
RR	Receiver ready	From DCE	
SQ	Signal quality	From DCE	
NS	New signal	To DCE	
SF	Select frequency	To DCE	
SR	Signal rate selector	To DCE	
SI	Signal rate indicator	From DCE	
SSD	Secondary send data	To DCE	Secondary channel data
SRD	Secondary receive data	From DCE	
SRS	Secondary request to send	To DCE	Secondary channel control
SCS	Secondary clear to send	From DCE	
SRR	Secondary receiver ready	From DCE	
LL	Local loopback	To DCE	Control
RL	Remote loopback	To DCE	
TM	Test mode	From DCE	
SS	Select standby	To DCE	Control
SB	Standby indicator	From DCE	

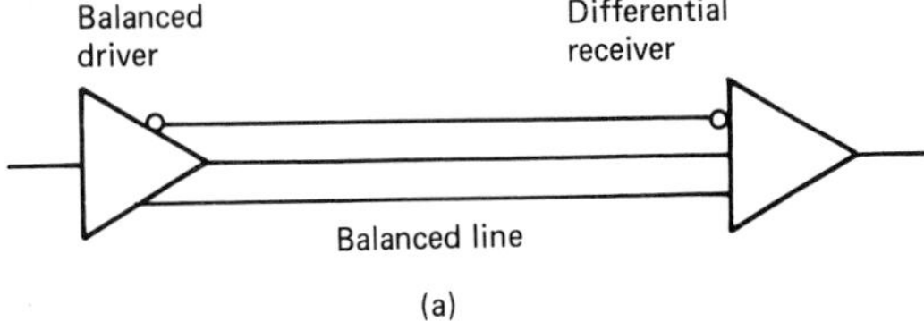

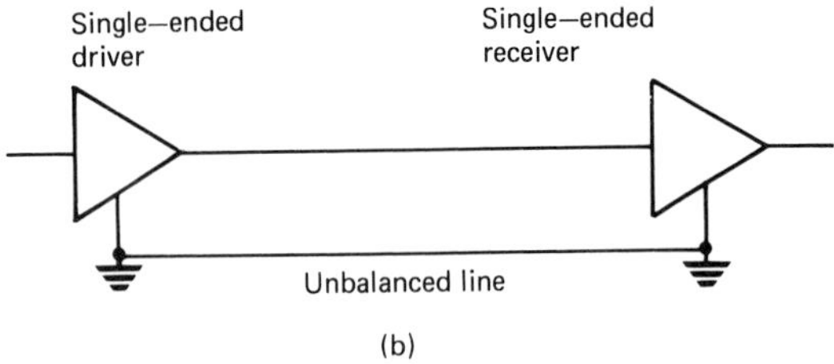

Figure 5.34 RS422 and RS423 driver/receiver systems.

The newer RS-449 interface standard which is used for higher data-transmission rates defines the mechanical characteristics in terms of the pin designations of a 37-pin interface. These are listed in Table 5.2. The electrical characteristics of the interface are specified by the two other associated standards, RS-422, which refers to communication by means of a balanced differential driver along a balanced interconnecting cable with detection being by means of a differential receiver, and RS423, which refers to communication by means of a single-ended driver on an unbalanced cable with detection by means of a differential receiver. These two systems are shown in Figure 5.34. The maximum recommended cable lengths for the balanced RS-422 standard are 4000 ft at 90 kbits/s, 380 ft at 1 Mbits/s and 40 ft at 10 Mbits/s. For the unbalanced RS-423 standard the limits are 4000 ft at 900 bits/s, 380 ft at 10 kbits/s and 40 ft at 100 kbits/s.

For further details of these interface standards the reader is directed to the standards produced by the EIA. These are listed in the References. Interfaces are also discussed in Volume 5.

The IEEE-488 Bus (IEEE, 1978), often referred to as the HPIB Bus (Hewlett Packard Interface Bus), is a standard which specifies a communications protocol between a controller and instruments connected onto the bus. The instruments typically connected on to the bus include digital voltmeters, signal generators, frequency meters and spectrum and impedance analysers. The bus allows up to 15 such instruments to be connected onto the bus. Devices talk, listen or do both, and at least one

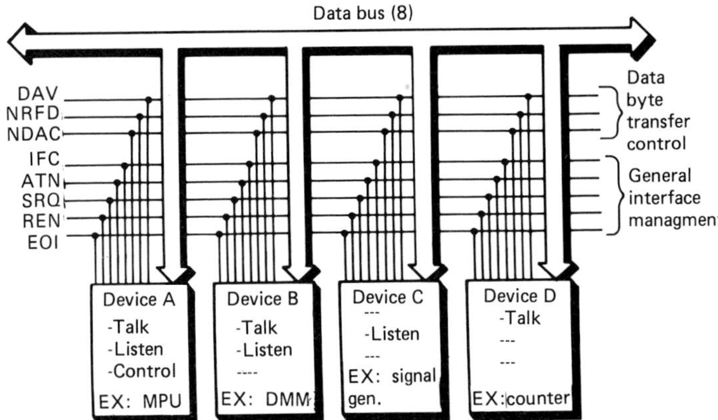

Figure 5.35 IEEE-488 bus system.

device on the bus must provide control, this usually being a computer. The bus uses 15 lines, the pin connections for which are shown in Table 5.3. The signal levels are TTL and the cable length between the controller and the device is limited to 2 m. The bus can be operated at a frequency of up to 1 MH. The connection diagram for a typical system are shown in Figure 5.35. Eight lines are used for addresses, program data and measurement data transfers, three lines are used for the control of data transfers by means of a handshake technique and five lines are used for general interface management.

CAMAC (which is an acronym for Computer Automated Measurement and Control) is a multiplexed interface system which not only specifies the connections and the communications protocol between the modules of the system which act as interfaces between the computer system and peripheral devices but also stipulates the physical dimensions of the plug-in modules. These modules are typically ADCs, DACs, digital buffers, serial to parallel converters, parallel to serial converters and level changers. The CAMAC system offers a 24-bit parallel data highway via an 86-way socket at the rear of each module. Twenty-three of the modules are housed in a single unit known as a 'crate', which additionally houses a controller. The CAMAC system was originally specified for the nuclear industry, and is particularly suited for systems where a large multiplexing ratio is required. Since each module addressed can have up to 16 subaddresses a crate can have up to 368 multiplexed inputs/outputs. For further details of the CAMAC system the reader is directed to Barnes (1981) and to the CAMAC standards issued by the Commission of the European Communities, given in the References.

The S100 Bus (also referred to as the IEEE-696 interface (IEEE, 1981)) is an interface standard devised for bus-oriented systems and was originally designed for interfacing microcomputer systems. Details of this bus can be found in the References.

5.10 References

BARNES, R. C. M. 'A standard interface: CAMAC', in *Minicomputers: A Handbook for Engineers, Scientists, and Managers*, ed. Y. Paker, Abacus, London (1981), pp. 167–187

BENTLEY, J., *Principles of Measurement Systems*, Longman, London (1983)

BOWDELL, K. 'Interface data transmission', in *Minicomputers: A Handbook for Engineers, Scientists, and Managers*, ed. Y. Paker, Abacus, London (1981), pp. 148–166

Table 5.3 Pin assignments for IEEE-488 interface

Pin no.	*Function*	*Pin no.*	*Function*
1	DIO 1	13	DIO 5
2	DIO 2	14	DIO 6
3	DIO 3	15	DIO 7
4	DIO 4	16	DIO 8
5	EOI	17	REN
6	DAV	18	GND twisted pair with 6
7	NRFD	19	GND twisted pair with 7
8	NDAC	20	GND twisted pair with 8
9	IFC	21	GND twisted pair with 9
10	SRQ	22	GND twisted pair with 10
11	ATN	23	GND twisted pair with 11
12	Shield (to earth)	24	Signal ground

DIO = Data Input–Output
EOI = End Or Identify
REN = Remote Enable
DAV = Data Valid
NRFD = Not Ready For Data
NDAC = Not Data Accepted
IFC = Interface Clear
SRQ = Service Request
ATN = Attention
GND = Ground

BLACKWELL, J. 'Long distance communication', in *Minicomputers: A Handbook for Engineers, Scientists, and Managers*, ed. Y. Paker, Abacus, London (1981), pp. 301–316

CATTERMOLE, K. W. *Principles of Pulse Code Modulation*, Iliffe, London (1969)

CCITT. Recommendation V 24. List of definitions for interchange circuits between data-terminal equipment and data circuit-terminating equipment, in CCITT, Vol. 8.1, *Data Transmission over the Telephone Network*, International Telecommunication Union, Geneva (1977)

COATES, R. F. W. *Modern Communication Systems*, 2nd edn, Macmillan, London (1982)

EEC Commission: CAMAC. *A Modular System for Data Handling. Revised Description and Specification*, EUR 4100e, HMSO, London (1972)

EEC Commission: CAMAC. *Organisation of Multi-Crate Systems. Specification of the Branch Highway and CAMAC Crate Controller Type A*, EUR 4600e, HMSO, London (1972)

EEC Commission: CAMAC. *A Modular Instrumentation System for Data Handling. Specification of Amplitude Analogue Signals*, EUR 5100e, HMSO, London (1972)

EIA. *Standard RS-232C Interface between Data Terminal Equipment and Data Communications Equipment Employing Serial Binary Data Interchange*, EIA, Washington, DC (1969)

EIA. *Standard RS-449 General-purpose 37-position and 9-position Interface for Data Terminal Equipment and Data Circuit-terminating Equipment Employing Serial Binary Data Interchange*, EIA, Washington, DC (1977)

HARTLEY, G., MORNET, P., RALPH, F. and TARRON, D. J. *Techniques of Pulse Code Modulation in Communications Networks*, Cambridge University Press, Cambridge (1967)

HMSO. *Private Point-to-Point Systems Performance Specifications (Nos W.6457 and W.6458) for Angle-Modulated UHF Transmitters and Receivers and Systems in the 450–470 Mc/s Band*, HMSO, London (1963)

HMSO. *Performance Specification: Medical and Biological Telemetry Devices*, HMSO, London (1978)

HMSO. *Performance Specification: Transmitters and Receivers for Use in the Bands Allocated to Low Power Telemetry in the PMR Service*, HMSO, London (1979)

HMSO. International Telecommunication Union World Administrative Radio Conference, 1979, *Radio Regulations. Revised International Table of Frequency Allocations and Associated Terms and Definitions*, HMSO, London (1980)

IEEE. *IEEE-488-1978 Standard Interface for Programmable Instruments*, IEEE, New York (1978)

IEEE. *IEEE-696-1981 Standard Specification for S-100 Bus Interfacing Devices*, IEEE, New York (1981)

JOHNSON, C. S. 'Telemetry data systems', *Instrument Technology*, Aug. (1976), 39–53: Oct. (1976), 47–53

KEISER, G. *Optical Fibre Communication*, McGraw-Hill International, London (1983)

SENIOR, J. *Optical Fiber Communications, Principles and Practice*, Prentice-Hall, London (1985)

SHANMUGAN, S. *Digital and Analog Communications Systems*, John Wiley, New York (1979)

STEELE, R. *Delta Modulation Systems*, Pentech Press, London (1975)

WARNOCK, J.D. Section 16.27 in *The Process Instruments and Controls Handbook* 3rd edition, edited by D.M. Considine, McGraw-Hill, London (1985)

WILSON, J. and HAWKES, J. F. B. *Optoelectronics: An Introduction*, Prentice-Hall, London (1983)

6 Display and recording

M.L. SANDERSON

6.1 Introduction

Display devices are used in instrumentation systems to provide instantaneous but non-permanent communication of information between a process or system and a human observer. The data can be presented to the observer in either an analogue or digital form. Analogue indicators require the observer to interpolate the reading when it occurs between two scale values, which requires some skill on the part of the observer. They are, however, particularly useful for providing an overview of the process or system and an indication of trends when an assessment of data from a large number of sources has to be quickly assimilated. Data displayed in a digital form require little skill from the observer in reading the value of the measured quantity, though any misreading can introduce a large observational error as easily as a small one. Using digital displays it is much more difficult to observe trends within a process or system and to quickly assess, for example, the deviation of the process or system from its normal operating conditions. Hybrid displays incorporating both analogue and digital displays combine the advantages of both.

The simplest indicating devices employ a pointer moving over a fixed scale; a moving scale passing a fixed pointer; or a bar graph in which a semi-transparent ribbon moves over a scale. These devices use mechanical or electromechanical means to effect the motion of the moving element. Displays can also be provided using illuminative devices such as light-emitting diodes (LEDs), liquid crystal displays (LCDs), plasma displays, and cathode ray tubes (CRTs). The mechanisms and configurations of these various display techniques are identified in Table 6.1.

Table 6.1 Commonly used display techniques

Display technique	*Mechanism*	*Configurations*
Indicating devices		
Moving pointer	Mechanical/electromechanical movement of pointer over a fixed scale	Horizontal/vertical, straight, arc. circular, or segment scales with edgewise strip, hairline, or arrow-shaped pointers
Moving scale	Mechanical/electromechanical movement of scale. Indication given by position of scale with respect to fixed pointer	Moving dial or moving drum analogue indicators, digital drum indicators.
Bar graph	Indication given by height or length of vertical or horizontal column	Moving column provided by mechanically driven ribbon or LED or LCD elements
Illuminative displays		
Light emitting diodes	Light output provided by recombination electroluminescence in a forward-biased semiconductor diode	Red, yellow, green, displays configured as lamps, bar graphs, 7- and 16-segment alphanumeric displays, dot matrix displays
Liquid crystal displays	The modulation of intensity of transmitted-reflected light by the application of an electric field to a liquid crystal cell	Reflective or transmissive displays, bar graph, 7-segment, dot matrix displays, alphanumeric panels
Plasma displays	Cathode glow of a neon gas discharge	Nixie tubes, 7-segment displays, plasma panels
CRT displays	Conversion into light of the energy of scanning electron beam by phosphor	Monochrome and colour tubes, storage tubes, configured as analogue, storage, sampling, or digitizing oscilloscopes, VDUs, graphic displays

Table 6.2 Commonly used recording techniques

Recording system	*Technique*	*Configurations*
Graphical recorders	Provide hard copy of data in graphical form using a variety of writing techniques, including pen-ink, impact printing, thermal, optical, and electric writing	Single/multichannel x–t strip chart and circular chart recorders, galvanometer recorders, analogue and digital x–y recorders, digital plotters
Printers	Provide hard copy of data in alphanumeric form using impact and non-impact printing techniques	Serial impact printers using cylinder, golf ball, daisywheel or dot matrix heads. Line printers using drum, chain-belt, oscillating bar, comb, and needle printing heads. Non-impact printers using thermal, electrical, electrostatic, magnetic, ink-jet, electrophotographic, and laser printing techniques
Magnetic recording	Use the magnetization of magnetic particles on a substrate to store information	Magnetic tape recorders using direct, frequency modulation or pulse code modulation technique for the storage of analogue or digital data. Spool to spool or cassette recorders. Floppy or hard discs for the storage of digital data
Transient recorders	Use semiconductor memory to store high-speed transient waveforms	Single/multichannel devices using analogue-to-digital conversion techniques. High-speed transient recorders using optical scanning techniques to capture data before transfer to semiconductor memory
Data loggers	Data-acquisition system having functions programmed from the front panel	Configured for a range of analogue or digital inputs with limited logical or mathematical functions. Internal display using LED, LCD, CRT. Hard copy provided by dot matrix ink or thermal or electrical writing technique. Data storage provided by semiconductor or magnetic storage using tape or disc

Recording enables hard copy of the information to be obtained in graphical or alphanumeric form or the information to be stored in a format which enables it to be retrieved at a later stage for subsequent analysis, display, or conversion into hard copy. Hard copy of graphical information is made by graphical recorders. x–t recorders enable the relationships between one or more variables and time to be obtained whilst x–y recorders enable the relationship between two variables to be obtained. These recorders employ analogue or digital drive mechanisms for the writing heads, generally with some form of feedback. The hard copy is provided using a variety of techniques, including ink pens or impact printing on normal paper, or thermal, optical, or electrical writing techniques on specially prepared paper. Alphanumeric recording of data is provided by a range of printers, including impact printing with cylinder, golf ball, daisywheel, or dot matrix heads; or non-impact printing techniques including ink-jet, thermal, electrical, electrostatic, electromagnetic, or laser printers.

Recording for later retrieval can use either magnetic or semiconductor data storage. Magnetic tape recorders are used for the storage of both analogue and digital data. Transient/waveform recorders (also called waveform digitizers) generally store their information in semiconductor memory. Data-logger systems may employ both semiconductor memory and magnetic storage on either disc or tape. Table 6.2 shows the techniques and configurations of the commonly used recording systems.

The display and recording of information in an instrumentation system provides the man/machine interface (MMI) between the observer and the system or process being monitored. It is of fundamental importance that the information should be presented to the observer in as clear and unambiguous a way as possible and in a form that is easily assimilated. In addition to the standard criteria for instrument performance such as accuracy, sensitivity, and speed of response, ergonomic factors involving the visibility, legibility, and organization and presentation of the information are also of importance in displays and recorders.

6.2 Indicating devices

In moving-pointer indicator devices (Figure 6.1) the pointer moves over a fixed scale which is mounted vertically or horizontally. The scale may be either straight or an arc. The motion is created by mechanical means as in pressure gauges or by electromechanical means using a moving coil movement. (For details of such movements the reader is directed to Electrical Measurements in Volume 3 of *Instrument Technology*.) The pointer consists of a knife edge, a line scribed on each side of a transparent member, or a sharp, arrow-shaped tip. The pointers are designed to minimize the reading error when the instrument is read from different angles. For precision work such 'parallax errors' are reduced by mounting a mirror behind the pointer. Additional pointers may be provided on the scale. These can be used to indicate the value of a set point or alarm limits.

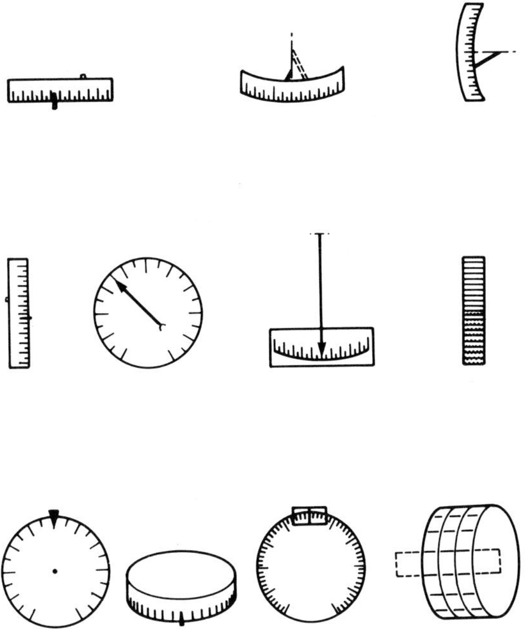

Figure 6.1 Moving-pointer and moving-scale indicators.

The pointer scales on such instruments should be designed for maximum clarity. BS 3693 sets out recommended scale formats. The standard recommends that the scale base length of an analogue indicating device should be at least $0.07D$, where D is the viewing distance. At a distance of 0.7 m, which is the distance at which the eye is in its resting state of accommodation, the minimum scale length should be 49 mm. The reading of analogue indicating devices requires the observer to interpolate between readings. It has been demonstrated that observers can subdivide the distance between two scale markings into five, and therefore a scale which is to be read to within 1 per cent of full-scale deflection (FSD) should be provided with twenty principal divisions. For electromechanical indicating instruments accuracy is classified by BS 89 into nine ranges, from ±0.05 per cent to ±5 per cent of FSD. A fast response is not required for visual displays since the human eye cannot follow changes much in excess of 20 Hz. Indicating devices typically provide frequency responses up to 1–2 Hz.

Moving-scale indicators in which the scale moves past a fixed pointer can provide indicators with long scale lengths. Examples of these are also shown in Figure 6.1.

In the bar graph indicator (Figure 6.2) a semitransparent ribbon moves over a scale. The top of the ribbon indicates the value of the measured quantity and the ribbon is generally driven by a mechanical lead. Arrays of LEDs or LCDs can be used to provide the solid state equivalent of the bar graph display.

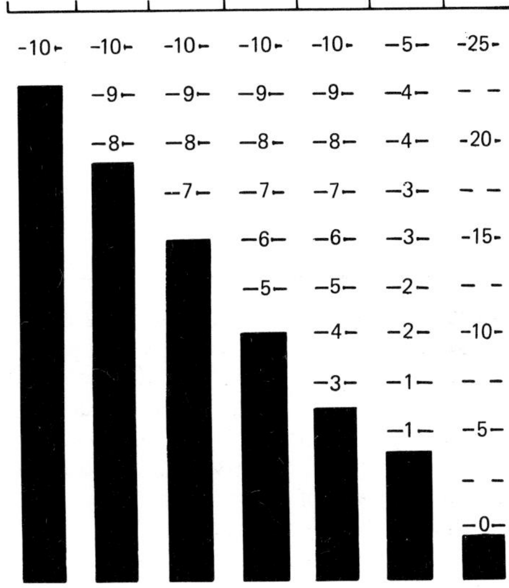

Figure 6.2 Bar-graph indicator.

6.3 Light-emitting diodes (LEDs)

These devices, as shown in Figures 6.3(a) and 6.3(b), use recombination (injection) electroluminescence and consist of a forward-biased p–n junction in which the majority carriers from both sides of the junction cross the internal potential barrier and enter the material on the other side, where they become minority carriers, thus disturbing the local minority carrier population. As the excess minority carriers diffuse away from the junction, recombination occurs. Electroluminescence takes place if the recombination results in radiation. The wavelength of the emitted radiation is inversely proportional to the band gap of the material, and therefore for the radiation to be in the visible region the band gap must be greater than 1.8 eV.

$GaAs_{0.6}P_{0.4}$ (gallium arsenide phosphide) emits red light at 650 nm. By increasing the proportion of phosphorus and doping with nitrogen the wavelength of the emitted light is reduced. $GaAs_{0.35}P_{0.65}N$ provides a source of orange light, whilst $GaAs_{0.15}P_{0.85}N$ emits yellow light at 589 nm. Gallium phosphide doped with nitrogen radiates green light at 570 nm. Although the internal quantum efficiencies of LED materials can be high, the external quantum efficiencies may be much lower. This is because the materials have a high refractive index and therefore a significant proportion of the emitted radiation strikes the material/air interface beyond the critical angle and is totally internally reflected. This is usually overcome by encapsulating the diode in a hemispherical dome made of epoxy resin, as shown in Figure 6.3(c). The construction of an LED element in a seven-segment display is shown in Figure 6.3(d).

The external quantum efficiencies of green diodes tend to be somewhat lower than those of red diodes, but, for the same output power, because of the

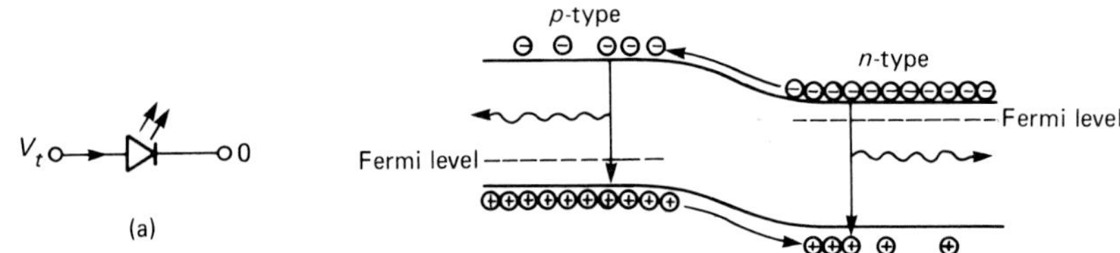

(a)

Injection of minority carriers and subsequent radiative recombination with the majority carriers in a forward biased p–n junction.

(b)

(c)

(d)

(e)

Figure 6.3 Light-emitting diodes.

sensitivity of the human eye the green diode has a higher luminous intensity.

Typical currents required for LED elements are in the range 10–100 mA. The forward diode drop is in the range 1.6–2.2 V, dependent on the particular device. The output luminous intensities of LEDs range from a few to over a hundred millicandela, and their viewing angle can be up to ±60°. The life expectancy of a LED display is twenty years, over which time it is expected that there will be a 50 per cent reduction in output power.

LEDs are available as lamps, seven- and sixteen-segment alphanumeric displays, and in dot matrix format (Figure 6.3(e)). Alphanumeric displays are provided with on-board decoding logic which enables the data to be entered in the form of ASCII or hexadecimal code.

6.4 Liquid crystal displays (LCDs)

These displays are passive and therefore emit no radiation of their own but depend upon the modulation of reflected or transmitted light. They are based upon the optical properties of a large class of organic materials known as liquid crystals. Liquid crystals have molecules which are rod shaped and which, even in their liquid state, can take up certain defined orientations relative to each other and also with respect to a solid interface. LCDs commonly use nematic liquid crystals such as *p*-azoxyanisole, in which the molecules are arranged with their long axes approximately parallel, as shown in Figure 6.4(a). They are highly anisotropic—that is, they have different optical or other properties in different directions. At a solid–liquid interface the ordering of the crystal can be either homogeneous (in which the molecules are parallel to the interface) or homeotropic (in which the molecules are aligned normal to the interface), as shown in Figure 6.4(b). If a liquid crystal is confined between two plates which without the application of an electric field is a homogeneous state, then when an electric field is applied the molecules will align themselves with this field in order to minimize their energy. As shown in Figure 6.4(c), if the E field is less than some critical value E_c then the ordering is not affected. If $E > E_c$ then the molecules furthest away from the interfaces are realigned. For values of the electric field $E >> E_c$ most of the molecules are realigned.

A typical reflective LCD consists of a twisted nematic cell in which the walls of the cell are such as to produce a homogeneous ordering of the molecules but rotated by 90 degrees (Figure 6.4(d)). Because of the birefringent nature of the crystal, light polarized on entry in the direction of alignment of the molecules at the first interface will leave the cell with its direction of polarization rotated by 90 degrees. On the application of an electric field in excess of the critical field (for a cell of thickness 10 μm a typical critical voltage is 3 V) the molecules align themselves in the direction of the applied field. The polarized light does not then undergo any rotation. If the cell is sandwiched between two pieces of polaroid with no applied field, both polarizers allow light to pass through them, and therefore incident light is reflected by the mirror and

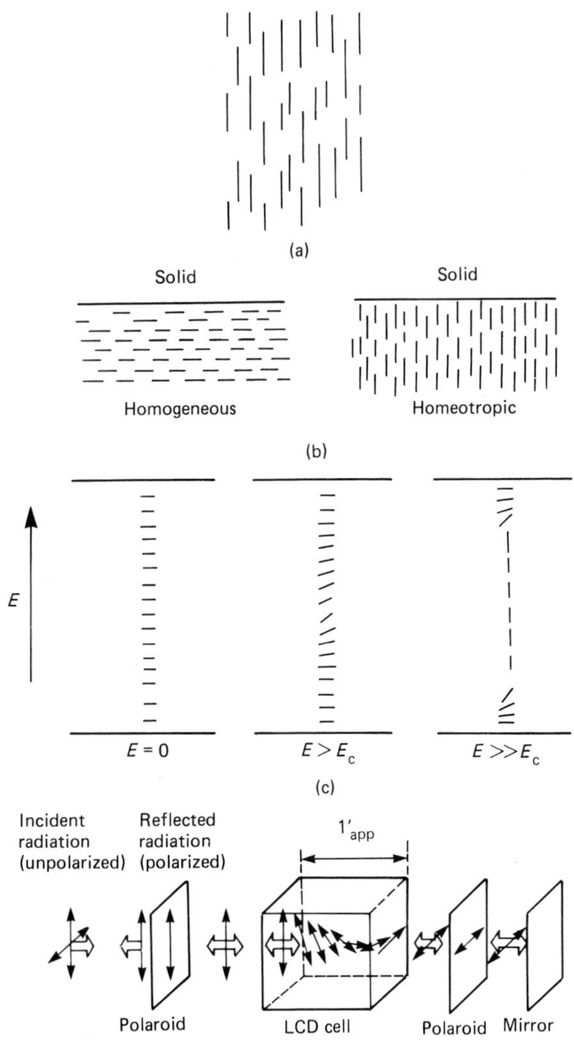

Figure 6.4 Liquid crystal displays. (a) Ordering of nematic crystals; (b) ordering at liquid crystal/solid interface; (c) application of an electric field to a liquid crystal cell; (d) reflective LCD using a twisted nematic cell.

the display appears bright. With the application of the voltage the polarizers are now crossed, and therefore no light is reflected and the display appears dark. Contrast ratios of 150:1 can be obtained.

D.C. voltages are generally not used in LCDs because of the electromechanical reactions. A.C. waveforms are employed with the cell having a response corresponding to the rms value of the applied voltage. The frequency of the a.c. is in the range 25 Hz to 1 kHz. Power consumption of LCD displays is low, with a typical current of 0.3–0.5 μA at 5 V. The optical switching time is typically 100–150 ms. They can operate over a temperature range of −10°C to +70°C.

Polarizing devices limit the maximum light which can be reflected from the cell. The viewing angle is also limited to approximately ±45 degrees. This can be improved by the use of cholesteric liquid crystals used in conjunction with dichroic dyes which absorb light whose direction of polarization is parallel to its long axis. Such displays do not require polarizing filters and are claimed to provide a viewing angle of ±90 degrees.

LCDs are available in bar graph, seven-segment, dot matrix, and alphanumeric display panel configurations.

6.5 Plasma displays

In a plasma display as shown in Figure 6.5(a) a glass envelope filled with neon gas, with added argon, krypton, and mercury to improve the discharge properties of the display, is provided with an anode and a cathode. The gas is ionized by applying a voltage of approximately 180 V between the anode and cathode. When ionization occurs there is an orange/yellow glow in the region of the cathode. Once ionization has taken place the voltage required to sustain the ionization can be reduced to about 100 V.

The original plasma display was the Nixie tube, which had a separate cathode for each of the figures 0–9. Plasma displays are now available as seven-segment displays or plasma panels as shown in Figures 6.5(a) and 6.5(b). The seven-segment display uses a separate cathode for each of the segments. The plasma panel consists, for example, of 512 × 512 vertical and horizontal x and y electrodes. By applying voltages to specific x and y electrode pairs (such that the sum of the voltages at the spot specified by the (x,y) address exceeds the ionization potential) then a glow will be produced at that spot. The display is operated by applying continuous a.c. voltages equivalent to the sustaining potential to all the electrodes. Ionization is achieved by pulsing selected pairs. The glow at a particular location is quenched by applying antiphase voltages to the electrodes.

The display produced by plasma discharge has a wide viewing angle capability, does not need back lighting, and is flicker free. A typical 50 mm seven-segment display has a power consumption of approximately 2 W.

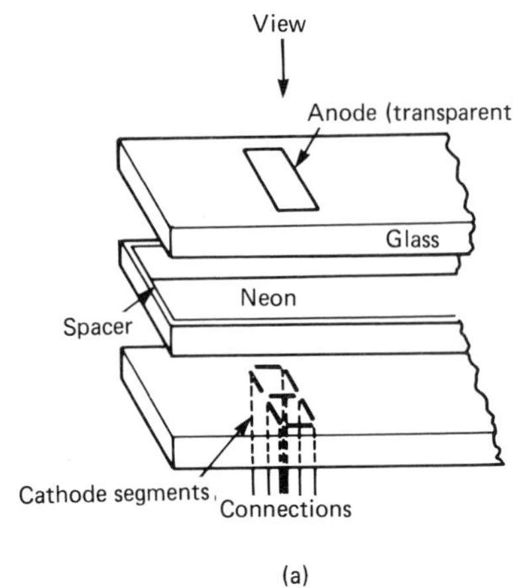

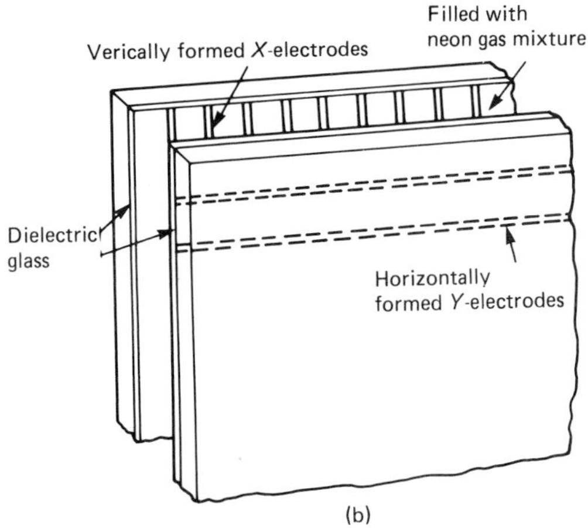

Figure 6.5 Plasma display. (a) Seven segment display; (b) plasma panel.

6.6 Cathode ray tubes (CRTs)

CRTs are used in oscilloscopes which are commonly employed for the display of repetitive or transient waveforms. They also form the basis of visual display units (VDUs) and graphic display units. The display is provided by using a phosphor which converts the energy from an electron beam into light at the point at which the beam impacts on the phosphor.

A CRT consists of an evacuated glass envelope in which the air pressure is less than 10^{-4} pascal (Figure 6.6). The thermionic cathode of nickel coated with oxides of barium, strontium, and calcium is indirectly heated to approximately 1100°K and thus gives off electrons. The number of electrons which strike the screen and hence control the brightness of the display is adjusted by means of the potential applied to a control grid surrounding the cathode. The control grid which has a pin hole through which the electrons can pass is held at a potential of between 0 and 100 V negative with respect to the cathode. The beam of electrons pass through the first anode A_1 which is typically held at a potential of 300 V positive with respect to the cathode before being focused, accelerated, and deflected.

Focusing and deflection of the beam can be by either electrostatic or magnetic means. In the electrostatic system shown in Figure 6.6(a) the cylindrical focusing anode A_2, which consists of disc baffles having an aperture in the centre of them, is between the first anode A_1 and the accelerating anode A_3, which is typically at a potential of 3–4 kV with respect to the cathode. Adjusting the potential on A_2 with respect to the potentials on A_1 and A_3 focuses the beam such that the electrons then travel along the axis of the tube. In a magnetic focusing system magnetic field coils around the tube create a force on the electrons, causing them to spiral about the axis and also inwardly. By employing magnetic focusing it is possible to achieve a smaller spot size than with electrostatic focusing. Deflection of the electron beam in a horizontal and vertical direction moves the position of the illuminated spot on the screen. Magnetic deflection provides greater deflection capability and is therefore used in CRTs for television, alphanumeric, and graphical displays. It is slower than electrostatic deflection, which is the deflection system commonly used in oscilloscopes.

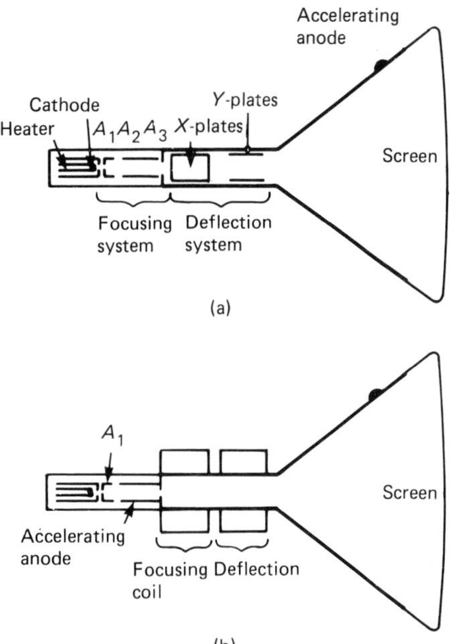

Figure 6.6 Cathode ray tube. (a) Electrostatic focusing and deflection; (b) electromagnetic focusing and deflection.

Acceleration of the beam is by either the use of the accelerating electrode A_3 (such tubes are referred to as monoaccelerator tubes) or by applying a high potential (10–14 kV) on to a post-deflection anode situated close to the CRT screen. This

Table 6.3 Characteristics of commonly used phosphors (courtesy of Tektronix)

Phosphor	*Fluorescence*	*Relative*[a] *luminance (%)*	*Relative*[b] *photographic writing speed (%)*	*Decay*	*Relative burn resistance*	*Comments*
P1	Yellow-green	50	20	Medium	Medium	In most applications replaced by P31
P4	White	50	40	Medium /short	Medium /high	Television displays
P7	Blue	35	75	Long	Medium	Long-decay, double-layer screen
P11	Blue	15	100	Medium /short	Medium	For photographic applications
P31	Green	100	50	Medium /short	High	General purposes, brightest available phosphor

[a]Measured with a photometer and luminance probe incorporating a standard eye filter. Representative of 10 kV aluminized screens with P31 phosphor as reference.
[b]P11 as reference with Polaroid 612 or 106 film. Representative of 10 kV aluminized screens.

technique, which is known as post-deflection acceleration (PDA), gives rise to tubes with higher light output and increased deflection sensitivity.

The phosphor coats the front screen of the CRT. A range of phosphors are available, the choice of which for a particular situation depends on the colour and efficiency of the luminescence required and its persistence time, that is, the time for which the afterglow continues after the electron beam has been removed. Table 6.3 provides the characteristics of some commonly used phosphors.

6.6.1 Colour displays

Colour displays are provided using a screen which employs groups of three phosphor dots. The material of the phosphor for each of the three dots is chosen such that it emits one of the primary colours (red, green, blue). The tube is provided with a shadow mask consisting of a metal screen with holes in it placed near to the screen and three electron guns, as shown in Figure 6.7(a). The guns are inclined to each other so that the beams coincide at

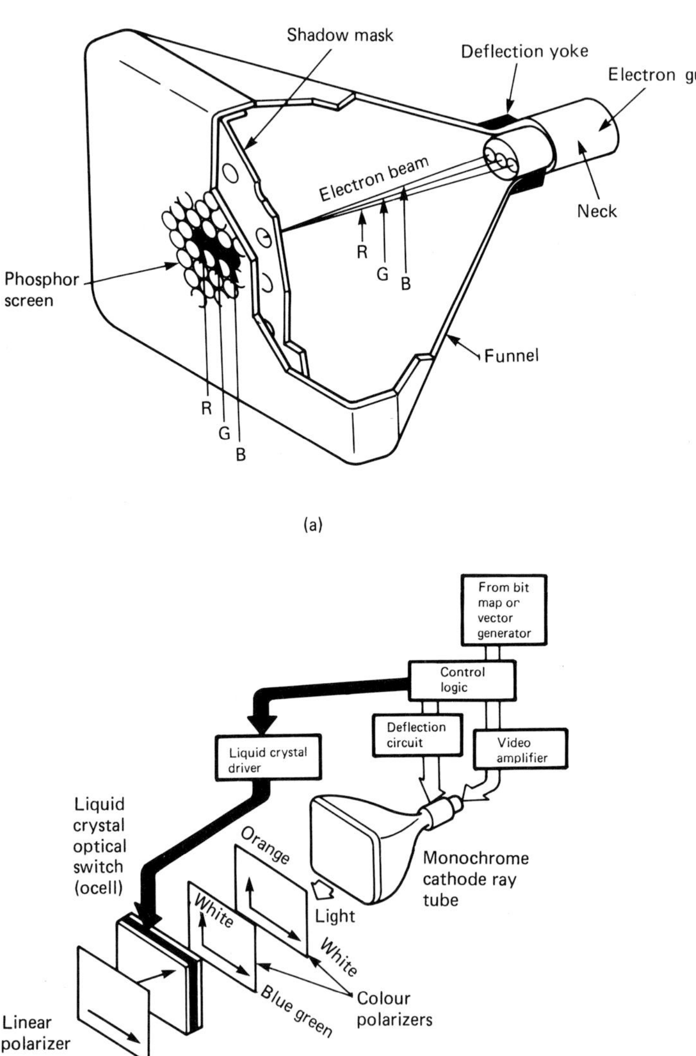

Figure 6.7 Colour displays. (a) Shadow mask colour tube; (b) liquid crystal colour display.

the plane of the shadow mask. After passing through the shadow mask the beams diverge and, on hitting the screen, energize only one of the phosphors at that particular location. The effect of a range of colours is achieved by adjusting the relative intensities of the three primary colours by adjusting the electron beam currents. The resolution of colour displays is generally lower than that of monochrome displays because the technique requires three phosphors to produce the effect of colour. Alignment of the shadow mask with the phosphor screen is also critical and the tube is sensitive to interfering magnetic fields.

An alternative method of providing a colour display is to use penetration phosphors which make use of the effect that the depth of penetration of the electron beam is dependent on beam energy. By using two phosphors, one of which has a non-luminescent coating, it is possible by adjusting the energy of the electron beam to change the colour of the display. For static displays having fixed colours this technique provides good resolution capability and is reasonably insensitive to interfering magnetic fields.

Liquid crystal colour displays employ a single phosphor having two separate emission peaks (Figure 6.7(b)). One is orange and the other blue-green. The colour polarizers orthogonally polarize the orange and blue-green components of the CRT's emission, and the liquid crystal cell rotates the polarized orange and blue-green information into the transmission axis of the linear polarizer and thus selects the colour of the display. Rotation of the orange and blue-green information is performed in synchronism with the information displayed by the sequentially addressed CRT. Alternate displays of information viewed through different coloured polarizing filters are integrated by the human eye to give colour images. This sequential technique can be used to provide all mixtures of the two primary colours contained in the phosphor.

6.6.2 Oscilloscopes

Oscilloscopes can be broadly classified as analogue, storage, sampling, or digitizing devices. Figure 6.8 shows the elements of a typical analogue oscilloscope. The signals to be observed as a function of time are applied to the vertical (Y) plates of the oscilloscope. The input stage of the vertical system matches the voltage levels of these signals to the drive requirements of the deflection plate of the oscilloscope which will have a typical deflection sensitivity of 20 V/cm. The coupling of the input stage can be either d.c. or a.c.

The important specifications for the vertical system include bandwidth and sensitivity. The bandwidth is generally specified as the highest frequency which can be displayed with less than 3 dB loss in amplitude compared with its value at low frequencies. The rise time, T_r, of an oscilloscope to a step input is related to its bandwidth, B, by $T_r = 0.35/B$. In order to measure the rise time of a

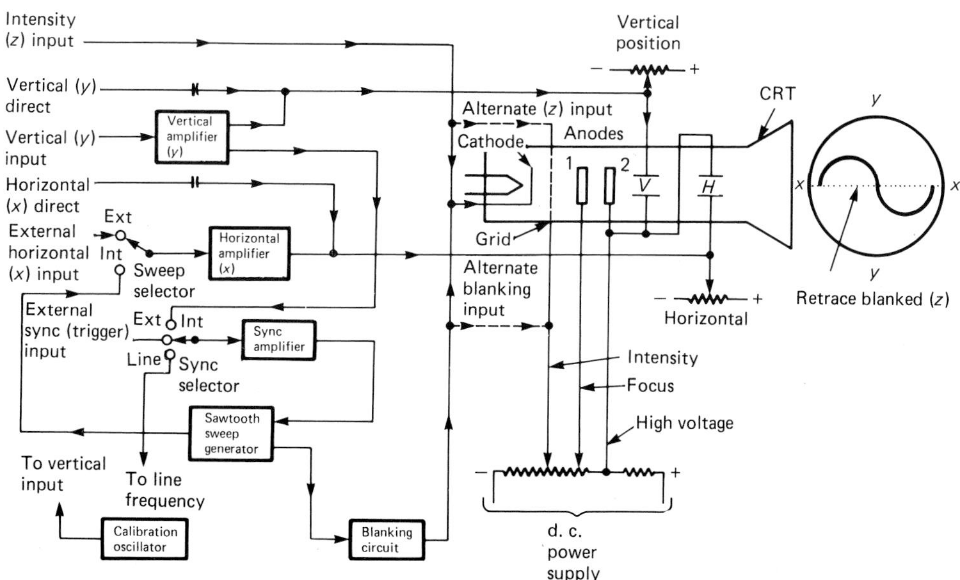

Figure 6.8 Analogue oscilloscope.

waveform with an accuracy of better than 2 per cent it is necessary that the rise time of the oscilloscope should be less than 0.2 of that of the waveform. Analogue oscilloscopes are available having bandwidths of up to 1 GHz.

The deflection sensitivity of an oscilloscope, commonly quoted as mV/cm, mV/div, or μV/cm, μV/div, gives a measure of the smallest signal the oscilloscope can measure accurately. Typically, the highest sensitivity for the vertical system corresponds to 10 μV/cm. There is a trade-off between bandwidth and sensitivity since the noise levels generated either by the amplifier itself or by pickup by the amplifier are greater in wideband measurements. High-sensitivity oscilloscopes may provide bandwidth-limiting controls to improve the display of low-level signals at moderate frequencies.

For comparison purposes, simultaneous viewing of multiple inputs is often required. This can be provided by the use of dual-trace or dual-beam methods. In the dual-trace method the beam is switched between the two input signals. Alternate sweeps of the display can be used for one of the two signals, or, in a single sweep, the display can be chopped between the two signals. Chopping can occur at frequencies up to 1 MHz. Both these methods have limitations for measuring fast transients since in the alternate method the transient may occur on one channel whilst the other is being displayed. The chopping rate of the chopped display limits the frequency range of the signals that can be observed.

Dual-beam oscilloscopes use two independent electron beams and vertical deflection systems. These can be provided with either a common horizontal system or two independent horizontal systems to enable the two signals to be displayed at different sweep speeds. By combining a dual-beam system with chopping it is possible to provide systems with up to eight inputs.

Other functions which are commonly provided on the Y inputs include facilities to invert one channel or to take the difference of two input signals and display the result. This enables unwanted common mode signals present on both inputs to be rejected.

For the display of signals as a function of time the horizontal system provides a sawtooth voltage to the X plates of the oscilloscope together with the blanking waveform necessary to suppress the flyback. The sweep speed required is determined by the waveform being observed. Sweep rates corresponding to as little as 200 ps/div can be obtained. In time measurements the sweep can either be continuous, providing a repetitive display, or single shot, in which the horizontal system is triggered to provide a single sweep. To provide a stable display in the repetitive mode the display is synchronized either internally from the vertical amplifier or externally using the signal triggering or initiating the signal being measured. Most oscilloscopes provide facilities for driving the X plates from an external source to enable, for example, a Lissajous figure to be displayed.

Delayed sweep enables the sweep to be initiated some time after the trigger. This delayed sweep facility can be used in conjunction with the timebase to provide expansion of one part of the waveform.

The trigger system allows the user to specify a position on one or more of the input signals in the case of internal triggering or on a trigger signal in the case of external triggering where the sweep is to initiate. Typical facilities provided by trigger level controls are auto (which triggers at the mean level of the waveform) and trigger level and direction control, i.e. triggering occurs at a particular signal level for positive-going signals.

6.6.3 Storage oscilloscopes

Storage oscilloscopes are used for the display of signals which are either too slow or too fast and infrequent for a conventional oscilloscope. They can also be used for comparing events occurring at different times.

The techniques which are used in storage oscilloscopes include bistable, variable persistence, fast transfer storage, or a combination of fast transfer storage with bistable or variable persistence storage. The storage capability is specified primarily by the writing speed. This is usually expressed in cm/μs or div/μs.

The phosphor in a bistable CRT has two stable states—written and unwritten. As shown in Figure 6.9(a), when writing the phosphor is charged positive in those areas where it is written on. The flood gun electrons hit the unwritten area but are too slow to illuminate it. However, in the written areas the positive charge of the phosphor attracts the electrons and provides them with sufficient velocity to keep the phosphor lit and also to knock out sufficient secondaries to keep the area positive. A bistable tube displays stored data at one level of intensity. It provides a bright, long-lasting display (up to 10 h), although with less contrast than other techniques. It has a slow writing speed with a typical value of 0.5 cm/μs. Split-screen operation, in which the information on one part of the screen is stored whilst the remainder has new information written onto it, can be provided using a bistable CRT.

The screen of the variable persistence CRT, shown in Figure 6.9(b), is similar to that of a conventional CRT. The storage screen consists of a fine metal mesh coated with a dielectric. A collector screen and ion-repeller screen are located behind

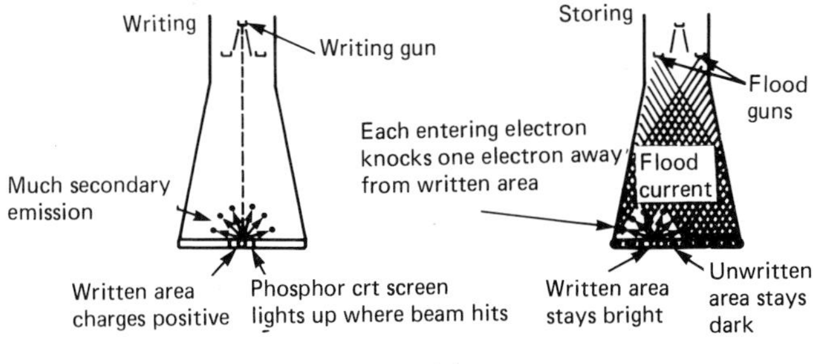

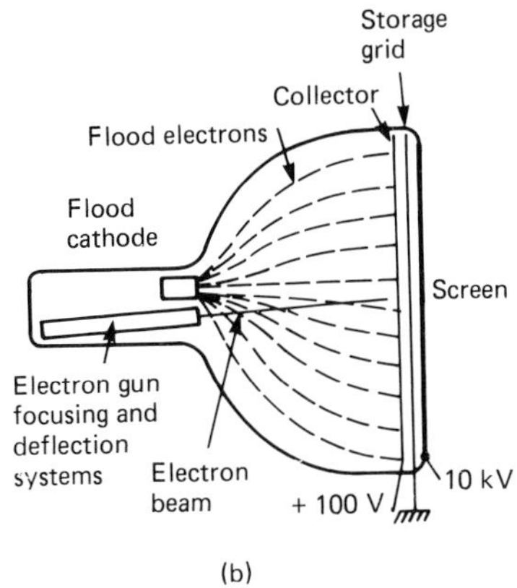

Figure 6.9 Storage CRTs. (a) Bistable; (b) variable persistence.

the storage screen. When the writing gun is employed a positive trace is written out on the storage screen by removing electrons from its dielectric. These electrons are collected by the collector screen. The positively charged areas of the dielectric are transparent to low-velocity electrons. The flood gun sprays the entire screen with low-velocity electrons. These penetrate the transparent areas but not other areas of the storage screen. The storage screen thus becomes a stencil for the flood gun. The charge on the mesh can be controlled, altering the contrast between the trace and the background and also modifying how long the trace is stored. Variable persistence storage provides high contrast between the waveform and the background. It enables waveforms to be stored for only as long as the time between repetitions, and therefore a continuously updated display can be obtained. Time variations in system responses can thus be observed. Integration of repetitive signals can also be provided since noise or jitter not common to all traces will not be stored or displayed. Signals with low repetition rates and fast rise times can be displayed by allowing successive repetitions to build up the trace brightness. The typical writing rate for variable persistence storage is 5 cm/μs. A typical storage time would be 30 s.

Fast transfer storage uses an intermediate mesh target which has been optimized for speed. This target captures the waveform and then transfers it to another mesh optimized for long-term storage. The technique provides increased writing speeds (typically up to 5500 cm/μs). From the transfer target storage can be by either bistable or variable persistence. Oscilloscopes are available in which storage by fast variable persistence, fast bistable, variable persistence, or bistable operation is user selectable. Such devices can provide a range of writing speeds, with storage time combinations ranging from 5500 cm/μs and 30 s using fast variable persistence storage to 0.2 cm/μs and 30 min using bistable storage.

6.6.4 Sampling oscilloscopes

The upper frequency limit for analogue oscilloscopes is typically 1 GHz. For the display of repetitive signals in excess of this frequency,

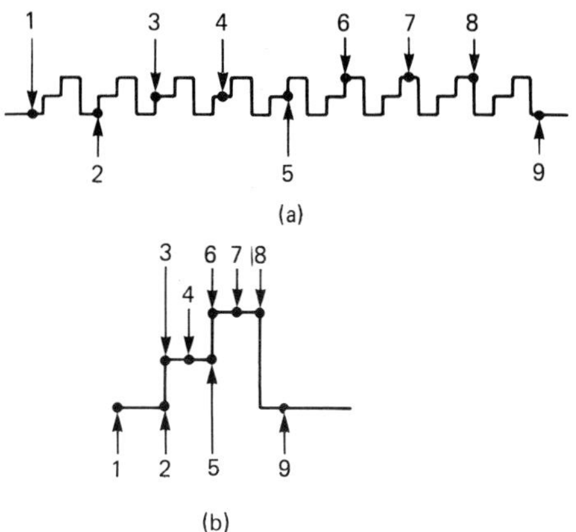

Figure 6.10 Sampling oscilloscope.

sampling techniques are employed. These extend the range to approximately 14 GHz. As shown in Figure 6.10, samples of different portions of successive waveforms are taken. Sampling of the waveform can be either sequential or random. The samples are stretched in time, amplified by relatively low bandwidth amplifiers, and then displayed. The display is identical to the sampled waveform. Sampling oscilloscopes are typically capable of resolving events of less than 5 mV in peak amplitude that occur in less than 30 ps on an equivalent timebase of less than 20 ps/cm.

6.6.5 Digitizing oscilloscopes

Digitizing oscilloscopes are useful for measurements on single-shot or low-repetition signals. The digital storage techniques they employ provide clear, crisp displays. No fading or blooming of the display occurs and since the data are stored in digital memory the storage time is unlimited.

Figure 6.11 shows the elements of a digitizing oscilloscope. The Y channel is sampled, converted to a digital form, and stored. A typical digitizing oscilloscope may provide dual-channel storage with a 100 MHz, 8-bit ADC on each channel feeding a 1 K × 8 bit store, with simultaneous sampling of the two channels. The sample rate depends on the timebase range but typically may go from 20 samples/s at 5 s/div to 100 M samples/s at 1 μs/div. Additional stores are often provided for comparative data.

Digitizing oscilloscopes can provide a variety of display modes, including a refreshed mode in which the stored data and display are updated by a triggered sweep; a roll mode in which the data and display are continually updated, producing the effect of new data rolling in from the right of the screen; a fast roll mode in which the data are continually updated but the display is updated after the trigger; an arm and release mode which allows a single trigger capture; a pre-trigger mode which in roll and fast roll allocates 0, 25, 75, and 100 per cent of the store to the pre-trigger signal; and a hold display mode which freezes the display immediately.

Communication to a computer system is generally provided by a IEEE-488 interface. This enables programming of the device to be undertaken, for stored data to be sent to an external controller, and, if required, to enable the device to receive new data for display. Digitizing oscilloscopes may also provide outputs for obtaining hard copy of the stored data on an analogue x–y plotter.

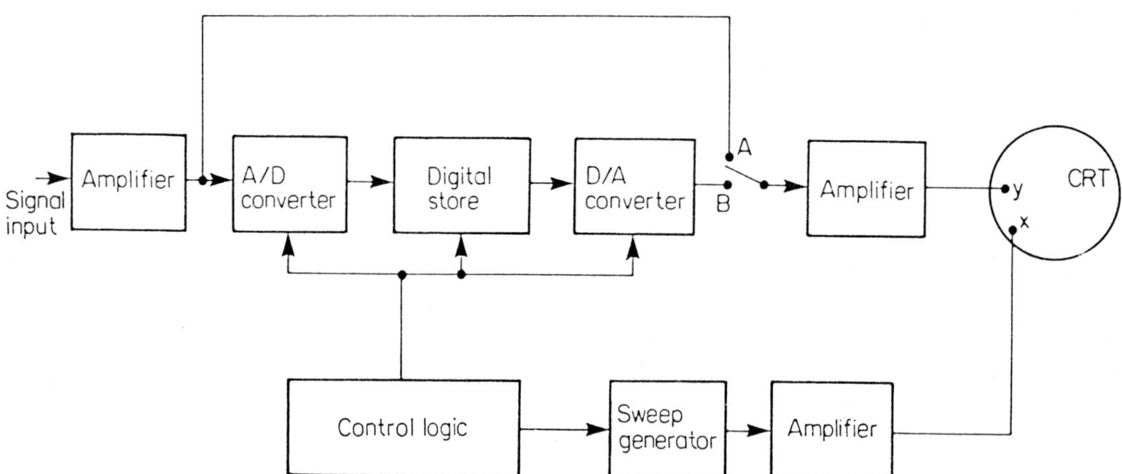

Figure 6.11 Digitizing oscilloscope.

6.6.6 Visual display units (VDUs)

A VDU comprising a keyboard and CRT display is widely used as a MMI in computer-based instrumentation systems. Alphanumeric VDU displays use the raster scan technique, as shown in Figure 6.12. A typical VDU will have 24 lines of 80 characters. The characters are made up of a 7 × 5 dot matrix. Thus seven raster lines are required for a single line of text and five dots for each character position. The space between characters is equivalent to one dot and that between lines is equivalent to one or two raster scans.

As the electron beam scans the first raster line the top row of the dot matrix representation for each character is produced in turn. This is used to

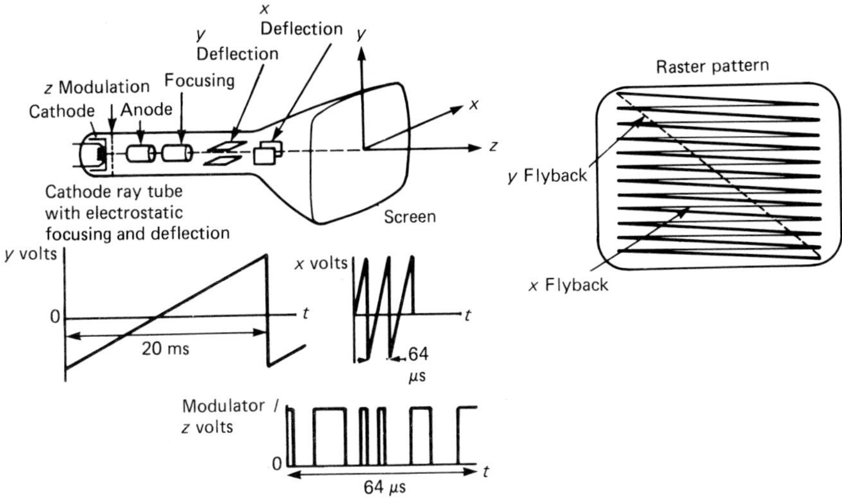

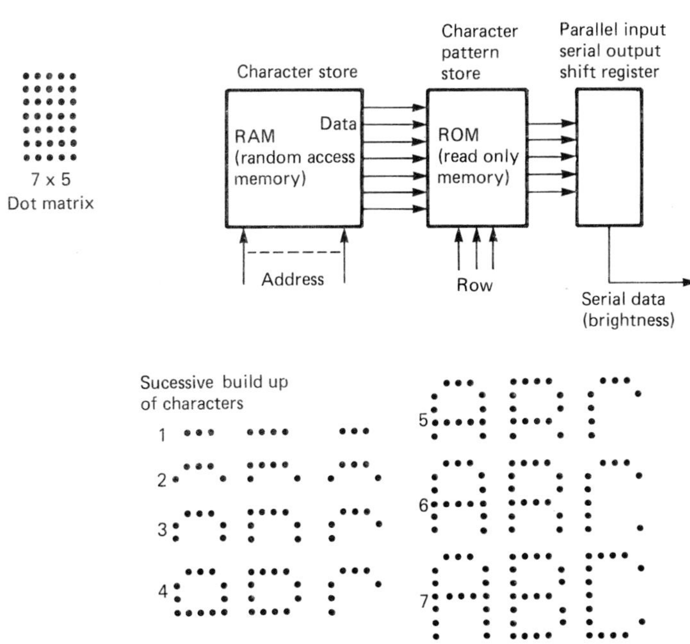

Figure 6.12 Visual display unit.

modulate the beam intensity. For the second raster scan the second row of the dot matrix representation is used. Seven raster scans generate one row of text. The process is repeated for each of the 24 lines and the total cycle repeated at a typical rate of 50 times per second.

The characters to be displayed on the screen are stored in the character store as 7-bit ASCII code, with the store organized as 24 × 80 words of 7 bits. The 7-bit word output of the character store addresses a character pattern ROM. A second input to the ROM selects which particular row of the dot matrix pattern is required. This pattern is provided as a parallel output which is then converted to a serial form to be applied to the brightness control of the CRT. For a single scan the row-selection inputs remain constant whilst the character pattern ROM is successively addressed by the ASCII codes corresponding to the 80 characters on the line. To build up a row of character the sequence of ASCII codes remains the same but on successive raster scans the row address of the character pattern ROM is changed.

6.6.7 Graphical displays

A graphical raster-scan display is one in which the picture or frame is composed of a large number of raster lines, each one of which is subdivided into a large number of picture elements (pixels). Standard television pictures have 625 lines, consisting of two interlaced frames of 313 lines. With each 313-line frame scanned every 20 ms the line scan rate is approximately 60 μs/line.

A graphic raster-scan display stores every pixel in random access or serial store (frame), as shown in Figure 6.13. The storage requirements in such systems can often be quite large. A system using 512 of the 625 lines for display with 1024 pixels on each line having a dual intensity (on/off) display requires a store of 512 Kbits. For a display having the same resolution but with either eight levels of brightness or eight colours the storage requirement then increases to 1.5 Mbits.

Displays are available which are less demanding on storage. Typically, these provide an on/off display having a resolution of 360 lines each having 720 pixels. This requires a 16K × 16 bit frame store. Limited graphics can be provided by alphanumeric raster scan displays supplying additional symbols to the ASCII set. These can then be used to produce graphs or pictures.

6.7 Graphical recorders

Hard copy of data from a process or system can be displayed in a graphical form either as the relationships between one or more variables and time using an x–t recorder or as the relationship between two variables using an x–y recorder. x–t recorders can be classified as either strip chart recorders, in which the data are recorded on a continuous roll of chart paper, or circular chart recorders, which, as their name implies, record the data on a circular chart.

6.7.1 Strip chart recorders

Most strip chart recorders employ a servo-feedback system (as shown in Figure 6.14) to ensure that the displacement of the writing head across the paper tracks the input voltage over the required frequency range. The position of the writing head is generally measured by a potentiometer system. The error signal between the demanded position and the actual position of the writing head is amplified using an a.c. or d.c. amplifier, and the output drives either an a.c. or d.c. motor. Movement of the writing head is effected by a mechanical linkage between the output of the motor and the writing head. The chart paper movement is generally controlled by a stepping motor.

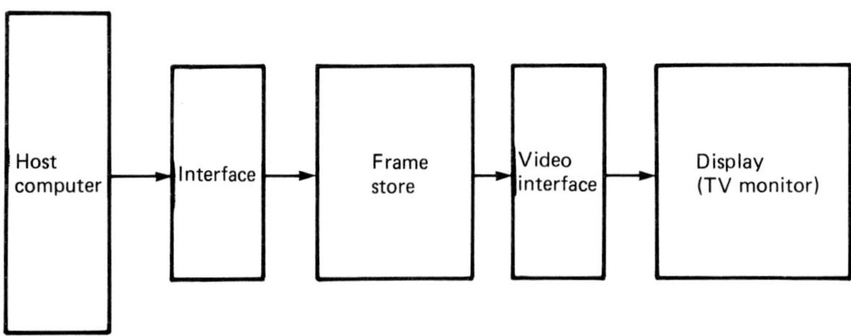

Figure 6.13 Elements of a graphical display.

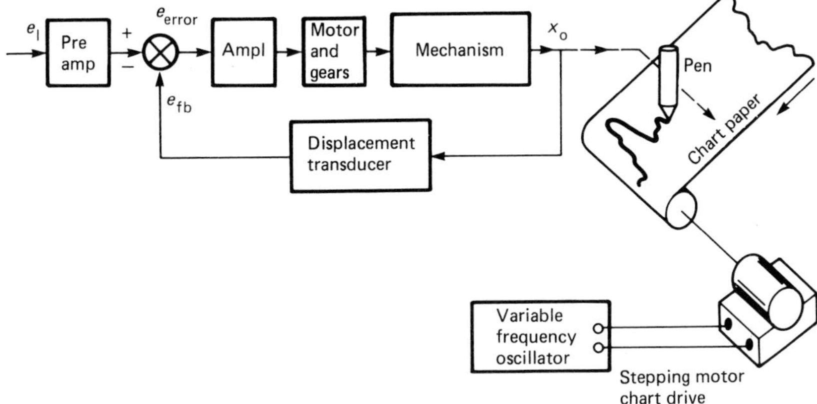

Figure 6.14 Strip chart recorder.

The methods used for recording the data onto the paper include:

(1) *Pen and ink*. In the past these have used pens having ink supplied from a refillable reservoir. Increasingly, such systems use disposable fibre-tipped pens. Multichannel operation can be achieved using up to six pens. For full-width recording using multiple pens, staggering of the pens is necessary to avoid mechanical interference.
(2) *Impact printing*. The 'ink' for the original impact systems was provided by a carbon ribbon placed between the pointer mechanism and the paper. A mark was made on the paper by pressing the pointer mechanism onto the paper. Newer methods can simultaneously record the data from up to twenty variables. This is achieved by having a wheel with an associated ink pad which provides the ink for the symbols on the wheel. By rotating the wheel different symbols can be printed on the paper for each of the variables. The wheel is moved across the paper in response to the variable being recorded.
(3) *Thermal writing*. These systems employ thermally sensitive paper which changes colour on the application of heat. They can use a moving writing head which is heated by an electric current or a fixed printing head having a large number of printing elements (up to several hundred for 100 mm wide paper). The particular printing element is selected according to the magnitude of the input signal. Multichannel operation is possible using such systems and time and date information can be provided in alphanumeric form.
(4) *Optical writing*. This technique is commonly used in galvanometer systems (see section 6.7.3). The source of light is generally ultraviolet to reduce unwanted effects from ambient light. The photographic paper used is sensitive to ultra-violet light. This paper develops in daylight or artificial light without the need for special chemicals. Fixing of the image is necessary to prevent long-term degradation,
(5) *Electric writing*. The chart paper used in this technique consists of a paper base coated with a layer of a coloured dye—black, blue, or red—which in turn is coated with a very thin surface coating of aluminium. The recording is effected by a tungsten wire stylus moving over the aluminium surface. When a potential of approximately 35 V is applied to this stylus an electric discharge occurs which removes the aluminium, revealing the dye. In multichannel recording the different channels are distinguished by the use of different line configurations (for example, solid, dashed, dotted). Alphanumeric information can also be provided in these systems.

The major specifications for a strip chart recorder include:

(1) *Number of channels*. Using a numbered print wheel, up to thirty channels can be monitored by a single recorder. In multichannel recorders, recording of the channels can be simultaneous or on a time-shared basis. The channels in a multichannel recording can be distinguished either by colour or by the nature of line marking.
(2) *Chart width*. This can be up to 250 mm.
(3) *Recording technique*. The recorder may employ any of the techniques described above.
(4) *Input specifications*. These are given in terms of the range of the input variable which may be

voltage, current, or from a thermocouple, RTD, pH electrode, or conductivity probe. Typical d.c. voltage spans are from 0.1 mV to 100 V. Those for d.c. current are typically from 0.1 mA to 1 A. The zero suppression provided by the recorder is specified by its suppression ratio, which gives the number of spans by which the zero can be suppressed. The rejection of line frequency signals at the input of the recorder is measured by its common and normal mode rejection ratios.

(5) *Performance specifications*. These include accuracy, deadband, resolution, response time, and chart speed. A typical voltage accuracy specification may be $\pm(0.3 + 0.1 \times$ suppression ratio) per cent of span, or 0.20 mV, whichever is greater. Deadband and resolution are usually expressed as a percentage of span, with 0.1 and ± 0.15 per cent, respectively, being typical figures. Chart recorders are designed for use with slowly varying inputs (< 1 Hz for full-scale travel). The response time is usually specified as a step response time and is often adjustable by the user to between 1 and 10 s. The chart speed may vary between mm/h and m/h, depending on the application.

6.7.2 Circular chart recorders

These recorders, as shown in Figure 6.15, generally use a 12-in diameter chart. They are particularly well suited for direct actuation by a number of mechanical sensors without the need for a transducer to convert the measured quantity into an electrical one. Thus they can be configured for a temperature recorder using a filled bulb thermometer system or as an absolute, differential, or gauge pressure recorder employing a bellows or a bourdon tube. Up to four variables can be recorded on a single chart. The rotation of the circular scale can be provided by a clockwork motor, which makes the recorder ideally suited in remote locations having no source of power.

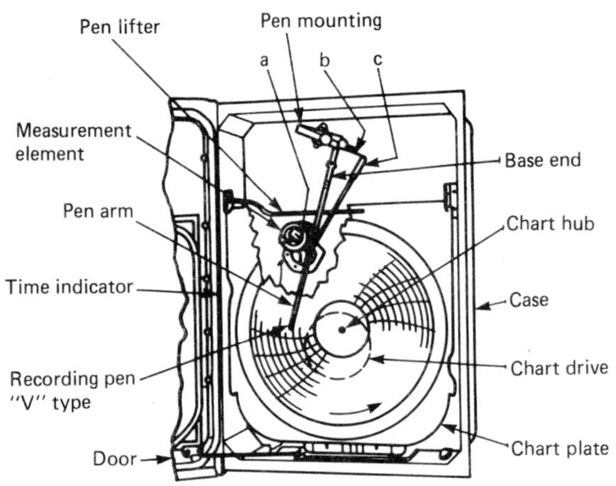

Figure 6.15 Circular chart recorder.

6.7.3 Galvanometer recorders

The D'Arsonoval movement used in the moving-coil indicating instruments can also provide the movement in an optical galvanometer recorder, as shown in Figure 6.16. These devices can have bandwidths in excess of 20 kHz. The light source in such devices is provided by either an ultra-violet or tungsten lamp. Movement of the light beam is effected by the rotation of a small mirror connected to the galvanometer movement. The light beam is focused into a spot on the light-sensitive paper. Positioning of the trace may also be achieved by mechanical means. A recorder may have several galvanometers and, since it is light that is being deflected, overlapping traces can be provided without the need for time staggering. Identification of individual traces is by sequential trace interruption in which the light from each trace in turn is interrupted by a series of pins passing in front of the galvanometers. Amplitude and time reference grids may also be provided.

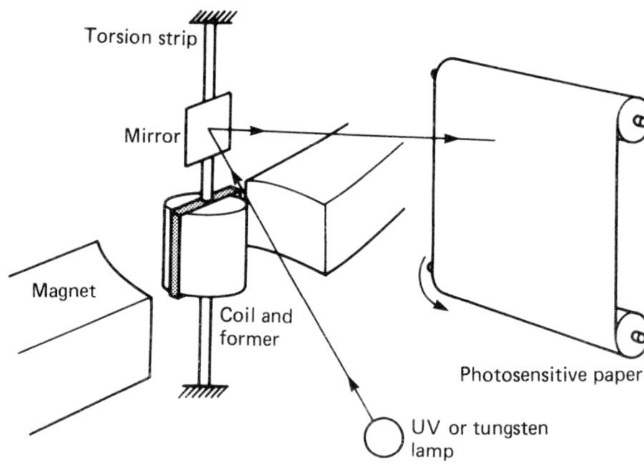

Figure 6.16 Galvanometer recorder.

Trade-offs are available between the sensitivity and frequency response of the galvanometers with high-sensitivity devices having low bandwidths. Manufacturers generally provide a range of plug-in galvanometers, having a range of sensitivities and bandwidths for different applications, which enables them to be quickly removed from the magnet block and replaced. Galvanometer systems are available which enable up to 42 channels to be recorded on a 300 mm wide chart drive. The drive speed of the paper can be up to 5000 mm/s.

6.7.4 *x–y* recorders

In an analogue *x–y* recorder (Figure 6.17) both the *x* and *y* deflections of the writing head are controlled by servo feedback systems. The paper, which is usually either A3 or A4 size, is held in position by electrostatic attraction or vacuum. These recorders can be provided with either one or two pens. Plug-in timebases are also generally available to enable them to function as *x–t* recorders. A typical device may provide *x* and *y* input ranges which are continuously variable between 0.25 mV/cm and 10 V/cm with an accuracy of ±0.1 per cent of full scale and a deadband of 0.1 per cent of full scale. Zero offset adjustments are also provided. A typical timebase can be adjusted between 0.25 and 50 s/cm with an accuracy of 1 per cent.

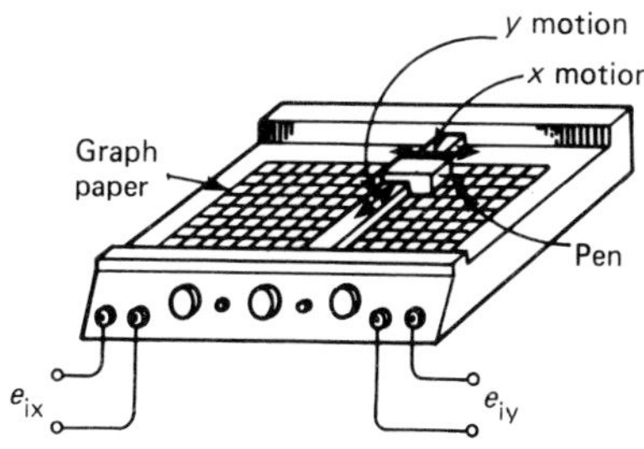

Figure 6.17 *x–y* recorder.

The dynamic performance of *x–y* recorders is specified by their slewing rate and acceleration. A very high-speed *x–y* recorder capable of recording a signal up to 10 Hz at an amplitude of 2 cm peak to peak will have a slewing rate of 97 cm/s and a peak acceleration of 7620 cm/s^2. Remote control of such functions as sweep start and reset, pen lift, and chart hold can be provided.

Digital *x–y* plotters replace the servo feedback with an open-loop stepping motor drive. These can replace traditional analogue recorders and provide increased measurement and graphics capabilities. A digital measurement plotting system can provide, for example, simultaneous sampling and storage of a number of input channels; a variety of trigger modes, including the ability to display pre-trigger data; multi-pen plotting of the data; annotation of the record with date, time, and set-up conditions; and an ability to draw grids and axes. Communication with such devices can be by means of the IEEE-488 or RS-232 interfaces.

For obtaining hard copy from digital data input, graphics plotters are available. With appropriate hardware and software these devices can draw grids, annotate charts, and differentiate data by the use of different colours and line types. They are specified by their line quality, plotting speed, and paper size. Intelligence built into the plotter will free the system's CPU for other tasks. The availability of a graphics language to control the plotter functions and graphics software packages also simplifies the user's programming tasks.

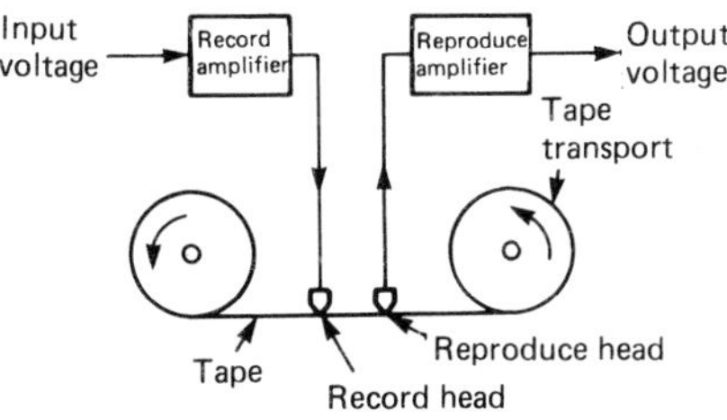

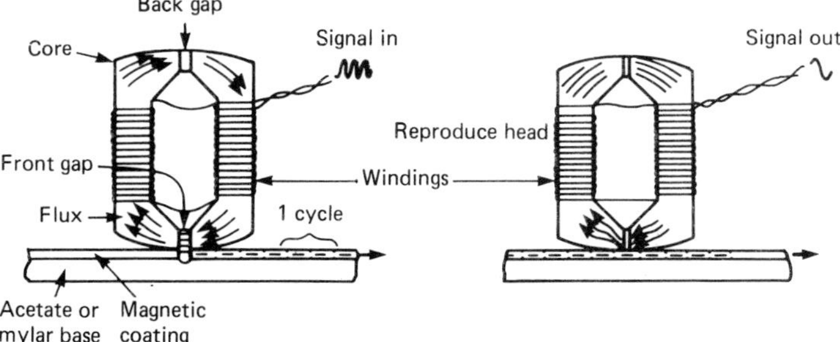

Figure 6.18 Elements of magnetic tape recorder system.

6.8 Magnetic recording

Using magnetic tape recording for data which are to be subsequently analysed has the advantage that, once recorded, the data can be replayed almost indefinitely. The recording period may vary from a few minutes to several days. Speed translation of the captured data can be provided in that fast data can be slowed down and slow data speeded up by using different record and reproduce speeds. Multichannel recording enables correlations between one or more variables to be identified.

The methods employed in recording data onto magnetic tape include direct recording, frequency modulation (FM), and pulse code modulation (PCM). Figure 6.18 shows the elements of a magnetic tape recorder system. Modulation of the current in the recording head by the signal to be recorded linearly modulates the magnetic flux in the recording gap. The magnetic tape, consisting of magnetic particles on an acetate or mylar base, passes over the recording head. As they leave from under the recording head the particles retain a state of permanent magnetization proportional to the flux in the gap. The input signal is thus converted to a spatial variation of the magnetization of the particles on the tape. The reproduce head detects these changes as changes in the reluctance of its magnetic circuit, which induces a voltage in its winding. This voltage is proportional to the rate of change of flux. The reproduce head amplifier integrates the signal to provide a flat frequency characteristic.

Since the reproduce head generates a signal which is proportional to the rate of change of flux the direct recording method cannot be used down to d.c. The lower limit is typically 100 Hz. The upper frequency limit occurs when the induced variation in magnetization varies over distances smaller than the gap in the reproduce head. This sets an upper limit for direct recording of approximately 2 MHz, using gaps and tape speeds commonly available.

In FM recording systems the carrier signal is frequently modulated by the input signal (frequency modulation is discussed in Chapter 5). The central frequency is chosen with respect to the tape speed and frequency deviations of up to ±40 per cent of the carrier frequency are used. FM systems provide a d.c. response but at the expense of the high-frequency recording limit.

PCM techniques, which are also described in Chapter 5, are used in systems for the recording of digital data. The coding used is typically Non-Return to Zero Level or Delay Modulation.

A typical portable instrumentation tape recorder can provide up to 14 data channels using ½-in tape. Using direct record/reproduce, such a system can record signals in a frequency band from 100 Hz to 300 kHz with an input sensitivity of between 0.1 to 2.5 V rms and a signal-to-noise ratio of up to 40 dB. FM recording with such a system provides bandwidths extending from d.c. to as high as 40 kHz. A typical input sensitivity for FM recording is 0.1 to 10 V rms with a signal-to-noise ratio of up to 50 dB. TTL data recording using PCM can be achieved at data transfer rates of up to 480 kbits/s using such a system.

6.9 Transient/waveform recorders

These devices are used for the high-speed capture of relatively small amounts of data. The specifications provided by general-purpose transient recorders in terms of sampling rate, resolution, number of channels, and memory size are similar to those of the digitizing oscilloscope. Pre-trigger data capture facilities are also often provided. High-speed transient recorders, using scan conversion techniques in which the signal is written onto a silicon-diode target array, can provide sampling rates of 10^{11} samples/s (10 ps/point) with record lengths of 512 points and are capable of recording single-shot signals having bandwidths of up to 500 MHz.

6.10 Data loggers

Data loggers can be broadly defined as data-acquisition systems whose functions are programmed from the front panel. They take inputs from a mixture of analogue and digital signals, perform limited mathematical and logical operations on the inputs, and provide storage either in the form of semiconductor memory or magnetic tape or disc systems. Many data loggers are provided with an

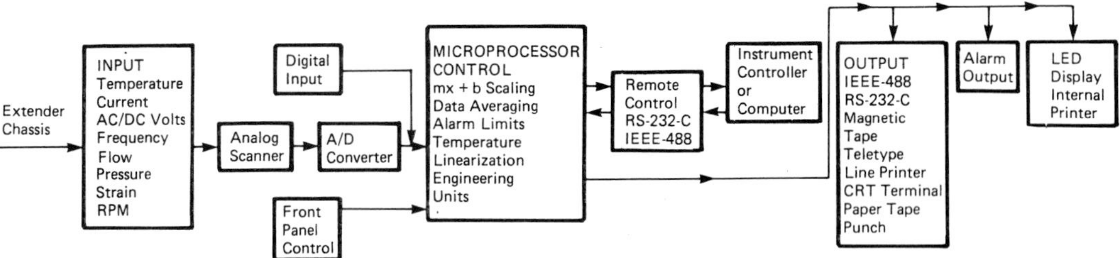

Figure 6.19 Data logger.

integral alphanumeric display and printer. Figure 6.19 shows the elements of a typical data-logging system. These systems can be characterized by:

(1) *The number and type of analogue or digital inputs which can be accepted.* The analogue inputs may be a.c. or d.c. current, d.c. current, or from thermocouples or RTDs.
(2) *The scanning rate and modes of scanning available.* These can include single-scan, monitor, interval scan, and continuous scan.
(3) *The method of programming.* This can be by one button per function on the front panel; by the use of a menu-driven approach by presenting the information to the user on a built-in CRT screen; or by using a high-level language such as BASIC.
(4) *The mathematical functions provided by the logger.* These may include linearization for thermocouple inputs, scaling to provide the user with an output in engineering units, and data averaging over a selectable number of scans.
(5) *The nature and capacity of the internal memory.* If the memory is semiconductor memory, is it volatile? If so, is it provided with battery back-up in case of power failure?
(6) *The printer technique and the width of the print output.* Data loggers typically use dot matrix ink printers or thermal or electric writing technique with continuous strip paper.
(7) *The display.* Data loggers generally provide display using LEDs or LCDs, although some incorporate CRTs.
(8) *Communication with other systems.* This is generally provided by RS 232/422/423 interfaces. Some data loggers are capable of being interrogated remotely using the public telephone network.

6.11 References

AGARD, P. J. *et al. Information and Display Systems in Process Instruments and Control Handbook*, eds D. M. Considine and G. Considine, McGraw-Hill, New York (1985)

BENTLEY, J. *Principles of Measurement Systems*, Longman, London (1983)

BOSMAN, D. 'Human factors in display design', in *Handbook of Measurement Science*, Volume 2, Practical Fundamentals, ed. P. Sydenham, John Wiley, Chichester (1983)

British Standards Institution, BS 89: 1977, Direct Acting Indicating Electrical Instruments and their Accessories (1977)

British Standards Institution, BS 3693 (Part 1: 1964 and Part 2: 1969). The Design of Scales and Indexes (1964 and 1969)

DOEBELIN, E. O. *Measurement Systems Application and Design*, 3rd edn, McGraw-Hill, London (1983)

LENK, J. D. *Handbook of Oscilloscopes, Theory and Application*, Prentice-Hall, Englewood Cliffs, New Jersey (1982)

WILKINSON, B. and HORROCKS, D. *Computer Peripherals*. Hodder and Stoughton, London (1980)

WILSON, J. and HAWKES, J.F.B. *Optoelectronics: An Introduction*. Prentice-Hall, Englewood Cliffs, New Jersey (1983)

7 Pneumatic instrumentation

E. H. HIGHAM

7.1 Basic characteristics

The early evolution of process control was centred on the petroleum and chemical industries, where the process materials gave rise to hazardous environments and therefore the measuring and control systems had to be intrinsically safe. Pneumatic systems were particularly suitable in this connection, and, once the flapper/nozzle system and its associated pneumatic amplifier (customarily called relay) had been developed for the detection of small movements, sensors to measure temperature, flow, pressure, level and density were devised. These were followed by pneumatic mechanisms to implement the control functions whilst air cylinders or diaphragm motors were developed to actuate the final control elements.

The pneumatic systems had further advantages in that the installation did not involve special skills, equipment or materials. The reservoir tanks, normally provided to smooth out the pulsations of the air compressor, also stored a substantial volume of compressed air which, in the event of failure of the compressor or its motive power, stored sufficient energy to enable the control system to remain in operation until an orderly shutdown had been implemented. The provision of comparable features with electronic or other types of control systems involves a great deal of additional equipment.

Although pneumatic control systems have many attractive features they compare unfavourably with electronic systems in two particular respects, namely signal transmission and signal conditioning or signal processing.

For the majority of process applications a distance/velocity lag of about 1 s is quite acceptable. This corresponds typically to a pneumatic transmission distance of about 100 m and is not a limitation for a great many installations, but in large plants, where measurement signals may have to be transmitted over distances of a kilometre or more, electrical methods for transmission have to be adopted. When the successful operation of a process depends on conditioning the signal (e.g. taking the square root, multiplying, dividing, summing or averaging, differentiating or integrating the signals) the pneumatic devices are undoubtedly more complex, cumbersome and very often less accurate than the corresponding electronic devices.

Pneumatic systems are virtually incompatible with digital ones, and cannot compete at all with their advantages for signal transmission, multiplexing, computation, etc. On the other hand, when all these opportunities have been exploited and implemented to the full, the signal to the final control element is nearly always converted back to pneumatics so that the necessary combination of power, speed and stroke/movement can be achieved with a pneumatic actuator.

7.2 Pneumatic measurement and control systems

Pneumatic systems are characterized by the simplicity of the technology on which they are based and the relative ease with which they can be installed, operated and maintained. They are based on the use of a flapper/nozzle in conjunction with a pneumatic relay to detect a very small relative movement (typically, <0.002 mm) and to control a supply of compressed air so that a considerable force can be generated under precise control.

A typical flapper/nozzle system is shown in Figure 7.1. It comprises a flat strip of metal attached to the

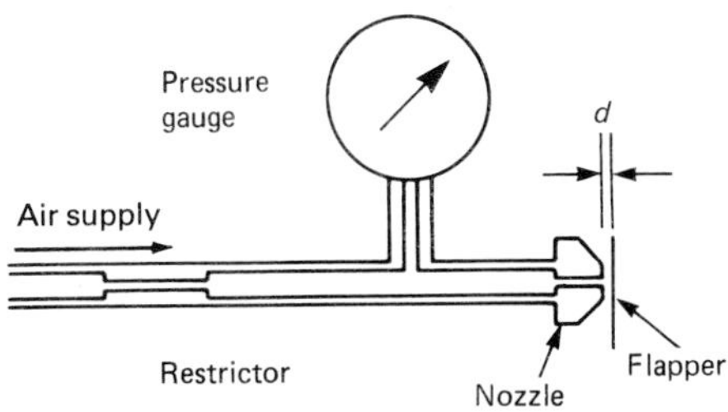

Figure 7.1 Typical flapper/nozzle system. (Most of the figures in this chapter are reproduced by courtesy of The Foxboro Company.)

device or member of which the relative motion is to be detected. This flapper is positioned so that when moved it covers or uncovers a 0.25 mm diameter hole located centrally in the 3 mm diameter flat surface of a truncated 90-degree cone. A supply of clean air, typically at 120 kPa, is connected via a restrictor and a 'T' junction to the nozzle. A pressure gauge connected at this 'T' junction would show that, with the nozzle covered by the flapper, the pressure approaches the supply pressure, but when the flapper moves away from the nozzle the pressure falls rapidly to a value determined by the relative values of the discharge characteristics of the nozzle and the restrictor, as shown in Figure 7.2.

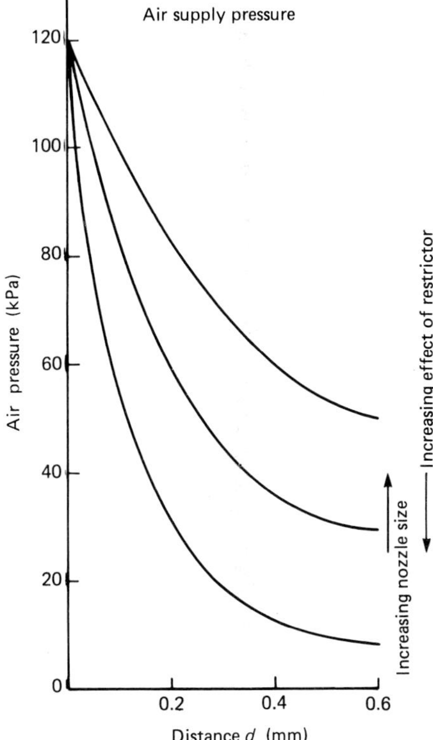

Figure 7.2 Relation between nozzle back pressure and flapper/nozzle distance.

For measurement purposes this change in pressure needs to be amplified, and this is effected by means of a pneumatic relay (which is equivalent to a pneumatic amplifier). In practice, it is convenient to incorporate the restrictor associated with the nozzle in the body of the relay, as shown in Figure 7.3. This figure also shows that the relay comprises two chambers isolated from each other by a flexible diaphragm which carries a cone and spigot that act as a valve to cover or uncover the exhaust port. The spigot acts against a small ball retained by the leaf spring so that it functions as a second valve which controls the flow of air from the supply to the output port.

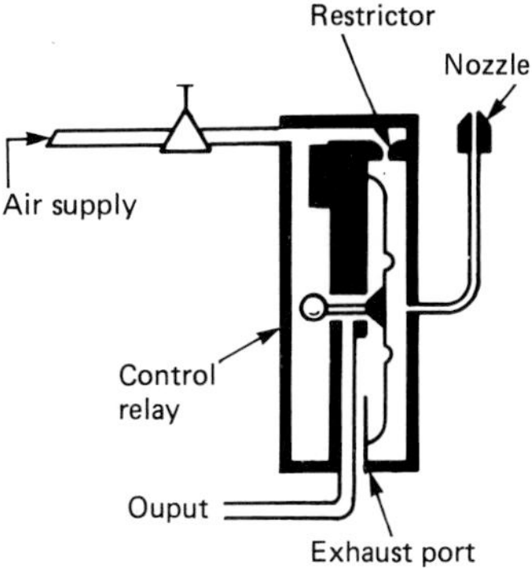

Figure 7.3 Pneumatic relay.

In operation, when the nozzle is covered the pressure in the associated chamber builds up, causing the conical valve to close the exhaust port and the ball valve to allow air to flow from the supply to the output port so that the output pressure rises.

When the nozzle is uncovered by movement of the flapper the flexible diaphragm moves so that the ball valve restricts the flow of air from the supply. At the same time the conical valve moves off its seat, opening the exhaust so that the output pressure falls.

With such a system the output pressure is driven from 20 to 100 kPa as a result of the relative movement between the flapper and nozzle of about 0.02 mm. Although the device has a non-linear character, this is relatively unimportant when it is included in the feedback loop of a measuring system.

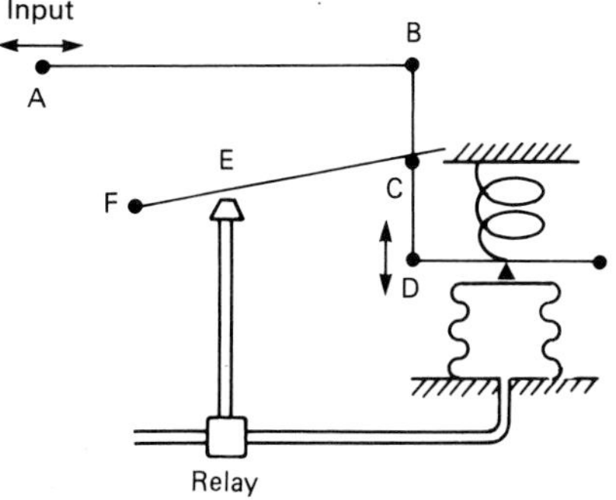

Figure 7.4 Basic pneumatic motion-balance system.

There are two basic schemes for utilizing the flapper/nozzle/relay system, namely the motion-balance and the force-balance systems. These are illustrated in Figures 7.4 and 7.5. Figure 7.4 shows a motion balance system in which the input motion is applied to point A on the lever AB. The opposite end (B) of this lever is pivoted to a second lever BCD which in turn has point D pivoted in a lever positioned by movement of the feedback bellows. At the centre (C) of the lever BD there is a spigot on which one end of the lever CEF is supported whilst it is pivoted at point F and has a flapper nozzle located at E. A horizontal displacement which causes A to move to the left is transmitted via B to C, and as a result the flapper at E moves off the nozzle so that the back pressure falls. This change is amplified by the relay so that the pressure in the bellows falls and the lever carrying the pivot D moves down until equilibrium is re-established. The output pressure is then proportional to the original displacement. By changing the inclination of the lever CEF the sensitivity or gain of the system may be changed.

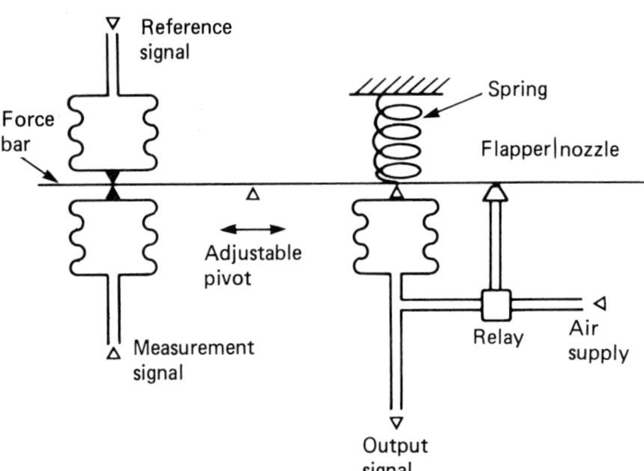

Figure 7.5 Basic pneumatic force-balance system.

Figure 7.5 illustrates a force-balance system. The measurement signal, in the form of a pressure, is applied to a bellows which is opposed by a similar bellows for the reference signal. The force difference applied to the lever supported on an adjustable pivot is opposed by a spring/bellows combination. Adjacent to the bellows is a flapper/nozzle sensor. In operation, if the measurement signal exceeds the reference signal the resultant force causes the force bar to rotate clockwise about the adjustable pivot so that the flapper moves closer to the nozzle, with the result that the pressure in the output bellows increases until equilibrium is re-established. The change in output pressure is then proportional to the change in the measurement signal.

7.3 Principal measurements

7.3.1 Introduction

Virtually all pneumatic measuring systems depend on a primary element such as an orifice plate, Bourdon tube, etc. to convert the physical parameter to be measured into either a force or a displacement which, in turn, can be sensed by some form of flapper/nozzle system or used directly to operate a mechanism such as an indicator, a recorder pen or a switch.

The measurements most widely used in the process industries are temperature, pressure, flow, level and density. In the following sections a description is given of the methods for implementing these measurements pneumatically, as opposed to describing the characteristics of the primary elements themselves. Also described are the pneumatic controllers which were evolved for the process industries and which are still very widely used.

7.3.2 Temperature

Filled thermal systems are used almost exclusively in pneumatic systems for temperature measurement and control. The sensing portion of the system comprises a bulb connected via a fine capillary tube to a spiral or helical Bourdon element or a bellows. When the bulb temperature rises, the increased volume of the enclosed fluid or its pressure is transmitted to the Bourdon element, which responds to the change by movement of its free end. This movement can be used directly to position a recording pen or an indicating pointer, either of which could also be coupled to a flapper/nozzle mechanism by a system of links and levers to actuate a pneumatic controller.

When a bellows is used to terminate the capillary the change in bulb temperature is converted into a force which, in turn, can be used to actuate a force-balance mechanism. Details of the materials used for filling the bulbs and their characteristics are given in Chapter 1 of Volume 2 of *Instrument Technology*.

In the motion balance systems the free end of the Bourdon tube is connected via adjustable links to a lever pivoted about the axis A in Figure 7.6. The free end of this lever bears on a second lever system pivoted about the axis B and driven by the feedback bellows. The free end of this second lever system is held in contact with a stem on a further lever system by a light spring. This latter lever is pivoted about the axis C and its free end is shaped to form the flapper of a flapper/nozzle system. The control relay associated with the flapper/nozzle system generates the output signal which is also applied to the feedback bellows.

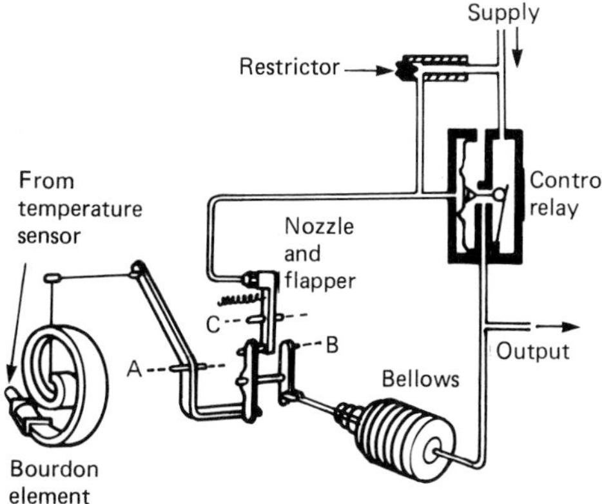

Figure 7.6 Motion-balance system for temperature measurement.

In operation, the links and levers are adjusted so that with the bulb held at the temperature corresponding to the lower range value the output signal is 20 kPa. If the measured temperature then rises, the lever pivoted at A moves in a clockwise direction (viewed from the left). In the absence of any movement of the bellows, this causes that associated lever pivoted about the axis C to rotate clockwise so that the flapper moves towards the nozzle. This, in turn, causes the nozzle back pressure to rise, a change which is amplified by the control relay, and this is fed back to the bellows so that the lever pivoted about the axis B moves until balance is restored. In this way, the change in the sensed temperature is converted into a change in the pneumatic output signal.

An example of the force-balance system is shown in Figure 7.7. There are two principal assemblies, namely the force-balance mechanism and the thermal system, which comprises the completely

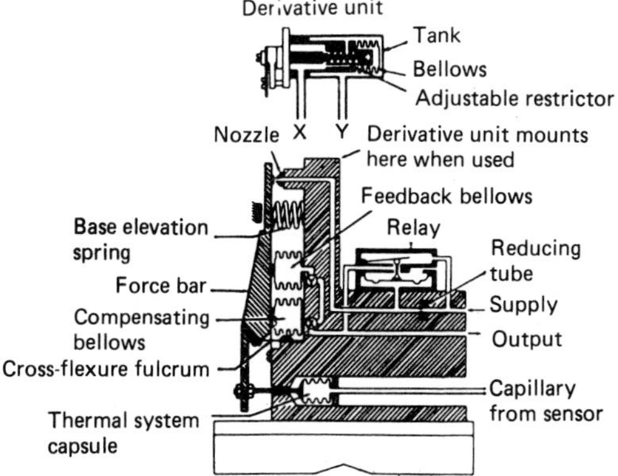

Figure 7.7 Force-balance system for temperature measurement.

sealed sensor and capillary assembly filled with gas under pressure. A change in temperature at the sensor causes a change in gas pressure. This change is converted by the thermal system capsule into a change in the force applied at the lower end of the force bar which, being pivoted on cross flexures, enables the force due to the thermal system to be balanced by combined forces developed by the compensating bellows, the feedback bellows and the base elevation spring. If the moment exerted by the thermal system bellows for the force exceeds the combined moments of the forces developed by the compensating bellows (which compensates the effect of ambient temperature at the transmitter), the feedback bellows (which develops a force proportional to the output signal) and the elevation spring (which provides means for adjusting the lower range value), the gap between the top of the force bar and the nozzle is reduced, causing the nozzle back pressure to rise. This change is amplified by the relay and applied to the feedback bellows so that the force on the force bar increases until balance is re-established. In this way, the forces applied to the force bar are held in balance so that the output signal of the transmitter is proportional to the measured temperature.

This type of temperature transmitter is suitable for measuring temperatures between 200 and 800 K, with spans from 25 to 300 K.

7.3.3 Pressure measurements

As explained in Volume 1, the majority of pressure measurements utilize a Bourdon tube, a diaphragm or a bellows (alone or operated in conjunction with a stable spring) as the primary elements which convert the pressure into a motion or a force. Both methods are used in pneumatic systems; those depending on motion use a balancing technique similar to that described in the previous section for temperature measurements, whilst those which operate on the force-balance principle utilize a mechanism that has wider application. It was initially developed for differential pressure measurements which, because they provide a common basis for measuring flow, level and density, have very wide application in industry. By selecting alternative primary elements the same force-balance mechanism can be used for measurement of gauge or absolute pressures. The basic arrangement of the mechanism is shown in Figure 7.8.

The force developed by the primary element is applied via a flexure to one end of the force bar which comprises two sections threaded so that they can be joined together with a thin circular diaphragm of cobalt–nickel alloy clamped in the joint.

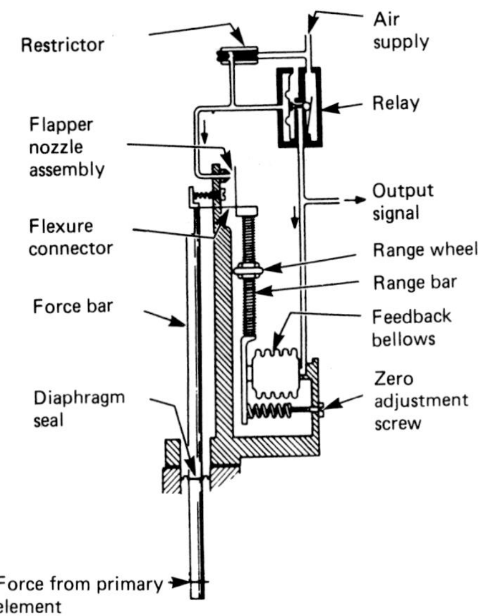

Figure 7.8 Basic arrangement of pneumatic force-balance mechanism.

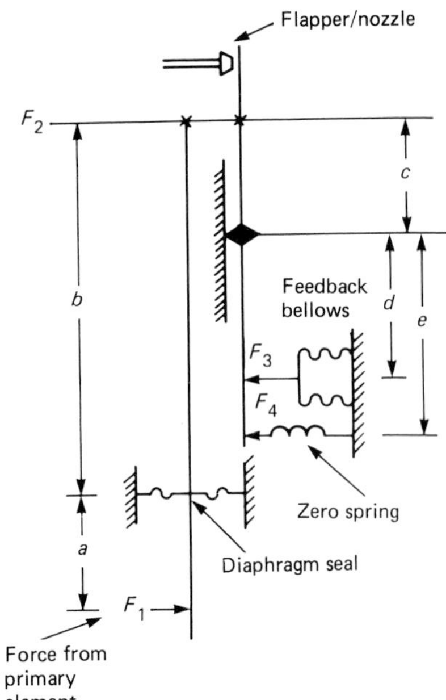

Figure 7.9 Diagram of forces involved in pneumatic force-balance mechanism.

This diaphragm serves as the pivot or flexure for the force bar as well as the seal between the process fluid and the force-balance mechanism, particularly in the differential pressure-measuring instruments.

The outer edge of the diaphragm seal is clamped between the body enclosing the primary element and the framework that supports the force-balance mechanism. This framework carries the zero adjustment spring, the feedback bellows, the pneumatic relay and the nozzle of the flapper/nozzle system.

At the lower end of the range bar is mounted the feedback bellows and zero spring, whilst at its upper end it carries the flapper and a flexure that connects it to the upper end of the force bar. The range bar is threaded so that the position of the range wheel (and hence the sensitivity of the system) can be varied. Figure 7.9 shows the diagram of forces for the mechanism.

In operation, force (F_1) from the primary element applied to the lower end of the force bar produces a moment (F_1a) about the diaphragm seal pivot which is transmitted to the upper end of the force bar where it becomes a force (F_2) applied via the flexural pivots and a transverse flexure connector to the upper end of the range bar. This force produces a moment (F_2c) about the range wheel, acting as a pivot, which is balanced by the combined moments produced by the forces F_3 and F_4 of the feedback bellows and zero spring, respectively.

Thus, at balance

$$F_1a = F_2b$$

and

$$F_2c = F_3d + F_4e$$

from which it follows that:

$$F_1 = \frac{bd}{ac} \cdot F_3 + \frac{be}{ac} \cdot F_4$$

By varying the position of the pivot on the range bar the ratio of F_1 to F_3 can be adjusted through a range of about 10 to 1. This provides the means for adjusting the span of an instrument.

The feedback loop is arranged so that when an increased force is generated by the primary element the resultant slight movement of the force bar causes the flapper to move closer to the nozzle so that its back pressure increases. This change is amplified by the relay and is applied to the bellows. As a result, the force that it applies to the range bar increases until a new equilibrium position is established and the various forces are balanced. Figure 7.10 illustrates the use of this force-balance mechanism in a gauge pressure transmitter if the low-pressure connection is open to the atmosphere or a high-range differential pressure transmitter if both high- and low-pressure signals are connected.

In this instrument the primary element is a bellows. Figure 7.11 shows essentially the same instrument but the bellows is evacuated and sealed on what was the low pressure side in the previous

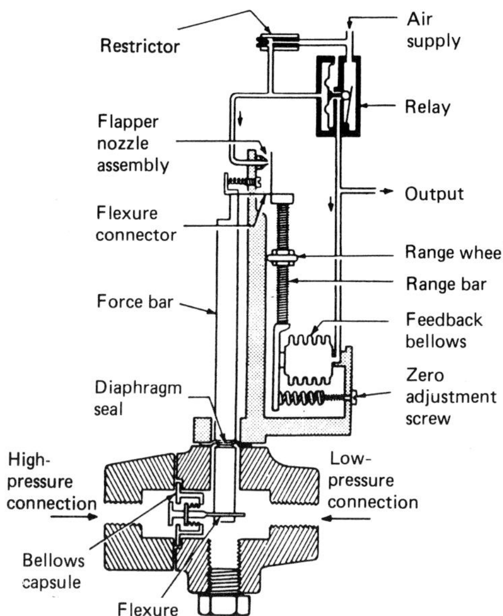

Figure 7.10 Force-balance mechanism incorporated into gauge pressure transmitter.

configuration, so that the instrument measures absolute pressure.

Figure 7.12 shows how the mechanism is used in a high-pressure transmitter in which the primary element is a Bourdon tube.

Figure 7.13 shows the use of the same mechanism attached to the differential pressure sensor which has become the most widely used form of pneumatic sensor.

The principal feature of the sensor is the diaphragm capsule shown in more detail in Figure 7.14. It comprises two identical corrugated diaphragms, welded at their perimeters to a back-up plate on which matching contours have been machined. At the centre, the two diaphragms are connected to a stem carrying the C-flexure by which the diaphragm is connected to the force bar. The small cavity between the diaphragms and the back-up plate is filled with silicone oil to provide damping.

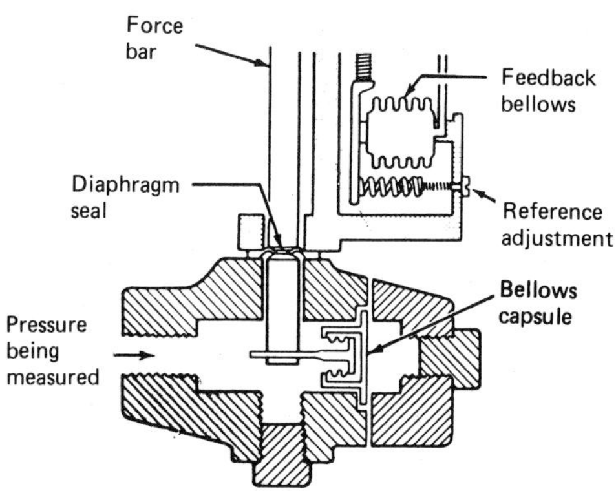

Figure 7.11 Force-balance mechanism incorporated into absolute pressure transmitter.

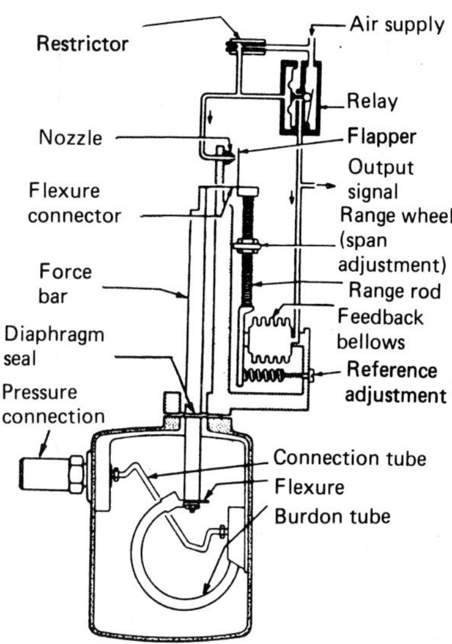

Figure 7.12 Force-balance mechanism incorporated into high-pressure transmitter incorporating a Bourdon tube.

If equal pressures are applied on either side of the capsule there is no resultant movement of the central stem. If, however, the force on one side is greater than that on the other, the resultant force is transmitted via the central stem to the C-flexure. If the force on one side greatly exceeds that on the other, then the diaphragm exposed to the higher pressure moves onto the matching contours of the back-up plate and is thereby protected from damage. This important feature has been a major factor in the successful widespread application of the differential pressure transmitter for measurement of many different process parameters, the most important being the measurement of flow in conjunction with orifice plates and the measurement of level in terms of hydrostatic pressures.

Figure 7.15 shows how the diaphragm capsule of the differential pressure transmitter is modified to convert it into an absolute pressure transmitter.

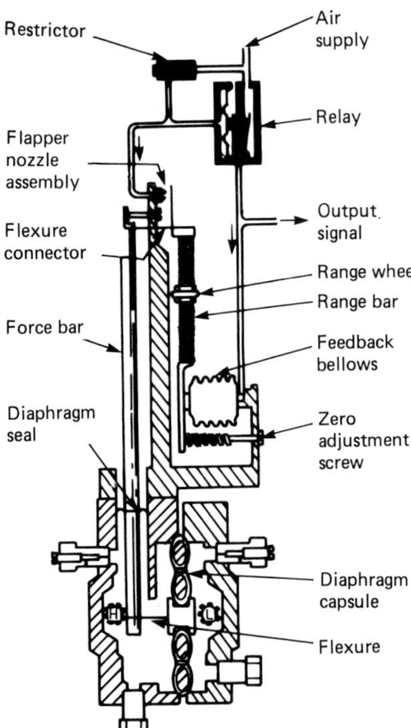

Figure 7.13 Force-balance mechanism incorporated into differential pressure transmitter.

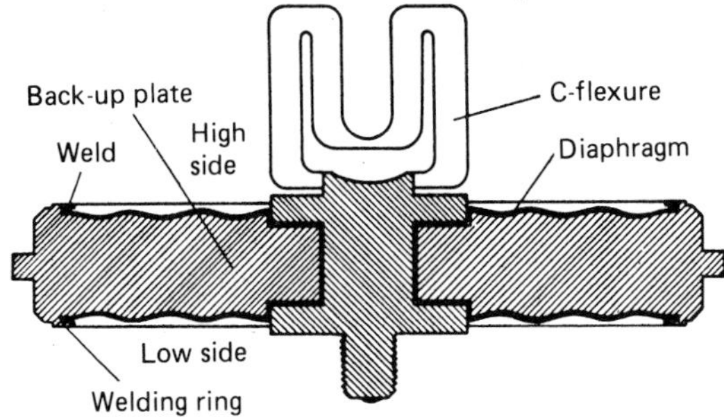

Figure 7.14 Construction of differential pressure sensor capsule.

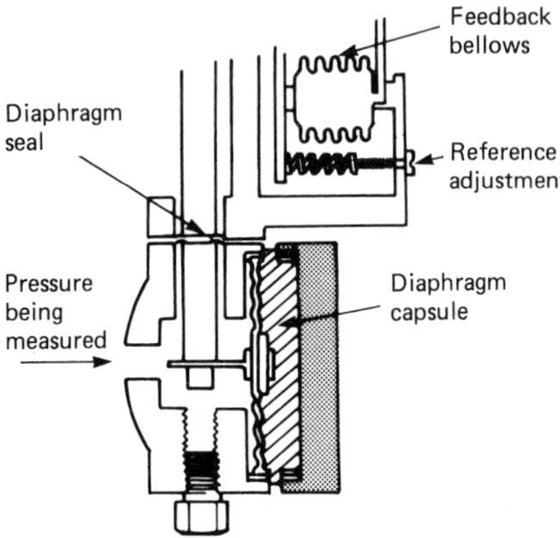

Figure 7.15 Modification of sensor capsule for absolute pressure measurements.

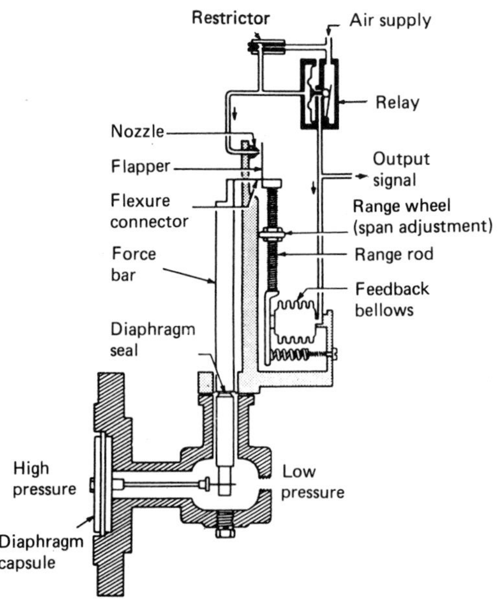

Figure 7.16 Force-balance mechanism incorporated into a flange-mounted level transmitter.

7.3.4 Level measurements

The diaphragm capsule and force balance mechanism can be adapted for measurement of liquid level. Figure 7.16 shows how it is mounted in a flange which, in turn, is fixed to the side of the vessel containing the liquid whose level is to be measured. If the tank is open then the low-pressure side of the capsule is also left open to the atmosphere. If, on the other hand, the measurement is to be made on a liquid in an enclosed tank, then the pressure of the atmosphere above the liquid must be applied to the rear of the capsule via the low-pressure connection. In operation, the hydrostatic pressure applied to the diaphragm being proportional to the head of liquid produces a force which is applied to the lower end of the force bar.

The same type of pneumatic force balance mechanism is used to measure this force and so generate an output signal which is directly proportional to the liquid level.

7.3.5 Buoyancy measurements

The same mechanism can be adapted to function as a buoyancy transmitter to measure either liquid density or liquid level, according to the configuration of the float which is adopted. This is shown in Figure 7.17 and further details of this method are given in Chapter 8 of Volume 1 of *Instrument Technology*.

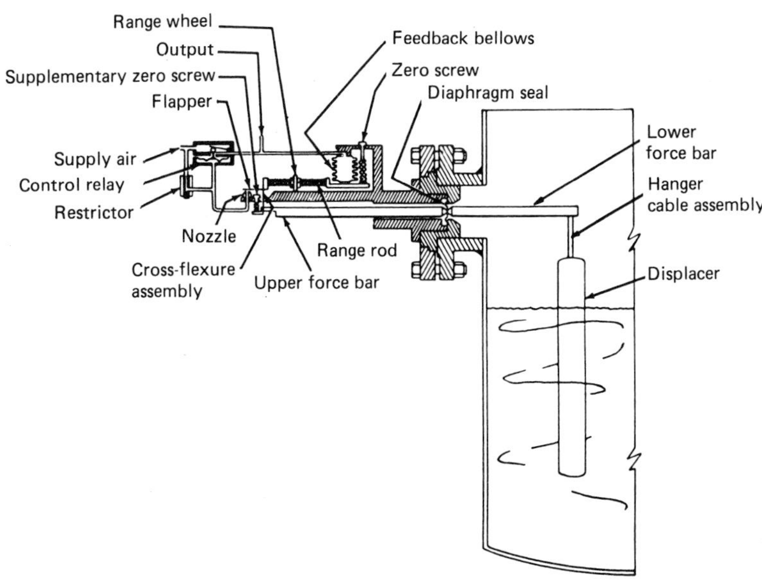

Figure 7.17 Force-balance mechanism incorporated into a buoyancy transmitter.

7.3.6 Target flow transmitter

This transmitter combines in a single unit both a primary element and a force-balance transmitter mechanism. As shown in Figure 7.18, the latter is essentially the same force-balance mechanism that is

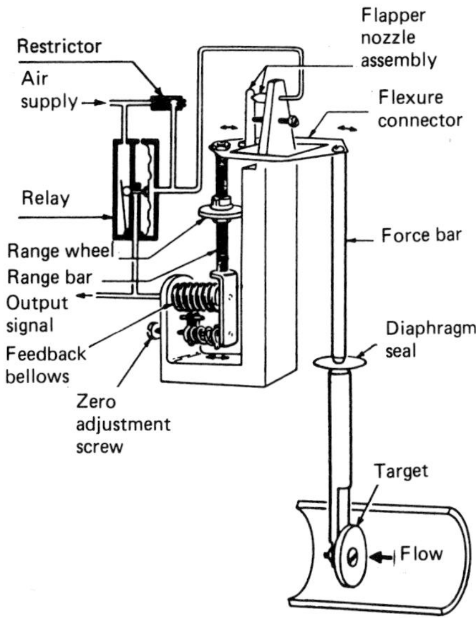

Figure 7.18 Force-balance mechanism incorporated into a target flow transmitter.

used in the other pneumatic transmitters described previously. The primary element is a disc-shaped target fixed to the end of the force bar and located centrally in the conduit carrying the process liquid.

As explained in Chapter 1 of Volume 1, the force on the target is the difference between the upstream and downstream surface pressure integrated over the area of the target. The square root of this force is proportional to the flow rate.

7.3.7 Speed

A similar force-balance technique can be used to generate a pneumatic signal proportional to speed, as shown in Figure 7.19. As the transmitter input shaft rotates, the permanent magnet attached to it generates a magnetomotive force. This force tends to cause the non-magnetic alloy disc to rotate in the same direction. Since the disc is connected to the flapper by means of flexures, any rotation of the disc causes a corresponding movement of the flapper, thus changing the clearance between the flapper and the nozzle.

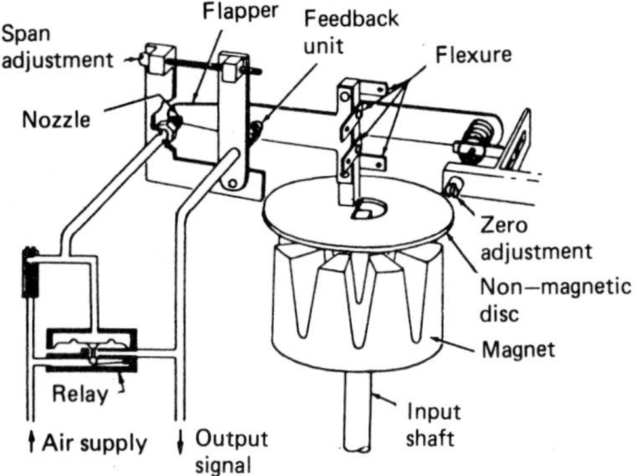

Figure 7.19 Modified force-balance mechanism incorporated into a speed transmitter.

As the flapper/nozzle relationship changes, the output pressure from the relay to the feedback unit changes until the force at the feedback unit balances the rotational force.

The output pressure which establishes the force balance is the transmitted pneumatic signal and is proportional to the speed of rotation. It may be used to actuate the pneumatic receiver in an indicator, recorder or controller.

7.4 Pneumatic transmission

In relatively simple control systems it is usually possible to link the primary sensing element directly to the controller mechanism and to locate this reasonably close to the final control element. However, when the process instrumentation is centralized, the primary sensing elements are arranged to operate in conjunction with a mechanism that develops a pneumatic signal for transmission between the point of measurement and the controller, which is usually mounted in a control room or sheltered area.

A standard for these transmission signals has been developed and is applied almost universally, with only small variations that arise as a result of applying different units of measure. If the lower range value is represented by a pressure P then the upper range value is represented by a pressure $5P$ and the span by $4P$. Furthermore, it is customary to arrange the nominal pressure of the air supplied to the instrument to be between $6.5P$ and $7.0P$.

In SI units, the zero or lower range value of the measurement is represented by a pressure of 20 kPa the upper range value by a pressure of 100 kPa and the span therefore by a change in pressure of 80 kPa. The corresponding Imperial units are 3 psi, 15 psi and 12 psi, whilst the corresponding metric units are 0.2 kg/cm^2 (0.2 bar), 1.0 kg/cm^2 (1.0 bar) and 0.8 kg/cm^2 (0.8 bar). (1 bar = 100 kPa = 14.7 psi.)

If a change in measured value occurs, this is sensed by the transmitter and its output pressure increases accordingly. When the transmitter is remote from the controller and connected to it by an appreciable length of tubing, there is a finite delay before the change of pressure generated at the transmitter reaches the controller. In the case of an increased signal, this delay is governed by the

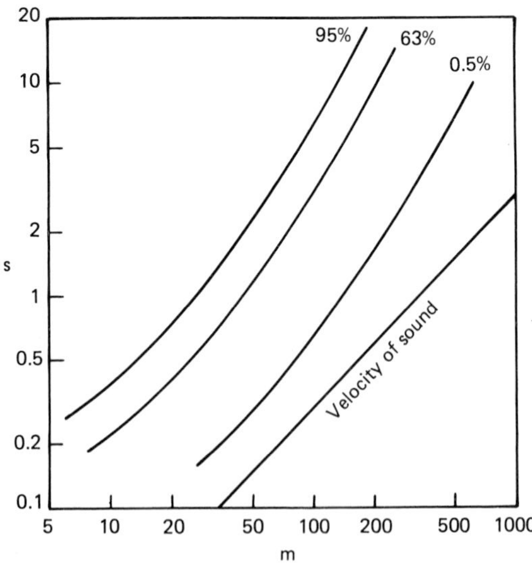

Figure 7.20 Time delay in response to step change of pneumatic pressure applied to various lengths of tube.

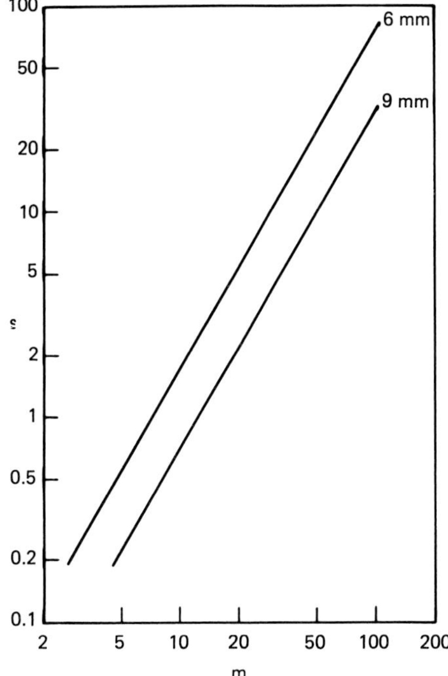

Figure 7.21 Time delay in response to a constant rate of change of pneumatic pressure applied to various lengths of tube.

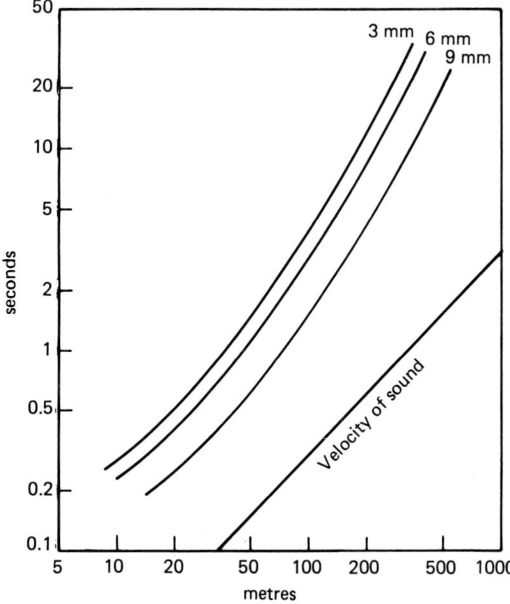

Figure 7.22 Time delay for 63.2 per cent response to step change of applied pressure for various lengths of tube.

magnitude of the change, the capability of the transmitter to supply the necessary compressed air to raise the pressure throughout the transmission line, the rate at which the change can be propagated along the line and finally the capacity of the receiving element.

A rigorous description of the overall characteristics of a pneumatic transmission system is beyond the scope of this book, but Figures 7.20–7.22 show the magnitude of the effects for reasonably representative conditions.

Figure 7.20 shows the time taken for the output to reach 95, 63 and 0.5 per cent of its ultimate value following a step change from 20 kPa to 100 kPa at the input according to the length of tube. Figure 7.21 shows the time lag versus tubing length when the input is changing at a constant rate. Figure 7.22 shows the time delay for a 63 per cent response to a step change of 20 to 100 kPa versus tubing length for 9 mm, 6 mm and 3 mm tubing.

7.5 Pneumatic controllers

7.5.1 Motion-balance controllers

Many of the early pneumatic controllers were based on the principle of motion balance because the sensor associated with the primary element produced a mechanical movement, rather than a force, to provide the signal proportional to the measured quantity. The technique is still widely used, and the Foxboro Model 43A, an example of a modern implementation of the concept embodying several variations of the control actions, is described in the following sections.

In most of these controllers a spring-loaded bellows or a Bourdon element converts the incoming signal into a motion. This motion is used directly to drive a pointer so that the measured value is displayed on a scale. On the same scale there is a second adjustable pointer the position of which identifies the set point or desired value for the controller action. For the majority of applications the required action is proportional plus integral, and is derived as follows.

As shown in Figure 7.23, a mechanical linkage between the two pointers is arranged so that movement of its midpoint is proportional to the difference between the measured value and the set point. This difference is applied horizontally at one end of the proportioning lever which is pivoted at its centre to a flat spring. A bellows connected to the pneumatic output of the controller and opposed by the integral action bellows applies a force to the flat spring, with the result that the proportioning lever is positioned virtually according to the magnitude of the output signal combined with the integral action.

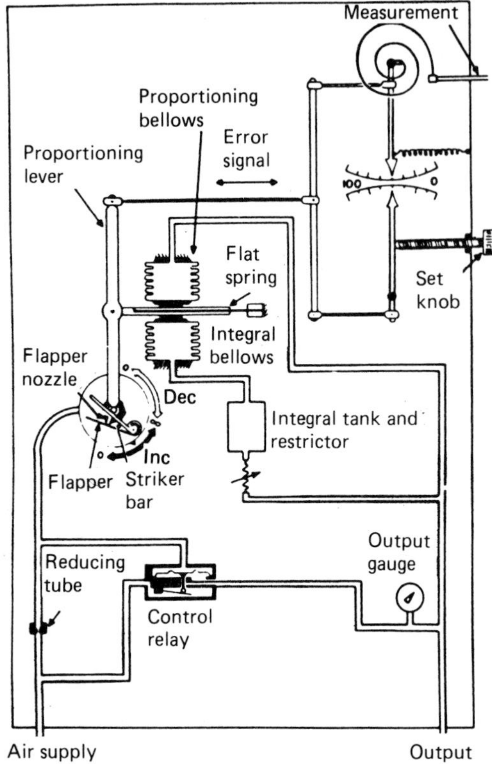

Figure 7.23 Basic configuration of pneumatic motion-balance two-term controller.

The lower free end of the proportioning lever bears on the striker bar of the flapper/nozzle system, and in so doing causes the flapper to cover or uncover the nozzle. Thus if the measurement exceeds the set point, the proportioning lever moves to the left (in the figure) and, being pivoted centrally, its lower free end moves to the right, off the striker bar, with the result that the flapper covers the nozzle. This causes the nozzle back pressure to increase, a change that is amplified by the control relay to a value that becomes the instrument output signal and is also applied to the proportional bellows, causing the proportioning lever to move downwards until it impinges again on the striker bar which, in turn, moves the flapper off the nozzle. Consequently the nozzle back pressure falls and the change, after being amplified by the control relay, is applied to the proportioning bellows as well as to the instrument output and via the integral tank and restrictor to the integral bellows. In this way any residual error between the measured value and the desired value is integrated and the output gradually adjusted until the error is eliminated.

This type of control action meets the majority of operational requirements. However, in a few instances proportional action alone is sufficient, in which case the integral bellows are replaced by a spring and the integral tank and restrictor are omitted.

On the other hand, there are a few instances where it is desirable to enhance the performance further by including derivative action, i.e. adding to the output signal a component that is proportional to the rate of change of the error signal. This is implemented by modifying the proportional bellows system as shown in Figure 7.24. In operation, a sudden change in the measurement signal actuates the flapper/nozzle mechanism so that the output signal changes. This change is fed back to the proportional bellows directly by the derivative mechanism, but the derivative restrictor causes the transient signal to die away so that the pressure in the proportioning bellows becomes equal to the

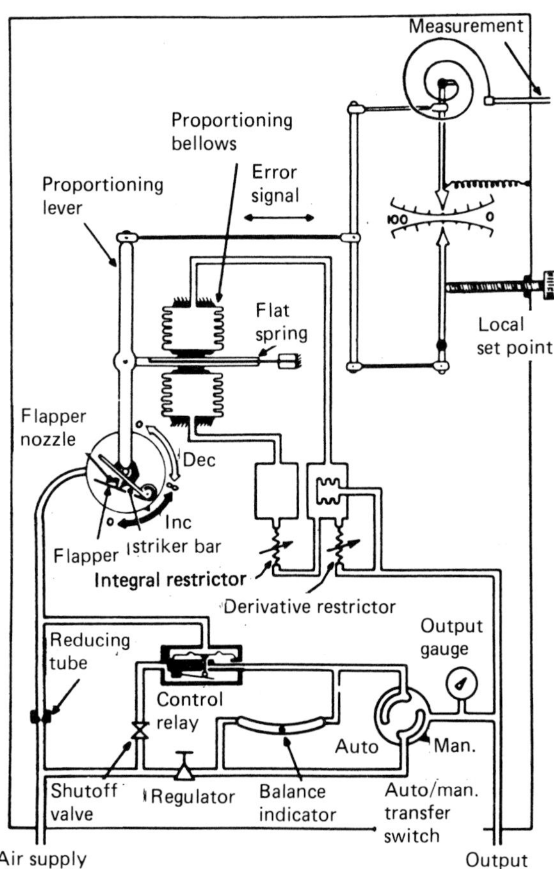

Figure 7.24 Basic configuration of pneumatic motion-balance three-term controller with auto/manual balance feature.

output pressure. In the meantime, the integral action builds up to reduce any difference between the measured value and the set point.

A further feature available in the instrument is the switch for transferring the controller from manual to automatic operation and vice versa. The switch itself is a simple two-way changeover device, but associated with it are a regulator and a sensitive balance indicator, comprising a metal ball mounted in a curved glass tube.

When it is desired to transfer the control loop from automatic to manual operation the regulator is adjusted until the ball in the balance indicator is positioned centrally to show that the regulator pressure has been set equal to the controller output. The process can then be transferred from automatic to manual control without imposing any transient disturbance. The reverse procedure is applied when the process has to be transferred from manual to automatic control, except that in this instance the set point control is adjusted to balance the controller output signal against the manually set value.

Other modes of operation which are available include differential gap action (also known as on/off control with a neutral zone), automatic shutdown (which is used to shut down a process when the measured value reaches a predetermined limit), on/off control (which is the simplest configuration of the instrument), remote pneumatic set (in which the manual set point control is replaced by an equivalent pneumatically driven mechanism) and batch operation (in which provision is made for avoiding saturation of the integral action circuit during the interval between successive batch process sequences). However, these configurations are rare compared with the simple proportional and proportional plus integral controllers.

7.5.2 Force-balance controllers

The Foxboro Model 130 Series of controllers serves to illustrate the method of operation of modern pneumatic force-balance controllers. The basic mechanism of the control unit is shown in Figure 7.25. There are four bellows, one each for the set point, measurement, proportional feedback and integral feedback, which bear on a floating disc with two bellows on each side of a fulcrum whose angular position can be varied. In operation, the forces applied via each bellows multiplied by the respective distances from the fulcrum are held in balance by operation of a conventional flapper/nozzle system which generates the pneumatic output signal.

If the angular position of the fulcrum is set so that it is directly above the proportional feedback bellows and the reset bellows (as shown in Figure 7.26(a)), then the unit functions as an on/off

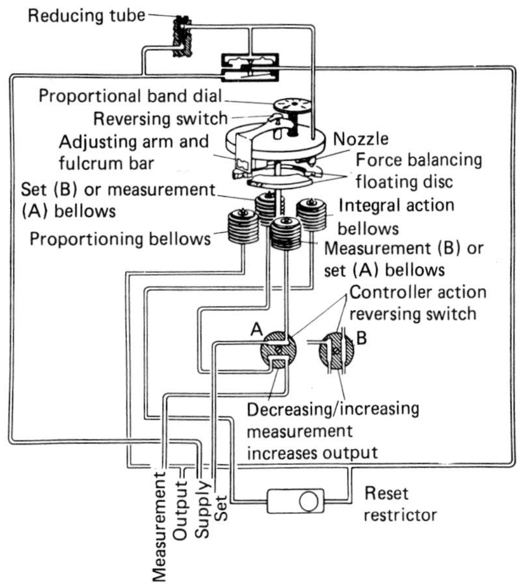

Figure 7.25 Basic mechanism of force-balance pneumatic controller.

controller. The slightest increase in measurement signal above the set point signal causes the nozzle to be covered so that output signal rises to the supply pressure. Any decrease in the measurement signal below the set point signal uncovers the nozzle so that the output signal falls to the zero level.

If the adjustable fulcrum is moved to the position shown in Figure 7.26(b), the proportional band is 25 per cent (or the gain is 4) (a/b = 1/4). If the measurement signal increases, the flapper/nozzle will be covered so that the output pressure rises until balance is restored. This will occur when the output pressure has increased by a factor of four (if the integral action is disregarded).

If the fulcrum is adjusted to the position shown in Figure 7.26(c), the proportional band is 400 per cent (or the gain is 0.25) (a/b = 4), then an increase in the measurement signal causes the flapper/nozzle to be covered so that the output pressure also rises until balance is restored. This will occur when the change in output pressure is one quarter that of the change in measurement signal.

Referring again to Figure 7.26 (b), if the measurement signal increases, so does the pressure in the output bellows by a factor of four. However, this change of output signal is applied via a restrictor to the reset bellows, which acts on the same side of the fulcrum. Thus as the pressure in the reset bellows rises, the output signal must rise proportionally more to restore balance. A difference in

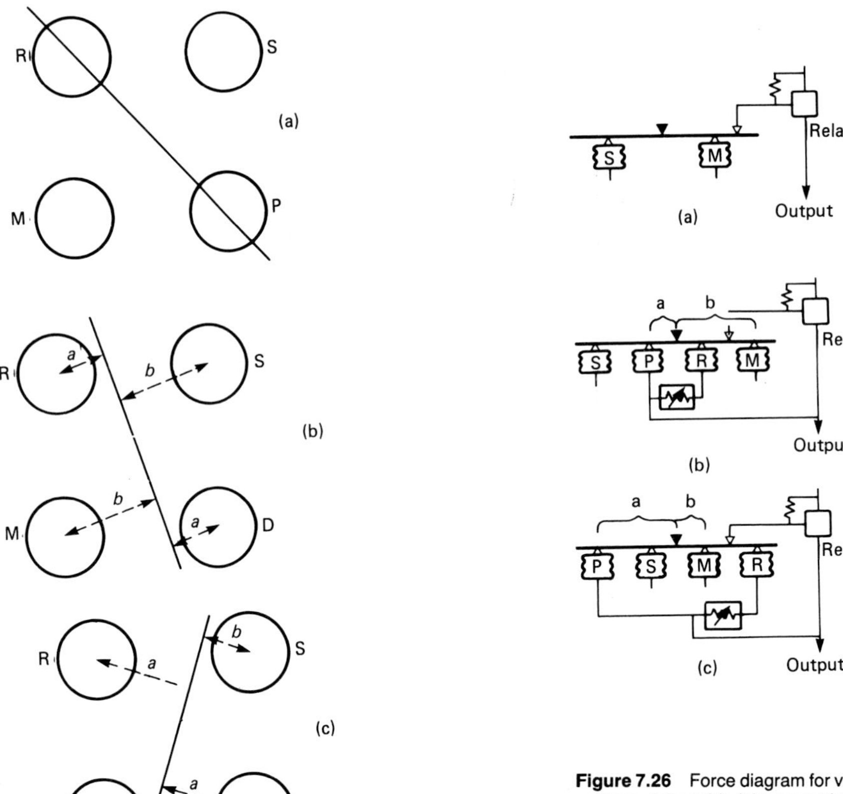

Figure 7.26 Force diagram for various controller settings. Adjustable fulcrum set for (a) on–off control action, (b) 25 per cent proportional band or (c) 400 per cent proportional band.

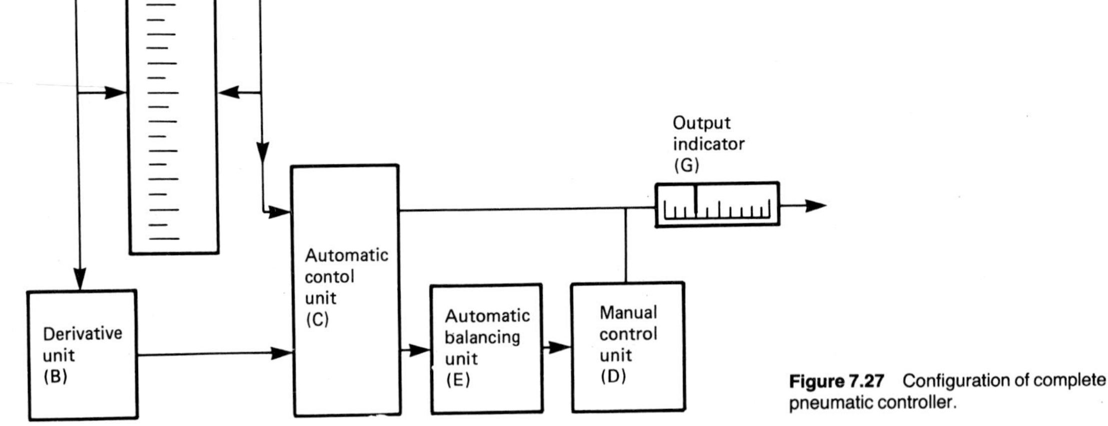

Figure 7.27 Configuration of complete pneumatic controller.

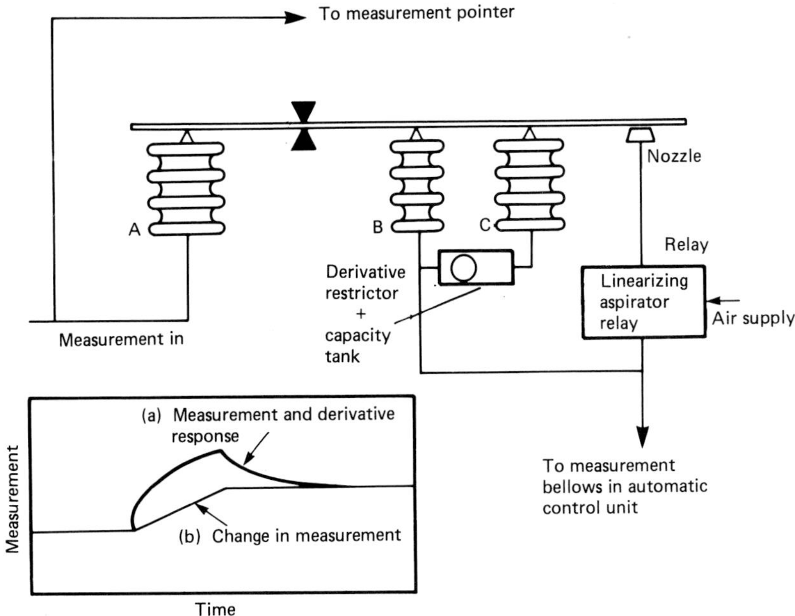

Figure 7.28 Basic mechanism of derivative function generation.

pressure then exists between the proportional bellows and the reset bellows until the process reacts to the controller output and reduces the measurement signal. This, in turn, reduces the pressure in the proportional bellows until the difference is eliminated. The reset action continues so long as there is a difference between the measurement and set point, and hence a difference between the reset and proportional bellows.

The configuration of the complete controller shown in Figure 7.27 is centred around the automatic control unit. The manual set point is adjusted by a knob in the front panel of the instrument. It drives a pointer on the scale and operates a mechanism that generates a proportional pressure to be applied to the automatic control unit.

The local/remote set point mechanism includes a receiver bellows which drives a second pointer to indicate the received value of the set point. It includes a switch which allows either the local or remote signal to be selected (Figure 7.27). The derivative unit is actuated from the measurement signal only and is not affected by changes of set point. As shown in Figure 7.28, it comprises a further force balance mechanism in which the moment generated by the signal to the measurement bellows A is balanced by the combined moments generated by two further bellows, one (C) arranged to generate a substantially larger moment than the other (B).

In steady conditions, the moment due to bellows A is equal to the combined moments of bellows B and C. Any increase in the measurement signal disturbs the balance, with the result that the relative position of the flapper/nozzle is reduced and the output of the linear aspirator relay rises. This signal is applied not only to the measurement bellows in the automatic control unit but also to bellows B and C.

However, the supply to bellows C passes through a restrictor so that, initially, balance is restored by the force generated by the bellows B alone. Subsequently, the force generated by bellows C rises and the effect is compensated by a fall in the output signal. After a time determined by the value of the restrictor, the pressures in bellows B and C become equal and they are then also equal to the pressure in bellows A. Thus, as a result of the transient, the effective measurement signal to the controller is modified by an amount proportional to the rate of change of the incoming signal, thereby providing the derivative controller action.

At the same time the full air supply pressure is applied via restrictors to chambers C and B so that the diaphragm takes up a position where the air vented to the atmosphere through the nozzle is reduced to a very low value.

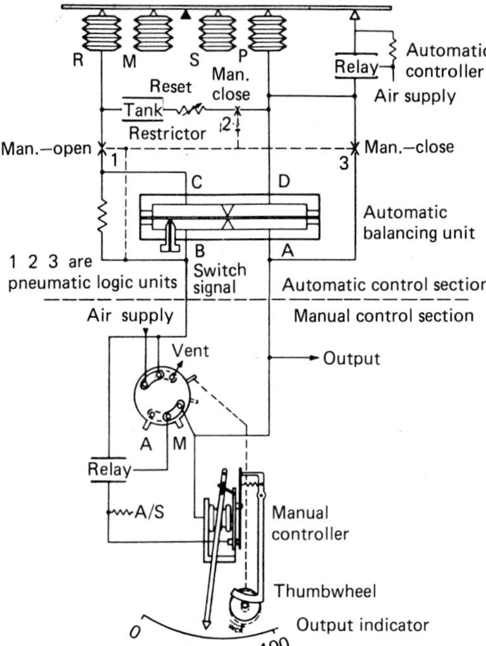

Figure 7.29 Manual-to-automatic transfer.

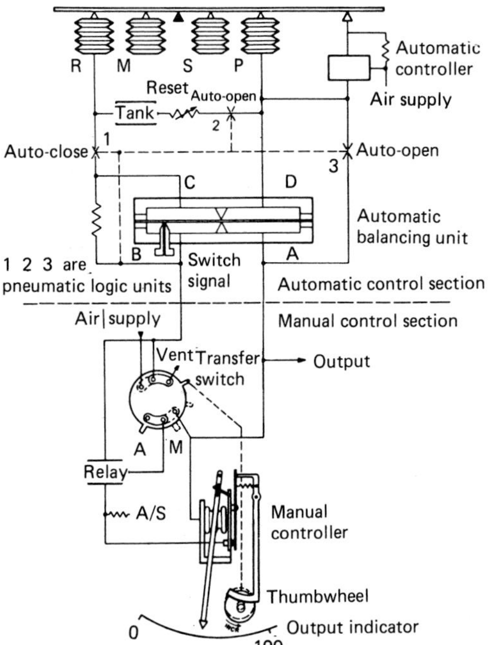

Figure 7.30 Automatic-to-manual transfer.

7.5.2.1 Automatic manual transfer switch

The design of previous pneumatic controllers has been such that, before transferring the control function from automatic to manual operation or vice versa, it is necessary to balance the two output signals manually, otherwise the process would be subjected to a 'bump', which may well cause unacceptable transient conditions.

To avoid this manual balancing operation, a unit has been devised and incorporated as a basic feature of the instrument. It is known as the automatic balancing unit, and, as shown in Figures 7.29 and 7.30, consists essentially of a chamber divided into four separate compartments isolated from each other by a floppy diaphragm pivoted at the centre. One of the chambers includes a nozzle through which air can escape slowly in normal operation as a result of the relative proximity of the diaphragm to the nozzle. When the position of the diaphragm moves away from the nozzle the flow of air increases and vice versa.

The interconnection of the unit when the controller is set in the manual operation mode is shown in Figure 7.29. In this mode, the manual controller generates the output signal which is also applied to the 'A' chamber in the automatic balancing unit. If the controller were in the automatic mode this same signal would be generated by the force balance unit operating in conjunction with the relay, in which case it would pass via the reset restrictor and tank to the reset bellows, but in the manual mode both these connections are closed by pneumatic logic switches.

Referring now to chamber D in the automatic balancing unit, this is connected directly to the proportional bellows (P) in the force-balance unit and so is held at that pressure. Any difference between the pressure in chambers A and D causes the floppy diaphragm to move with respect to the nozzle and so modify the pressure in chamber B which (in manual mode) is supplied via a restrictor. Thus as the output signal is changed by adjustment of the manual controller, the pressure in chamber A varies accordingly, causing the position of the floppy diaphragm to change. This, in turn, alters the rate at which air escapes via the nozzle from chamber B. This change is transferred via the restrictor to both chamber C and the reset bellows R in the force-balance unit so that the latter causes the pressure in its output bellows P to change until balance is restored through its normal *modus operandi*.

However, this same signal is also applied to chamber D, so that, in effect, the pressure in the proportional bellows P continuously follows that set by the manual controller. Consequently, when the

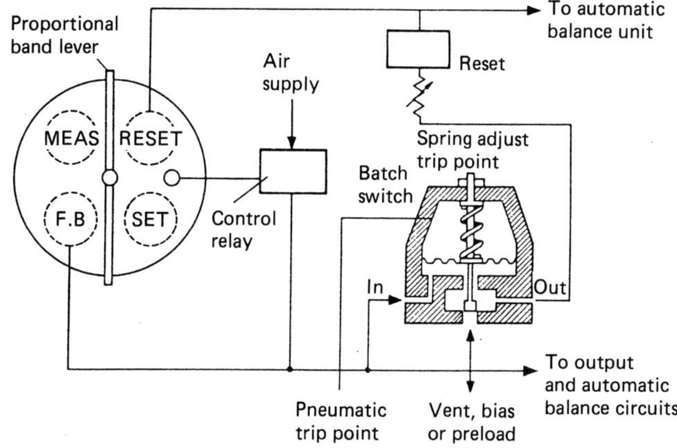

Figure 7.31 Functional diagram of batch-switch system. (*Notes*: (1) Bellows are beneath circular plate, nozzle is above; (2) an increase in measurement causes a decrease in output.

overall operation is transferred from manual to automatic, the force-balance control unit will have previously driven its own output signal to the value set by the Manual Controller so that the process is not subjected to a transient disturbance.

Before the controller action is transferred from automatic to manual operation the mechanism in the manual controller will have been receiving the output signal. Therefore the manual control lever is continually driven to a position corresponding to the output signal so that it is always ready for the controller to be transferred from automatic to manual control.

When the transfer switch is operated, the thumbwheel becomes engaged so that the output signal is now generated by the manual controller instead of the force-balance automatic controller. Prior to this, the automatic controller output signal is applied via the pneumatic logic switch to both chambers A and D in the automatic balancing unit so that half of the unit does not apply any moment.

7.5.2.2 Batch operation

When the controller is used to control a batch process or one in which the controller is held in the quiescent condition for an appreciable time it is necessary to include an additional feature which prevents saturation of the integral action that would otherwise occur because the measured value is held below the set point. (This is sometimes known as reset or integral wind-up.) When the process is restarted after being held in the quiescent state, the measured value overshoots the set point unless the normal *modus operandi* of the reset action is modified.

The modification involves inclusion of a batch switch, which, as shown in Figure 7.31, is essentially a pressure switch actuated by the output signal from the controller but with the trip point set by a spring or by an external pneumatic signal. While the controller is functioning as a controller, the batch switch has no effect, but when the process is shut down and the measurement signal moves outside the proportional band, the batch switch is tripped, whereupon it isolates the controller output from the reset bellows which is vented to atmosphere.

When the measurement returns within the proportional band the batch switch resets and the integral action immediately becomes operative in the normal manner.

7.6 Signal conditioning

7.6.1 Integrators

The most frequent requirement for integrators in pneumatic systems is to convert the signal from head-type flowmeters into direct reading or count of flow units. Since head-type flowmeters generate signals that are proportional to the square of flow rate, the integrator must extract the square root before totalizing the flow signal. In operation, the Foxboro Model 14A Integrator accepts a standard pneumatic signal, proportional to 0–100 per cent of differential pressure from a flow transmitter, which is applied to the integrator receiver bellows A in Figure 7.32. The force exerted by the bellows positions a force bar B in relation to a nozzle C. With an increase in differential pressure, the force bar approaches the nozzle and the resulting back pressure at the relay regulates the flow of air to drive the turbine rotor E. As the rotor revolves, the weights F, which are mounted on a cross-flexure assembly G on top of the rotor, develop a centrifugal force. This force feeds back through the thrust pin H to balance the force exerted on the force bar by the bellows.

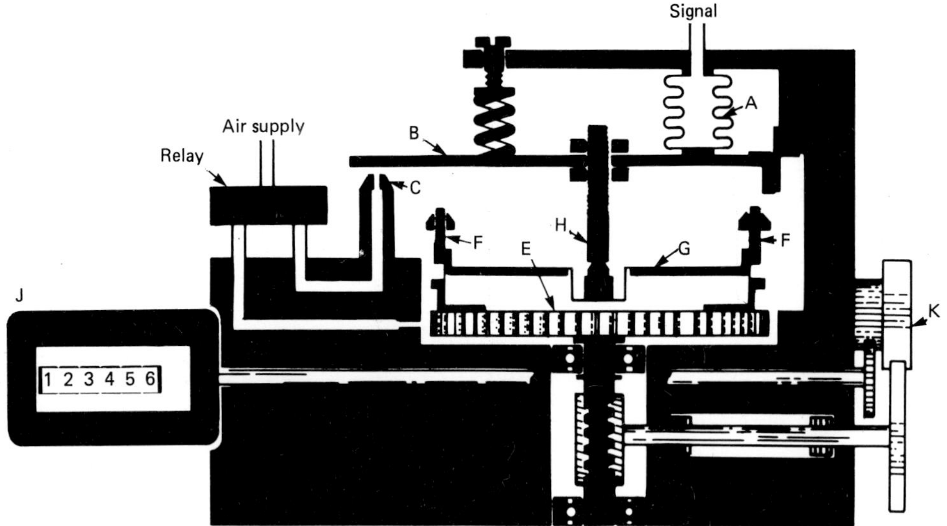

Figure 7.32 Functional diagram of pneumatic integrator.

The centrifugal force is proportional to the square of the turbine speed. This force balances the signal pressure which, for head-type flowmeters, is proportional to the square root of the flow rate. Therefore, turbine speed is directly proportional to flow and the integrator count, which is a totalization of the number of revolutions of the turbine rotor, is directly proportional to the total flow.

The turbine rotor is geared directly to counter J through gearing K. Changes in flow continuously produce changes in turbine speed to maintain a continuous balance of forces.

7.6.2 Analog square root extractor

The essential components of the square root extractor are shown in Figure 7.33, whilst Figure 7.34 shows the functional diagram. The input signal is applied to the A bellows and creates a force which disturbs the position of the nozzle with respect to the force arm. If the signal increases, the force arm is driven closer to the nozzle so that the back pressure increases. This change is amplified by the relay and its output is applied to both the C bellows and the B diaphragm.

Because the flexure arm is restrained so that the end remote from the flexure can only move along an arc, the combined effect of forces B and C is to drive the force arm away from the nozzle. This causes the nozzle back pressure to fall, which, in turn, reduces forces B and C until balance is restored.

Consideration of the vector force diagram shows that

$$\tan\theta = \frac{A}{B} \text{ or } B\tan\theta = A$$

For small changes, $\tan\theta$ is approximately equal to θ. Hence $B\theta = A$. Because (1) force A is proportional to the input signal, (2) force B is proportional to the

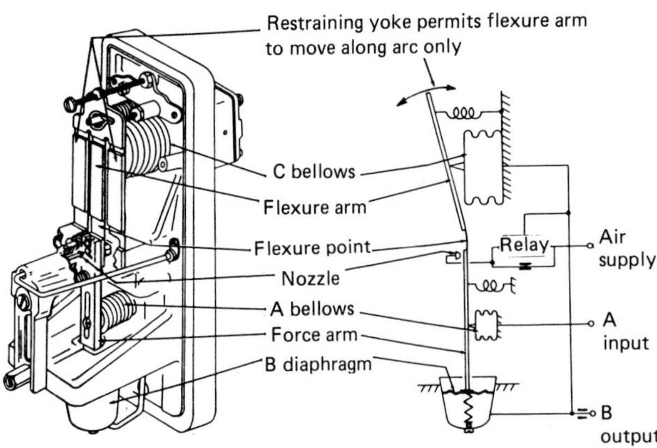

Figure 7.33 Functional diagram of pneumatic analog square root extractor.

output signal and (3) the position of the flexure arm to establish the angle θ is proportional to the force C, it follows that $B \times C \propto A$. As the bellows C is internally connected to B it follows that $B^2 \propto A$ or $B \propto \sqrt{A}$.

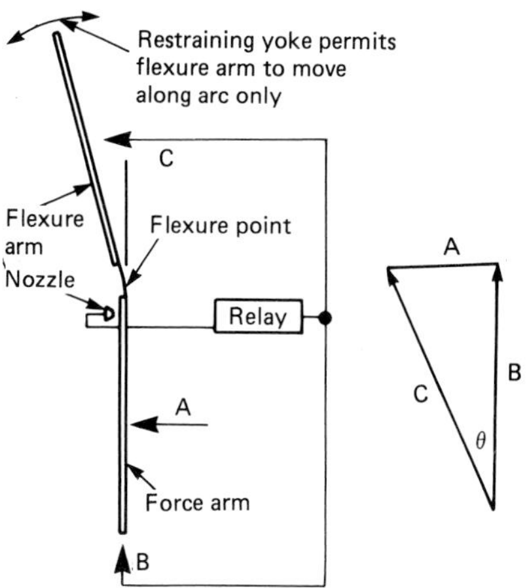

Figure 7.34 Force diagram for analog square root extractor.

7.6.3 Pneumatic summing unit and dynamic compensator

There are numerous process control systems which require two or more analog signals to be summed algebraically, and feed-forward control systems require lead/lag and impulse functions to be generated. The force-balance mechanism of the controller can be adapted to serve these functions. Figure 7.35 represents the arrangement of the bellows with respect to the fulcrum. It can be seen that with the gain set at unity (i.e. $a = b$) the two signals to be summed applied to the A and B bellows, respectively, the P and C bellows connected in parallel and supplied with air from the relay (which also supplies the output signal), then the output signal will be the average of the two input signals. If summing of the input signals is required, then only either the P or C bellows should be used. Similarly, signals may be subtracted by applying them to the A or B and C bellows, in which case the output is taken from the P bellows. In all these arrangements, the positioning of the fulcrum allows a constant to be introduced into the equation.

To generate a lead/lag, the mechanism is arranged as shown in Figure 7.36. The input signal is applied to the A bellows and the B and C bellows are connected together and supplied via a restriction and capacity tank from the P bellows, which, in common with the output, is supplied by the relay. As shown in Figure 7.37, the response of the system is determined by the setting of the gain and the restrictor.

Figure 7.38 shows the arrangement of the mechanism which generates an impulse response. The input signal is applied to bellows B, bellows P is

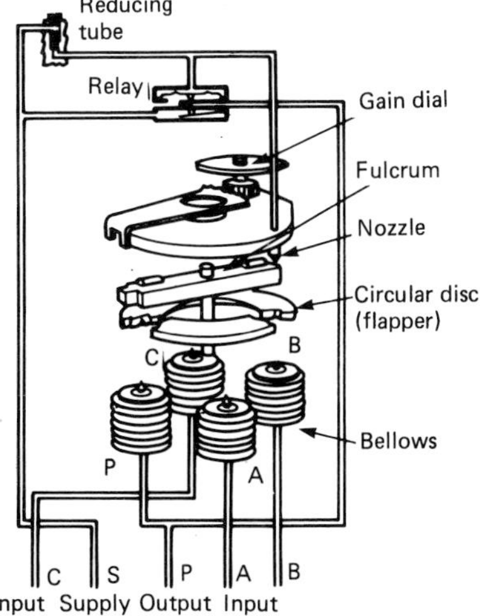

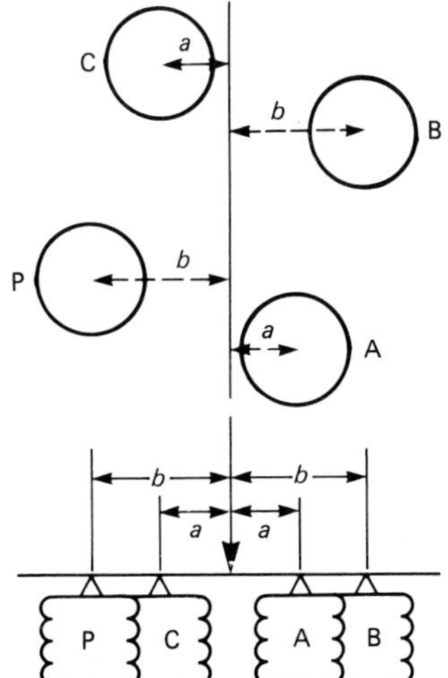

Figure 7.35 Basic configuration of pneumatic summing unit and dynamic compensator and force diagram.

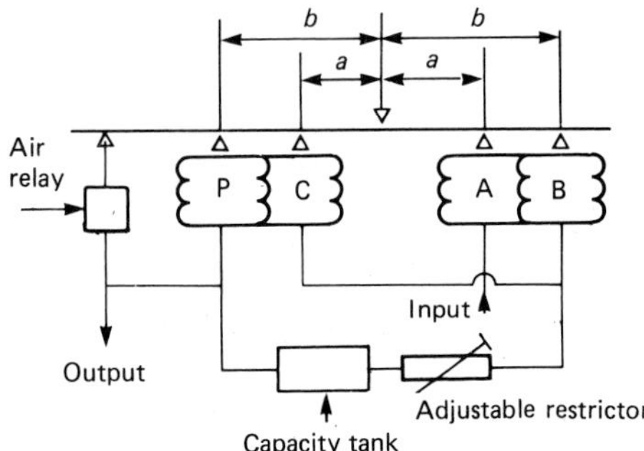

Figure 7.36 Force diagram for lead/lag unit.

connected to bellows B via a restrictor and a capacity tank, a plug valve is included so that one or the other of these two bellows can be vented, whilst the relay generates the signal for bellows C and the output from the relay. For reverse action, the roles of B and P are interchanged.

As shown in Figure 7.39, the output signal includes a positive- or negative-going impulse, according to the setting of the fulcrum and whether bellows P or B is vented. The recovery time is determined by the setting of the restrictor.

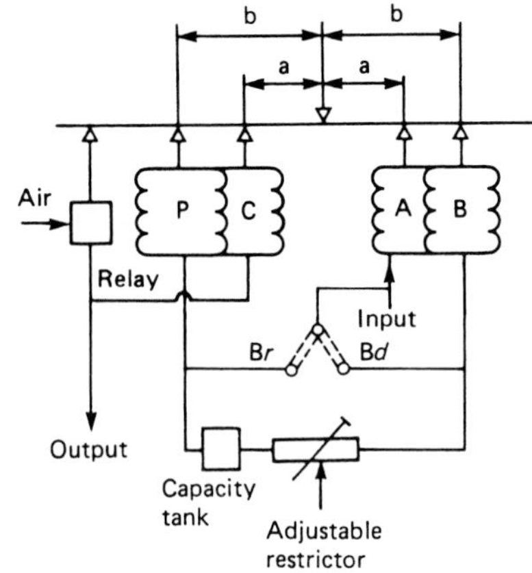

Figure 7.38 Force diagram for impulse generator.

7.6.4 Pneumatic-to-current converters

It is sometimes necessary to provide an interface between pneumatic and electronic control systems. This is particularly true when an existing pneumatic measurement and control system is being extended in a manner that involves the transmission of signals

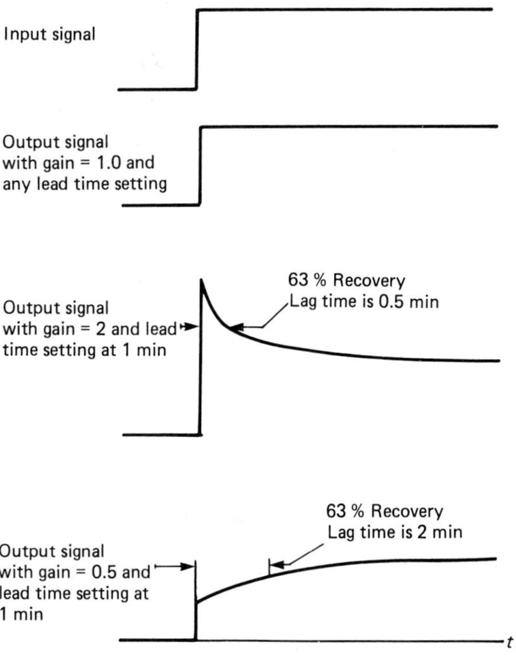

Figure 7.37 Response characteristic of lead/lag unit.

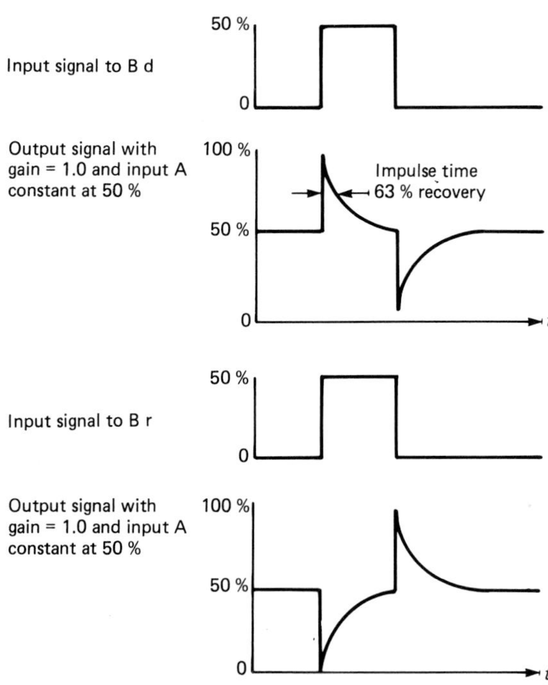

Figure 7.39 Response characteristic of impulse generator.

over long distances. In general, pneumatic transmission systems are more costly to install than the equivalent electronic current transmission systems, and they suffer from a transmission lag which detracts from the system performance.

Various methods have been used in the past to convert the pneumatic signals into a proportional electric current; the majority of these units are now based on the piezoresistive sensors described in Volume 1. These are fabricated on a wafer of silicon where a circular portion at the centre is etched away or machined to form a thin diaphragm. One side of the diaphragm is exposed to the pressure to be measured while, on the reverse side, the strain and temperature sensors are formed by ion implantation or similar techniques which have been developed for semiconductor manufacture. The strain sensors are connected in the arms of a Wheatstone bridge from which the out-of-balance signal provides the measurement signal, but, because the gauge factor is affected by any change in the temperature of the silicon wafer, the temperature sensors are used to compensate for this by varying the excitation applied to the bridge network. There are several proprietary ways of implementing this compensation, but most require selection or adjustment of some components to optimize the compensation over a useful temperature range. Compared with most other pressure transmitters, these units are only intended for converting the output signal from a pneumatic transmitter into a proportional current, and, although they may be subjected to equally hostile environmental conditions, the sensor itself is only exposed to 'instrument type' air pressures. In the majority of cases, this is a pressure between 20 and 100 kPa or the equivalent in metric or imperial units of measure. Occasionally there is a requirement to measure signals in the range 20–180 kPa, or the equivalent in other units, when power cylinders or positioners are involved.

A typical converter is shown in Figure 7.40. Its accuracy, including linearity, hysteresis and repeatability, is ±0.25 per cent of span and the ambient temperature effect is less than ±0.75 per cent per 30 K change within an overall temperature range from 0 to 50°C and ±1 per cent per 30 K change within the range −30 to +80°C. In some instances the converters can be located in a clean or protected environment such as a room in which other instrumentation is accommodated. For these applications, the robust enclosure is not required and the sensors, together with the associated electronic circuits, can be assembled into smaller units so that up to 20 of them can be stacked together and mounted in a standard 19-in rack, as shown in Figure 7.40(b).

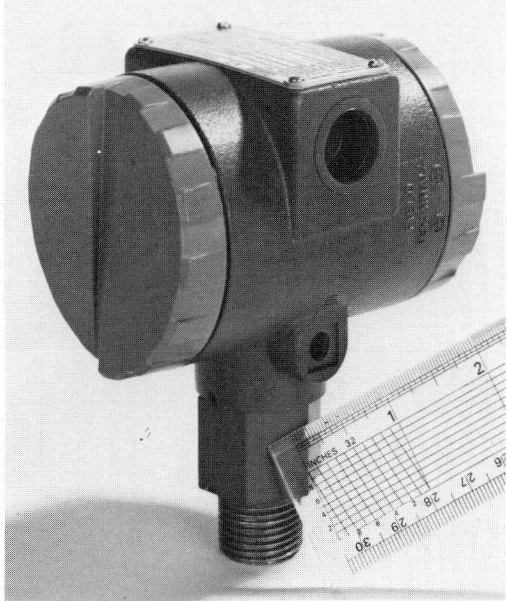

(a)

(b)

Figure 7.40 (a) Pneumatic-to-current converter; (b) pneumatic-to-current converters stacked in rack.

7.7 Electropneumatic interface

7.7.1 Diaphragm motor actuators

The pneumatic diaphragm actuator remains unchallenged as the most effective method of converting the signal from a controller into a force that can be used to adjust the setting of the final operator. In the

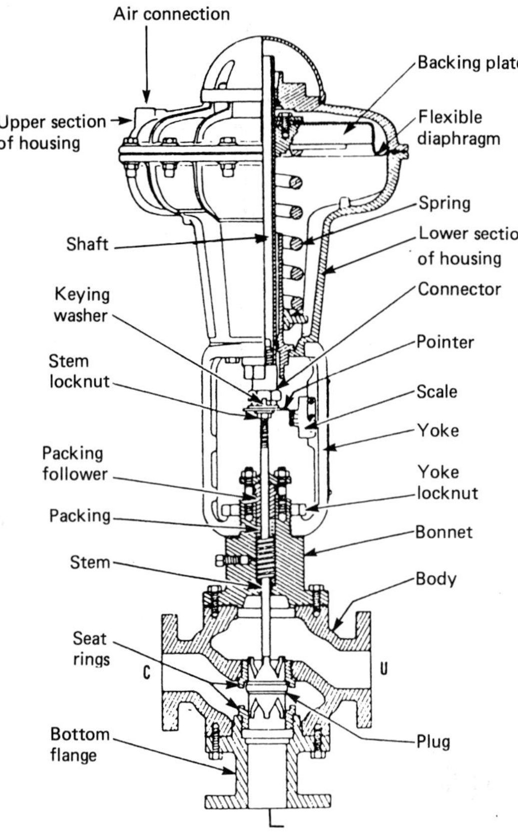

Figure 7.41 Pneumatic diaphragm motor actuator (mounted on two-way valve).

majority of process plants, the final control element is a control valve and the pneumatic diaphragm actuator is particularly well suited to provide the necessary force and stroke.

A typical actuator is shown in Figure 7.41. A flexible diaphragm that separates the upper and lower sections of the airtight housing is supported against a backing plate mounted on the shaft. A powerful spring, selected according to the required stroke and the air-operating pressure, opposes motion of the stem when compressed air is admitted to the upper section of the actuator housing. The stroke is limited by stops operating against the diaphragm backing plate.

The arrangement of the actuator and valve shown in Figure 7.41 is the customary configuration in which the spring forces the valve stem to its upper limit if the air supply or the air signal fails. A two-way valve is shown in the figure and in this case a spring would force the plug to direct the flow from the input port C to the exit port L in the event of an air failure. If the actuator were to be attached to a straightthrough valve, as would be the case if the exit port were blanked off, then the valve would close in the event of an air failure. In many instances this would represent a 'fail-safe' mode of operation (see Chapter 8), but in some plants the safe mode following failure of the air signal would be for the valve to be driven fully open. To deal with this eventuality, the actuator body can be inverted so that instead of the usual position shown in Figure 7.42(a) it is assembled as shown in Figure 7.42(b), in which case the spring would drive the valve stem downwards in the event of an air failure.

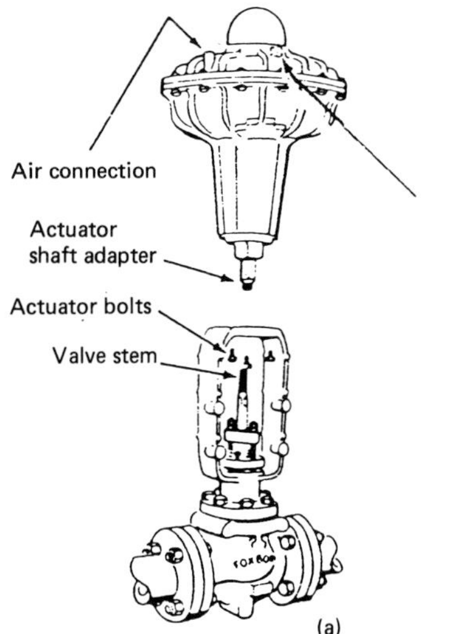

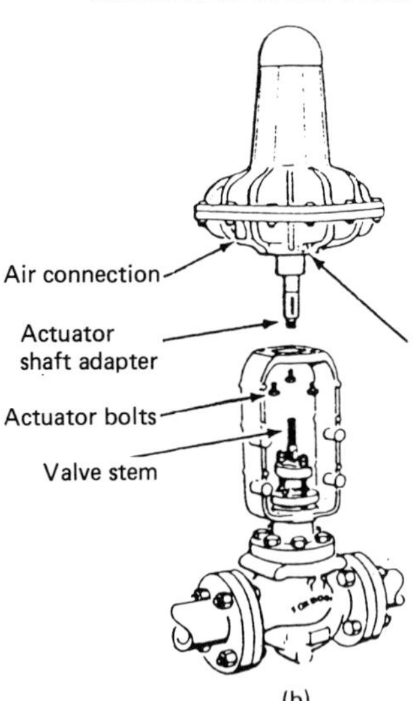

Figure 7.42 (a) Mounting for direct action; (b) mounting for reverse action.

Pneumatic valve stem positioners, electropneumatic converters or electropneumatic positioners, mounted on the valve yoke, can be used to enhance the precision or speed of response of the system.

7.7.2 Pneumatic valve positioner

A valve positioner is used to overcome stem friction and to position a valve accurately in spite of unbalanced forces in the valve body. One such unit is shown in Figure 7.43. It is usually mounted on the yoke of the valve and, in its normal mode of operation, a peg mounted on the valve stem and located in a slot in the feedback arm converts the stem movement into a shaft rotation.

Within the instrument, a flexure in the form of a 'U' with one leg extended is mounted on the shaft. The incoming pneumatic signal is fed to a bellows which applies a proportional force to the flexure at a point in line with the shaft. The free end of the flexure carries a steel ball which bears on a flapper which, together with the associated nozzle, is mounted on a disc that can be rotated about an axis perpendicular to that of the shaft.

In the normal mode of operation, an increase in the input signal causes the bellows to apply a force to the flexure so that the ball at its free end allows the flapper to move closer to the nozzle. This causes the back pressure to rise, and the change after amplification by the relay becomes the output signal, which is applied to the pneumatic actuator and so causes the valve stem to move until balance is re-established. The rotatable disc provides the means for adjusting the sensitivity as well as the direct or reverse action when used with either 'air-to-lift' or 'air-to-lower' actuators.

7.7.3 Electropneumatic converters

Although individual control loops may utilize electronic devices for sensing the primary measurement and deriving the control function, in the great majority of instances the final operator is required to provide a force or motion or both which can most readily be implemented pneumatically. Hence there

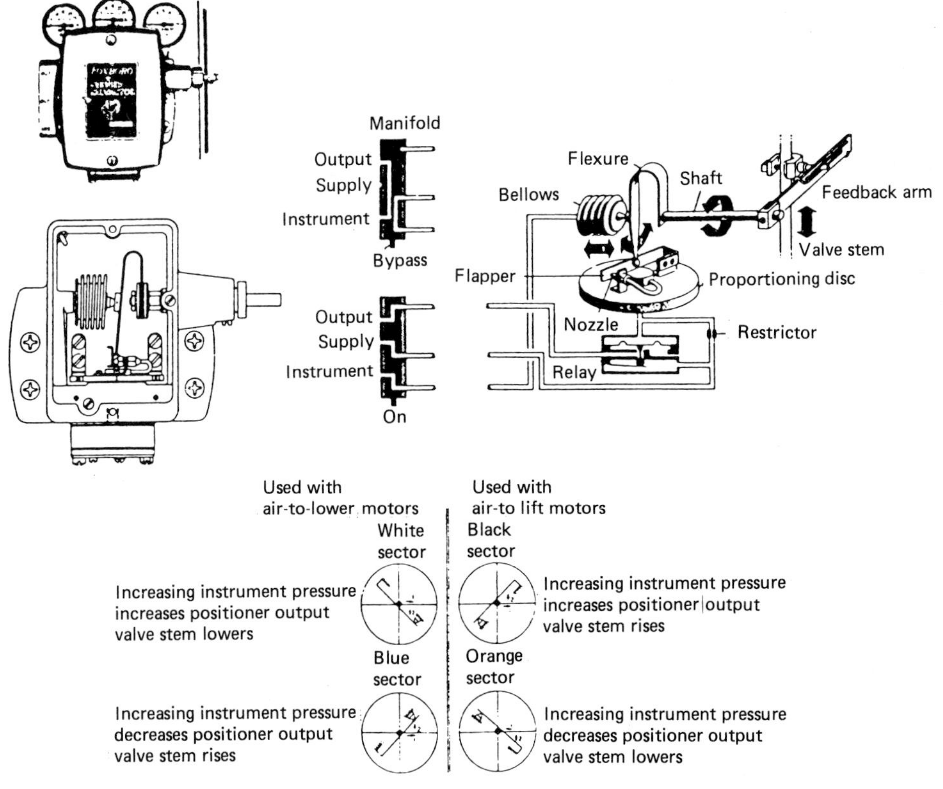

Figure 7.43 Pneumatic valve positioner.

is a requirement for devices which provide an interface between the electronic and pneumatic systems either to convert a current into a proportional air pressure or to convert a current into a valve setting by controlling the air supply to a diaphragm actuator. In most instances the devices have to be mounted on the process plants, where they are likely to be subjected to severe environmental conditions. Therefore it is important for them to be insensitive to vibration and well protected against mechanical damage and extremes of temperatures as well as corrosive atmospheres.

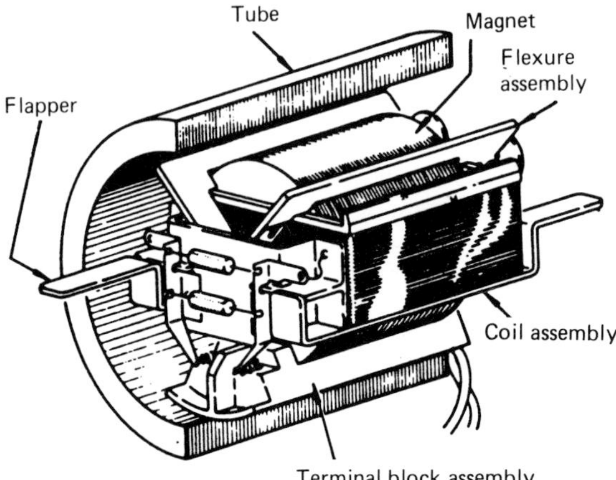

Figure 7.44 Galvanometer mechanism from electropneumatic converter.

The Foxboro E69F illustrates one method of achieving these requirements. It involves a motion-balance system based on a galvanometer movement, as shown in Figure 7.44. The system comprises a coil assembly mounted on cross flexures which allow it relative freedom to rotate about its axis but prevent any axial movement. The coil is suspended in a powerful magnetic field so that a current passing through the coil causes it to rotate. In the case of the electropneumatic converter, this rotation is sensed by a flapper/nozzle system, as shown in Figure 7.45.

The pneumatic section of the instrument comprises a feedback bellows and a bias spring which apply a force to a lever pivoted at one end by a flexure and carrying a nozzle at the free end. The nozzle is supplied via a restrictor and its back pressure is applied to a pneumatic relay whose output is applied to the feedback bellows and is also used as the pneumatic output from the unit.

With the current corresponding to the lower range value (e.g. 4 mA for a 4 to 20 mA converter) the relative position of the flapper and nozzle are adjusted so that the pneumatic output pressure is

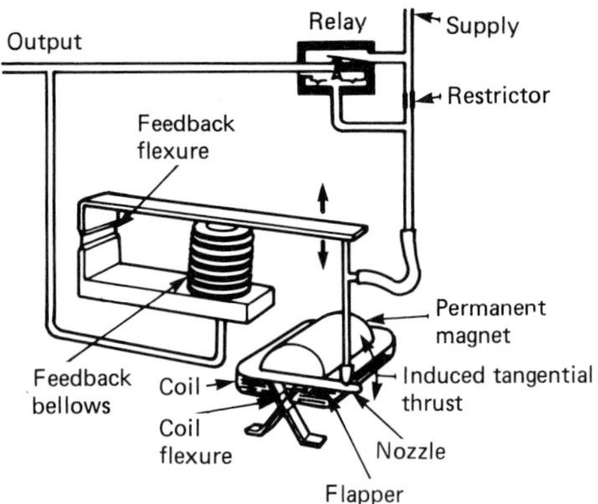

Figure 7.45 Basic configuration of electropneumatic converter.

equal to the required value (e.g. 20 kPa for a 20 to 100 kPa system).

An increase in the input current causes the coil to rotate, and in so doing moves the flapper towards the nozzle so that the back pressure is increased. The change is amplified by the relay and applied to the feedback bellows, so that the lever moves the nozzle away from the flapper until a new balance position is established.

The system is arranged so that when the coil current reaches the upper-range value (e.g. 20 mA) the pneumatic output signal reaches its corresponding upper-range value (e.g. 100 kPa). A limited range of adjustment is available by radial movement of the nozzle with respect to the axis of the coil.

7.7.4 Electropneumatic positioners

The Foxboro E69P shown in Figure 7.46 uses the same sensing mechanism in a positioner that drives the stem of a valve to a setting which is proportional to the incoming current signal. The positioner is

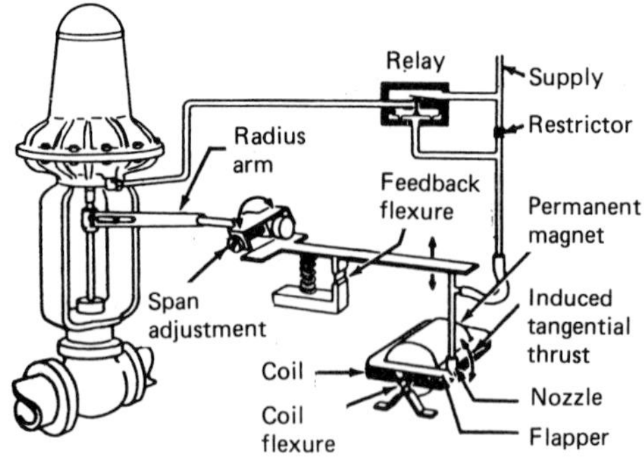

Figure 7.46 Basic configuration of electropneumatic valve-stem positioner.

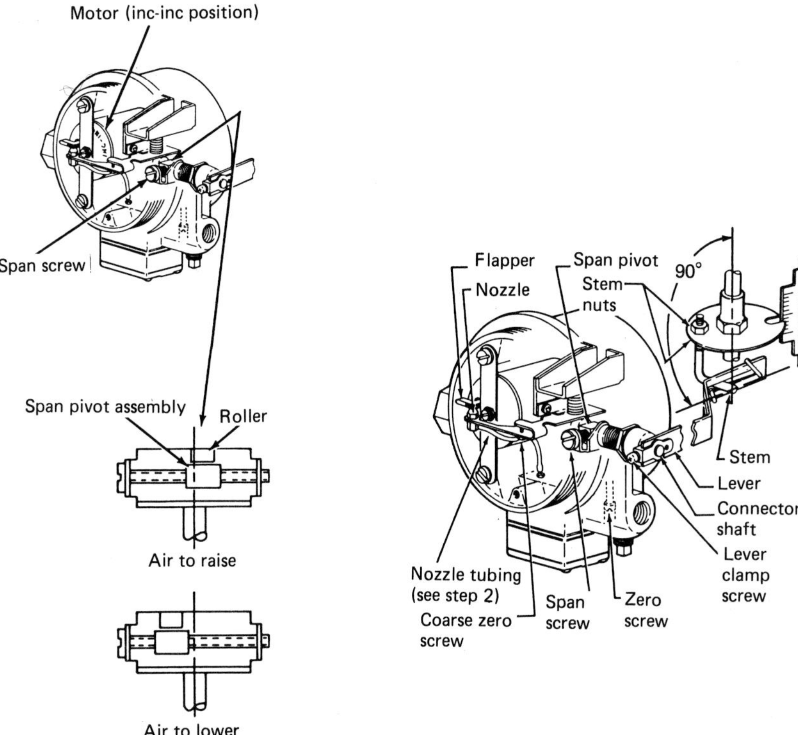

Figure 7.47 Mounting and adjustment of electro-pneumatic valve stem positioner.

mounted on the valve yoke and the valve stem is mechanically linked to it via a peg that is held by a spring against one side of a slot in the radius arm. As shown in Figure 7.47, movement of the valve stem causes the radius arm to rotate a shaft which passes through the instrument housing and the span pivot assembly. This comprises a roller whose axis is parallel to that of the shaft but the offset can be adjusted (to vary the span). The roller bears on the spring-loaded lever which carries the nozzle at its free end.

In operation, an increase in the current signal causes the coil to rotate so that the flapper moves closer to the nozzle. This increases the nozzle back pressure and the change, after being amplified by the relay, is applied to the valve actuator, causing the valve stem to move. This movement is transmitted via the radius arm to the shaft carrying the roller, with the result that the spring-loaded lever is repositioned until the valve stem has moved to a position corresponding to the new input current.

Compared with straightforward air-operated actuators, positioners have the advantage of virtually eliminating the effects of friction and stiffness as well as the reaction of the process pressure on the valve stem.

7.8 References

ANDERSON, N. A. *Instrumentation for Process Measurement and Control*, Chilton, London (1980)

CONSIDINE, D. M. (ed.). *Process Instruments and Controls Handbook*, 3rd edn, McGraw-Hill, New York (1985)

FOXBORO *Introduction to Process Control* (PUB 105B), Foxboro (1986)

MILLER, J. T. (ed.). *The Instrument Manual*, United Trades Press (1971)

8 Reliability

B.E. NOLTINGK

8.1 Introduction

The words 'reliable' and 'reliability' have been used in a general sense for a very long time. The value of the property they refer to has been increasingly recognized. In the military field, equipment with a superlative performance specification was worthless if it would not work when called upon to do so; for industrial processes involving some risk, there was a demand to quantify that risk instead of just calling it 'very low'. Consequently, since the 1950s the subject of reliability has been put on a sounder scientific and mathematical basis. In this brief account, attempting to relate it to instrumentation, we try to steer a middle course between broad qualitative generalities and a recapitulation of the sometimes abstruse mathematics that has been developed. As well as the whole military field, civil transport—particularly aeroplane systems—and process control plant, including that for nuclear power generation, have been the objects of extensive reliability analysis.

Much attention has been paid to the prediction of the performance of equipment from a reliability point of view. When considering different design approaches and when devising a strategy of management it is obviously of value to have figures for the rates at which different items will fail. There will probably be large statistical—and other—uncertainties, but the main purpose is often achieved if a failure rate is known to within an order of magnitude or even worse.

It might be thought that it is more important to increase reliability than to predict it, but the analysis inherent in prediction will often suggest economical ways to effect improvements. An atmosphere in which attention is focused on reliability will tend to produce reliable systems. Thought will also have to be given to the question of what is an acceptable risk. It will be realized that there are different modes of failure, some of which affect safety while others—through unnecessary shutdowns—influence the economical operation of plant; these two outcomes must both receive appropriate consideration.

It is convenient to think of equipment—particularly for instrumentation—at three different levels: components, modules and systems. They may be treated rather differently when their reliability is considered. There may be some uncertainty which category an item should be allotted to, but in general a component is an item that is replaced and never repaired, a module is a collection of components into something like an instrument while a system is the totality we are concerned with in a particular exercise, often including many modules with complex interconnections.

8.2 Components

The word 'component' most commonly brings to mind an electronic device—resistor, capacitor, etc. In integrated circuits many such are combined together, but with the definition that it is something that is replaced, not repaired, the whole device must be thought of as a component. The subject of reliability was first developed for equipment that was mainly electronic, partly because of the need and partly because the large population of nominally identical items used in electronics lent itself more obviously to a statistical approach. Note that soldered joints would be thought of as components, although their replacement would often be called a repair. In a similar way, small mechanical items are components, although there may be more uncertainty about classification: for example, an electric motor may be treated as a whole or it may be emphasized that the brushes within it can be replaced.

8.2.1 Physics of failure

How does a component fail? Three headings can be used: wear-out, misuse and inherent weakness. Some items are known from the outset to have limited lives; hot filaments must be expected to go open circuit eventually and gears to wear out. Components are designed to withstand only certain stresses of temperature, voltage, etc., and if these are exceeded they are likely to fail. During manufacture there may have been some mistake such as a foreign particle introduced or a locked-in mechanical stress. All three kinds of happening can cause failure in service—the overstressing may occur at some unpredictable time. All three interact with each other—manufacturing faults may shorten the life to wear-out and increase the sensitivity to overstressing.

The physical description of failure on a microscopic scale is commonly in chemical or mechanical terms. Corrosion changes composition and properties; a conducting foreign particle can move to bridge two conductors and short them out or stress can rupture and open circuit a conductor. A two-stage process is not uncommon, such as a broken seal leading subsequently to corrosion. In several such ways a delay can be introduced so that there is a time lapse between initiation and the failure becoming apparent, but it can be seen as plausible that the time scale is much less than the hoped-for life of the component.

8.2.2 Mathematical analysis

The instantaneous failure rate of an item at time t_1 can be thought of as the conditional probability that, having survived until t_1, it will fail during the short interval $t_2 - t_1$, divided by the duration of this interval. As in most probability concepts, probability for a single item can be replaced by the fraction of the total when considering a large number of identical items.

For many components, the instantaneous failure rate is not constant. At the beginning of life, there tend to be excessive failures, as discussed above, while items where there is a mechanism for wear-out will show a higher rate also as the end of life on that score is approached. This is illustrated in Figure 8.1.

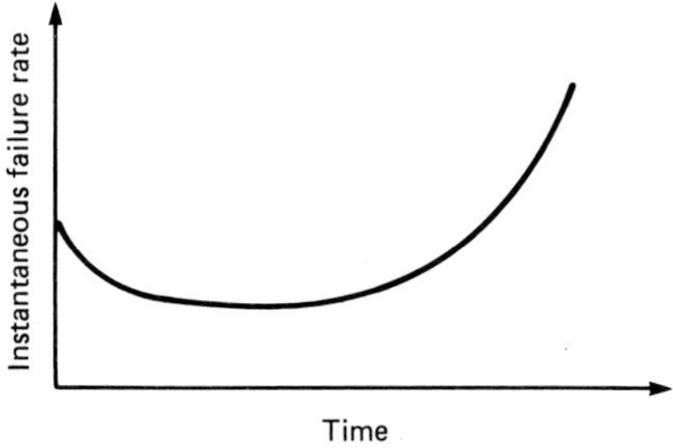

Figure 8.1 Variation of failure rate with time (the 'bath tub' curve).

The shape of the curve relating failure rate to time is often likened to a bath tub. However, it is much simpler to think in terms of a constant failure rate λ (dimension = 1/time), and we do that here. The justification is that the useful life occurs mainly between the periods when, on the one hand, early mortality and, on the other, wear-out are effective (i.e. the bottom of the 'bath tub' in Figure 8.1); λ is anyhow so imprecisely known that refinements are scarcely worth while. Then

$$\text{Mean time to failure} = \frac{1}{\lambda} \quad \text{(dimension = time)}$$

and reliability R, which must always be associated with some time, being defined as the probability of survival through that time, is

$$R(t) = \exp(-\lambda t) \qquad \text{(dimensionless)}$$

The probability density function (PDF) $f(t)$ giving the probability of failure during Δt at t, divided by Δt is

$$f(t) = \lambda \exp(-\lambda t)$$

(distinguished from the instantaneous failure rate in that it is not conditional on survival to t). If PDF is plotted against time, we get the exponential curve shown in Figure 8.2. The wide uncertainty in the statistics of small numbers is illustrated here, for if the mean time to failure is τ, there is still, for a single item, a 5 per cent probability that it will fail before 0.05τ and another 5 per cent probability that it will survive until after 3τ, corresponding to the areas shown under the curve.

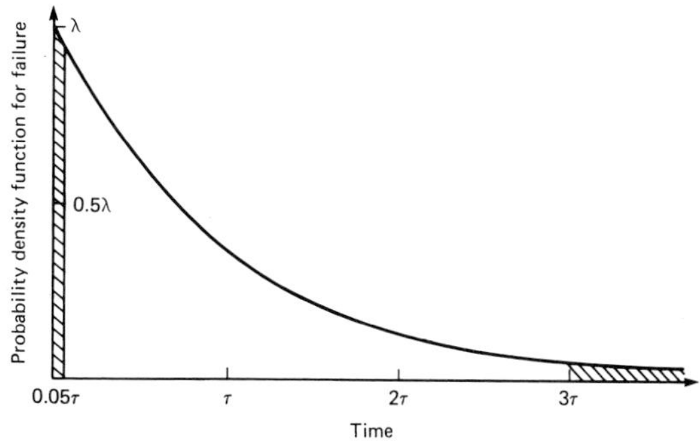

Figure 8.2 Probability density function for failure at different times.

8.2.3 Modes of failure

Failure of a component means that some characteristic changes in such a way as to prevent the component performing its required function, but there are several characteristics and several new values to which they can change. So we have to consider the *mode* of failure. Often, in electronic devices, it is to open circuit or to short circuit, but sometimes the shift is to a value not very different from the correct one. This commonly occurs relatively slowly, when it is described as 'degradation', whereas a sudden and complete failure is called 'catastrophic'. Degradation is observed more often in mechanical components than in electronic ones.

Different consequences of different modes of component failure are found when we consider the higher levels of modules and systems. There is a possibility of anticipating degradation errors by monitoring performance, whereas catastrophic failures are unpredictable (in individual cases, that is, as distinct from statistically).

8.2.4 Failure rates

In order to make practical use of theoretical concepts numerical values must be adopted for the failure rates of different components. It may be questioned whether there is such a thing as a failure rate that should be associated with any particular component. The concept of human mortality rate has been used by actuaries over many years and has been validated by the success of the predictions it has led to, but instrument components have an even wider variety than human beings. Probably, only the pragmatic answer can be given that, by adopting quantitative component reliability concepts, useful conclusions can be drawn. Much work has been devoted to establishing practical figures for failure rates, notably (in Britain) by the National Centre of Systems Reliability, part of the Safety and Reliability Directorate at Warrington; they maintain a continuously updated databank using contributions from many sources. Some observed failure rates reflect operational experience and some come from deliberate tests of isolated components.

Anyone seriously attempting to predict reliability should make use of comprehensive data from such publications as *Electronic Reliability Data* (1981), *Reliability and Maintainability* (1985) or MIL-HDBK-217D (1982) (see the References). The data should only be applied to items similar to those used to give the data.

Figure 8.3 gives an idea of the failure rates of different components and shows the enormous range over which they are spread. Some of the range is accounted for by operational conditions: temperature stress may introduce a factor of 3:1 for an increase from 0°C to 140°C, electrical stress a further

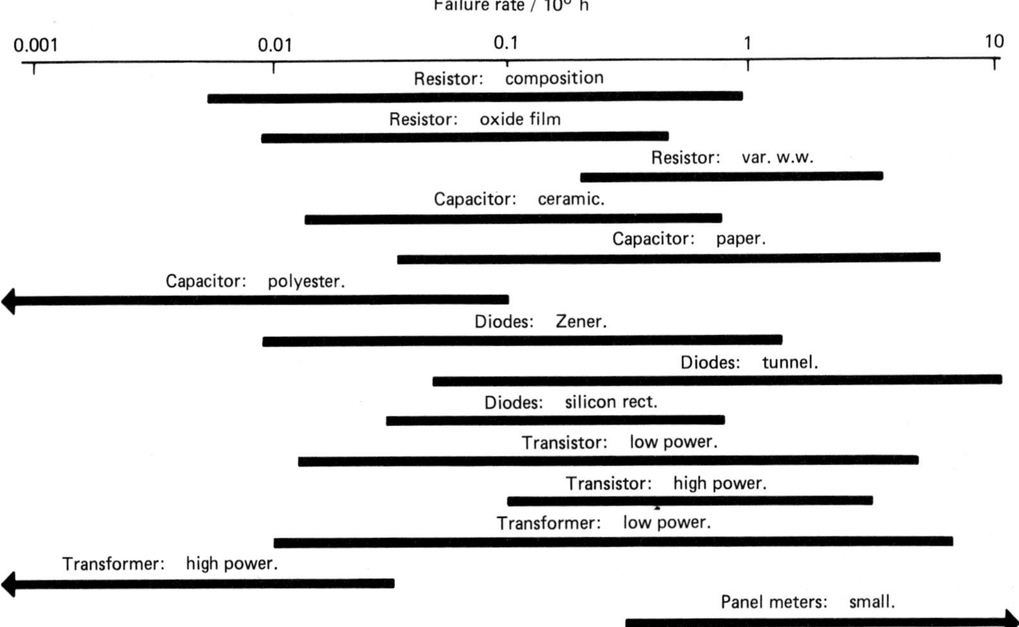

Figure 8.3 Failure rates of some components. (From Item 3 in the References, courtesy of the publishers.)

factor for many electronic components, while general severity of environment may alter the failure rate to be taken by as much as 50:1.

8.3 Modules

Ultimately, it is the behaviour of the whole system that is of interest, but it is helpful to consider also what happens at the module level, intermediate between component and system.

8.3.1 Failure rates

If all its components must be functioning correctly for the module to work, then its failure rate is determined by summing the failure rates of each component:

$$\lambda_{mod} = {}_1\lambda_{comp} + {}_2\lambda_{comp} + {}_3\lambda_{comp} + \ldots$$

and other parameters can be expressed in terms of λ_{mod}.

As we noted different modes of component failure, so we find different consequences ensue according to how a module fails. The commonest distinction is between fail-safe and fail-to-danger, the latter tending to damage either directly or if associated with some other eventuality, while the former tends only to cause an unnecessary shut-down. A simple example is a thermometer failing safe by reading too high when monitoring a process that becomes dangerous at excessive temperatures, but it is not always obvious which mode is fail-safe. I find this conveniently illustrated from a human situation. Thus, my wife worries about my safety if I have not arrived home by when I said I would, so a fail-safe feature of the information channel would lead to the expectation of a later-than-true return time. However, I can understand that with other wives and other worries the embarrassment would be associated with an unexpectedly early return, in which case the fail-safe failure would be in the opposite direction.

To determine module failure rates corresponding to different modes it is, of course, necessary to analyse the roles of different components—and the consequences of their failing in different modes—and sum the appropriate component rates.

8.3.2 Partial failures

Failure is defined as the termination of an item's ability to perform its required function. The precise function required, however, may vary from time to time. If an item can perform some of the functions required of it, but not meet its full specification, it is said to have undergone partial failure. The question arises sometimes with components, where it would commonly be associated with degradation, and more often with modules. Examples would be a capacitor with a high leakage current that still does not amount to a short circuit, a multimeter with one range out of action, a thermometer element with a slow response.

The possibility of partial failures complicates reliability analysis, which indeed becomes almost impossible if their number is likely to be comparable with that of total failures. A conservative value for failure rates will be derived if partial failures are counted in with total ones. The major problem they produce is in the field of monitoring the integrity of equipment, which we touch on under Systems (section 8.4) because, if some item has partially failed, it cannot be presumed that tests giving a satisfactory outcome under one set of conditions imply that the equipment will work equally well under a different set.

8.3.3 Design

A module that has been well designed will be more reliable because of lower failure rates in its components. This arises in several ways. Wear-out can be postponed, for instance, by underrunning incandescent lamps or by reducing the harshness of mechanical regimes. Understressed components were seen to have lower failure rates; stresses can generally be reduced by minimizing temperature rises and, for electronic components, reducing operating voltages. Design skills come into play in seeing that all this is done in a cost-effective way.

Good design also reduces the number of degradation failures. This can be appreciated from Figure 8.4. We plot there a typical probability density function showing the expected value of some component characteristic—say, the resistance of a

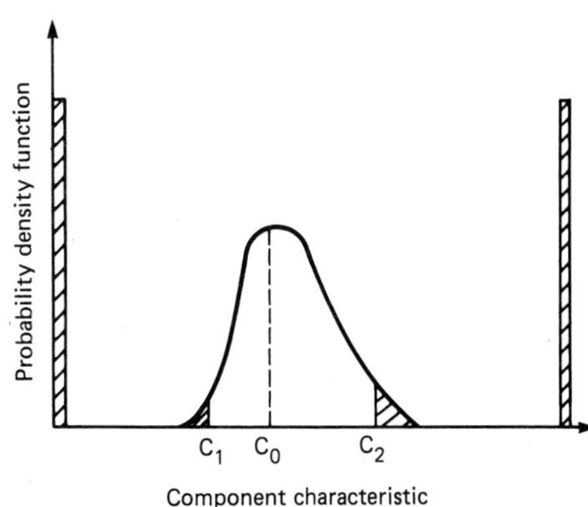

Figure 8.4 Spread of component characteristics.

resistor—after a certain time of operation. When installed, the characteristic had the value C_0 and for its module to work properly, the value has to lie between the limits C_1 and C_2. The probability that failure has occurred is thus given by the hatched area under the curve. This comprises the extremes, which correspond to catastrophic failure, and the flanks of the central curve, to which the characteristic may have drifted. The skill of the designer should ensure that the range of limits C_1–C_2 is wide enough for all the distribution curve for planned operating times to lie inside it.

In fact, weakness of design may account for some failures early in the life of some equipment, and some of the generally assumed high early failure rates. It is not unusual for development of a module to be completed at the same time as early trials, and if these suggest anomalously frequent failures the situation of a suspected component will be re-examined to see whether stresses are exceptionally high or whether there is an unusual sensitivity to drift. Component failure rates normally quoted are on the assumption of a good design from which teething troubles have been eliminated.

8.4 Systems

When we come to deal with complete systems there is scope for increasing reliability by introducing complex configurations which include 'redundancy'. The alternatives of fail-safe and fail-to-danger which we mentioned under modules now become important. The strategy adopted for repairs also plays a considerable part.

8.4.1 Redundancy

Redundancy in an item is formally defined just as the existence of more than one means of performing a given function. We can understand it best by illustrations. In the smoothing circuit of an electrical power supply unit, we need, say, at least 100 μF capacitance. If, then, we install two capacitors in parallel, each of this capacitance, we have a *redundant* component and the unit will continue to function should either of them go open circuit. However, should either develop a short circuit there is a total failure of the module. We have reduced the sensitivity to one mode of failure but increased the sensitivity to another mode. Incidentally, this shows how redundancy principles can be applied also at the module level.

Again, consider the protection of some plant against excessive temperature rise. We install a thermometer, arranging for the plant to be shut down if the thermometer gives a reading greater than some critical value. There is a certain small probability q_d that the thermometer will fail to show a high temperature if one arises. That would be

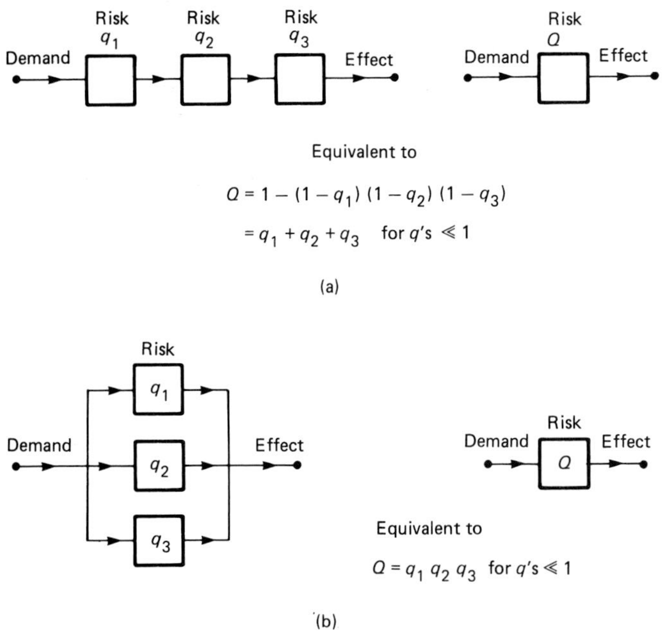

Figure 8.5 Reliability diagrams.

disastrous for the plant so we install another, identical thermometer and arrange for shutdown if either reads high; this reduces the probability of a dangerous failure to q_d^2 (q_d is assumed to be very small). However, there is also a finite probability q_s of a safe failure, corresponding to an incorrectly high reading of temperature and leading to an unnecessary shutdown. Introduction of the second thermometer has doubled this probability to $2q_s$, and we have a safer system at the cost of less economical working. All this is on the assumption that failures of two separate items—components or modules—are *independent*. It can be seen that the assumption is not always justified from examples such as a single overvoltage surge destroying two components or a fire in a cable duct damaging the connections between several modules. Much thought is given to ensuring independence at the stage of system design.

Arrangements in systems can be depicted in reliability diagrams, as shown in Figure 8.5. We generalize by talking of whether a demand gets through to cause an effect, the different blocks having probabilities q of not performing (hence $1 - q$ that they will perform) correctly. In the multi-thermometer case we have discussed, safe failures must be regarded as using the series configuration in Figure 8.5(a) because all elements must be performing for the signal 'Cool' to get through, but for failures to danger, the parallel arrangement in Figure 8.5(b) is appropriate, since any working element allows the signal 'Too hot' to pass.

'Partial redundancy' configurations are used to reduce the incidence of both safe and dangerous failures. A 'two out of three' example is depicted in Figure 8.6; it is arranged that when any two out of the three channels installed indicate danger, the danger signal is transmitted. For channels with equal risks q of failure, the risk of the total arrangement $Q = 3q^2$, appropriate values q_s or q_d being taken for the probability of elements having failed safe or to danger, respectively. In this simple case, $Q = 3q^2$ for both failure modes because a failure of two out of the three channels produces an effect in either mode; for the more general r out of n case, formulae will be different for the two modes. The importance of the logic element making the two out of three judgement should be noted: if that cannot be assumed to be 100 per cent reliable it must be given careful attention.

The total reliability of a complex control system can be examined by setting out the appropriate reliability diagram and inserting values for the risks associated with each element.

When some but not all redundant channels have failed, the system can be thought of as in a state of partial failure because it is operational but with a lower than specified reliability.

8.4.2 Repairs and availability

When considering the effect of redundancy on the performance of a whole system, we included values q for the probability that a unit was not working. If we start with a perfect system and simply let it deteriorate indefinitely, q will increase progressively from 0 (to 1 after infinite time) and can be calculated from failure rate data for each item at the time we are concerned with.

That unidirectional change is a correct picture for some situations, but with most large installations of instrumentation some maintenance and repair is undertaken. This plays an important part in the reliability achieved over long periods. To analyse the situation quantitatively, we think of the mean time to repair (MTTR) an assembly; this includes both the time elapsing before it is realized there has been a failure—which will be very short for 'self-revealing' faults—and the time for maintenance personnel to be deployed and achieve their repair mission.

In these continuing situations, we have to distinguish between a system's mean time to fail

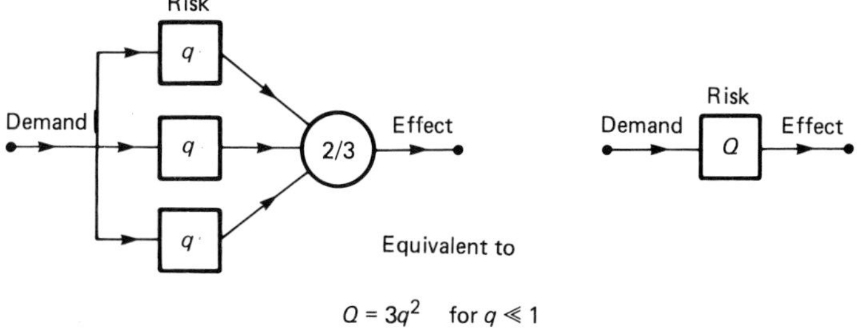

Figure 8.6 Partial redundancy of a 'two out of three' system.

(MTTF) and mean time between failures (MTBF). In fact, it can be seen that MTBF = MTTF + MTTR. We can also appreciate the concept of Availability, the fraction of time for which something can perform its design function:

$$\text{Availability} = \frac{\text{MTTF}}{\text{MTTF} + \text{MTTR}}$$

To avoid ambiguity of definition, it must be made clear whether shelf-life (i.e. periods when equipment is not switched on) is to be included.

The availability of modules or subsystems should be taken into consideration when calculating system reliability: it can be seen how this complicates calculations which have to take into account partial failures (and their modes) in redundant systems.

Maintainability is defined as 'the probability that a device that has failed will be restored to operational effectiveness within a given period of time when the maintenance action is performed in accordance with prescribed procedures'. With the (rather unrealistic) assumption of a *constant repair rate*, the situation can be analysed as were reliability and failure (section 8.2.2), giving

$$\text{Maintainability (in time } t) = 1 - \exp\left(\frac{-t}{\text{MTTR}}\right)$$

Good design can reduce MTTR as it can increase MTTF; the former is also influenced by maintenance procedures.

8.4.3 Software reliability

The expression *software reliability* is used because of the realization that when a complex computer system goes online it may contain errors that will only show up in certain infrequently occurring situations. The errors may be simple programmers' mistakes or they may arise from a misunderstanding of the physical system to which the computer is linked. It is, however, almost invariably the case for a large system that some software errors will only be discovered after the system has been brought into use.

There is no 'physics of failure' for software; perhaps there is a psychology of failure! Neither is there an instant of failure: software does not change with time except by human intervention. If we are contrasting the behaviour of hardware and software, a further difference is that in operational situations we are only concerned with partial failures of software because a system with it totally failed could never be launched.

It is difficult to describe the situation with a plausible mathematical model. The timescale for a failure is not that concerned with physical damage to a component, as in hardware failures. Instead, it is that for a set of circumstances to arise which will show up—and cause errors from—a partial failure that has been there all along.

Realization of the problem has led to attempts to devise techniques resulting in more reliable software. In practical instrumentation, the main conclusion is that it is wrong to presume on the perfect integrity of computer software.

8.5 Practical implementation

The foregoing sections give a brief outline of how the reliability of instruments and systems can be analysed and—very approximately—predicted. When setting up instrumentation, some practical steps should be taken which increase reliability and indeed must be presumed to have been effected if semi-quantitative predictions are to be valid.

8.5.1 Design and operation

We cannot do more than mention the vast question of good design. Some aspects are dealt with in Chapter 1 on Construction. Sound tolerancing of both electronic and mechanical components is important.

When availability was discussed, the need for a good maintenance procedure was apparent. If possible, components subject to wear-out (e.g. incandescent lamps and rubbing mechanical parts) should be replaced before they approach the ends of their lives—implying that the mean lives must be known and that the standard deviations about the means are not impossibly large. Adequate records, of course, should be kept; higher-than-expected failure rates for some components may imply poor design, which can be corrected.

In the reliability structure of a complete system, human action in response to a warning signal may play a part. This opens the door to human errors. It must certainly not be assumed that such errors are impossible, although it is very difficult to assign a probability in a particular situation. Smith suggests it ranges from 10^{-5} for overfilling the bath to 0.9 after 1 min in a situation of real emergency. Where the highest integrity is called for, the human element should be eliminated from the direct control chain and replaced by a fully automatic system. Human intervention should only be allowed when a time scale of hours gives an adequate period for leisurely thought.

8.5.2 Environment

A large part of providing reliable equipment consists

of ensuring that the equipment is suitable for the environment in which it will be operated. Many aspects of an environment are relevant.

High temperature is commonly recognized as an adverse environment. This is reflected in the factors by which failure rates are increased in quoted data. The useful properties of most materials degenerate as they get hotter. Not only temperature must be thought of; steep temperature gradients within a component or assembly can also give trouble, as can rapid and repeated temperature changes.

The atmosphere surrounding equipment may be the reason for early failure. Traces of corrosive gas or moisture can cause corrosion: remember that variations in temperature have an influence on whether vapour condenses out as liquid. Dust deposited from dust-laden atmospheres is often responsible for malfunctioning of moving parts or for changed electrical characteristics. Dust penetrates to the interior of imperfectly sealed containers through what is called 'breathing': when internal air cools and so contracts, air from outside is drawn in and this is repeated as cycles of temperature change are experienced.

Vibration and, indeed, exposure to any mechanical hazard should be avoided. The latter may originate from human tampering by those who do not realize the damage they cause—or by those who do, and welcome it. Appropriate protection is always important. On the other hand, inaccessibility may in practice reduce the maintenance given to an instrument, whether that inaccessibility arises from a remote location or from overprotective housing.

In some situations, radiation must be taken into account as an adverse environment. More likely to be overlooked is electrical interference. There is a danger, notably in cable runs, of electrical pick-up from one conductor to another. This can introduce false signals and so corrupt communication channels. It can also, at a higher level, cause physical damage; it might be thought difficult to transfer enough energy for this, but some active semiconductors are very sensitive, while if a protective system is engaged in protecting against a major disturbance, that disturbance itself can be the source of very energetic pulses.

Constancy of conditions is generally desirable, in particular a steady temperature. It is thus good practice to leave equipment switched on unless the consequent wear-out of components having a limited life is unacceptable.

Items will normally have specifications as to what environments they can withstand. From a reliability point of view, the limits indicated should not be thought of as precise go/no-go figures within which performance is perfect and outside which the item is useless. Rather is reliability increased progressively as the environment is made more favourable. Designer and user have to apply their skills so that this principle is used in the most cost-effective way.

8.5.3 Diversity

It was mentioned in section 8.4.1 that the technique of increasing reliability by introducing redundancy depended on failures being independent. Failures that have a common cause are a serious danger, because they can greatly reduce the protection given by redundancy.

To counter this, it is desirable to aim for *diversity*. The word is used to cover basic differences in doing things. If, for instance, two separate instruments provide redundant protection in a system, it could be specified that their components should come from different manufacturers or at least different batches; a potential source of failure that had occurred inadvertently would not then degrade the reliability of both instruments. In other situations, it is desirable that links between separate items of equipment should not follow the same path and so be susceptible to disruption by the same external event.

More fundamentally, diversity can provide some safeguard against faulty human analysis. In nuclear reactor protection systems, for instance, it may have been assumed that increased activity would always lead to more neutrons being found. If a redundant protection channel is based on the primary observation of raised temperature, this will prevent such drastic consequences if for any reason an increased neutron population should not be detected when the reactor power goes up.

It can be seen that, although it may tend to be complicated and expensive, diversity is a sound principle to aim at.

8.6 References

CLULEY, J. C. *Electronic Equipment Reliability*, Macmillan, London (1981)

GREEN, A.E. and BOURNE, A. J. *Reliability Technology*, John Wiley, Chichester (1972)

National Centre of Systems Reliability and Inspec. *Electronic Reliability Data*, Institution of Electrical Engineers (1981)

SMITH, D. J. *Reliability and Maintainability*, Macmillan, London (1985)

US Department of Defense. *Military Handbook: Reliability Prediction of Electronic Equipment* (MIL-HDBK-217D) (1982)

Reliability and Maintainability Data for Industrial Plants, A. P. Harris and Associates (1984)

Some British Standards relate to reliability, notably:
BS 4200, Part 2, Guide on the reliability of electronic equipment and parts used therein: terminology (1974)
BS 5760, Part 2, Guide on the reliability of engineering equipment and parts

9 Safety

L.C. TOWLE

9.1 Introduction

The interactions between the design and application of instrumentation and safety are many and diverse. The correct utilization of instrumentation for monitoring and control reduces risk. An obvious example is a fire detection and control system, but even a simple cistern control which prevents a water tank from overflowing affects overall safety. Any instrumentation which contributes to maintaining the designed status of an installation can arguably affect safety. However, instrumentation can increase the danger in an installation, usually by being incorrectly designed or used. The principal direct risks from electrical instrumentation are electrocution and the possibility of causing a fire or explosion by interaction between the electricity and flammable materials, which range from various insulating materials used on cables to the more sensitive oxygen-enriched hydrogen atmosphere of a badly ventilated battery charging room. Some aspects of the safety of lasers and the risks from radiation are dealt with elsewhere in *Instrument Technology*, Volume 3, Chapters 2, 3 and 5. Toxic materials should also be considered (see *Substances Hazardous to Health* in the References). These risks pale into insignificance when compared with the full range of possibilities of misapplying instrumentation to a process plant, but nevertheless in an overall safety analysis all risks must be minimized.

It is important to recognize that nowhere is absolute safety achievable, and that the aim is to achieve a socially acceptable level of safety. Quite what level has to be achieved is not well defined; it is perhaps sufficient to say that people are even more reluctant to be killed at work than elsewhere, and hence the level of safety must be higher than is generally accepted. For example, the risk level accepted by a young man riding a motorcycle for pleasure would not be acceptable to a process operator in a petrochemical plant. There are similar problems in determining how much financial expenditure is justified in achieving safety.

As well as the moral responsibilities implicit in not wishing to harm fellow mortals there are, in the majority of countries, strong legal sanctions, both civil and criminal, which can be used to encourage all designers to be careful. In the United Kingdom, the Health and Safety at Work Act 1974 together with the Electricity Regulations provides a framework for prosecuting anyone who carelessly puts at risk any human being, including himself. The act places responsibilities on manufacturers, users and individuals in some considerable detail, and the requirements are applied in almost all circumstances which can conceivably be regarded as work. For example, manufacturers are required to sell only equipment which is safe for its intended use, test it to check that it is safe, provide adequate installation instructions and be aware of the 'state of the art'. The Act was derived from the Robens Report, which is a very readable, well-argued discussion document which sets a reasonable background to the whole subject of industrial safety. The Act lays great stress on the need to recognize, record and evaluate levels of danger and the methods of reducing the risk to an acceptable level, and consequently there is a need for adequate documentation on the safety aspects of any installation. In the majority of installations the enforcing organization is the Factory Inspectorate, who have awesome powers to enter, inspect and issue various levels of injunction to prevent hazards. Fortunately, the majority of factory inspectors recognize that they do not have quite the infinite wisdom required to do their job, and proceed by a series of negotiated compromises to achieve a reasonable level of safety without having to resort to extreme measures. It is important to realize that the legal requirement in most installations is to take 'adequate precautions'. However, in the real world the use of certified equipment applied to the relevant British Standard Code of Practice is readily understood, easy to document and defensible, and is consequently the solution most frequently adopted.

9.2 Electrocution risk

In designing any electrical equipment it is necessary to reduce the risk of electrocution as far as possible. Many sectors of industry have special standards of construction and inspection combined with certification schemes to take into account their particular risks. For example, electro-medical equipment has to meet stringent standards, particularly in cases where sensors are inserted in the body.

It is useful to try to assess the equivalent circuit of the human body, and there are a large number of references on the subject which show quite wide discrepancies between experimental results. A few facts appear to be common. Figure 9.1 shows the generally accepted figures for the ability to detect the presence of current, and the level of current which causes muscular contraction, although it must again be stressed that individuals vary considerably. Muscular contraction is a fascinating process, involving an electrical impulse signal releasing a chemical which causes the mechanical movement. The currents required are about 15 mA, and to maintain a muscle contracted it requires about 10 pulses/s. When a direct current is applied it causes the muscle to contract once and then relax; consequently direct current tends to be safer. However, at higher levels direct current does cause paralysis, since variation in body resistance due to burns, etc. causes the current to fluctuate and hence contract the muscles. The 50–60 Hz normally used for domestic supplies is ideally chosen to make certain that paralysis occurs.

Body resistance is quite a complex picture, since much of the initial resistance is in the skin. A dry outer layer of skin, particularly in the areas which are calloused, gives quite high resistance at low voltage, typically 10–100 kΩ, but this falls to 1 kΩ at 500 V. Other, more sensitive areas of the body such as elbows have a much lower resistance (2 kΩ). Once the outer layer of skin is broken, the layer immediately below it has many capillaries filled with body fluid and has very low resistance. The bulk resistance of humans is mostly concentrated in the limbs and is taken to be 500 Ω. Figure 9.2 shows one curve of body resistance and a possible equivalent circuit of a human being at low voltage when the skin resistance is converted to a threshold voltage.

The process of killing someone directly by electricity is also quite complex. Generally, it is agreed that a current of 20–30 mA applied to the

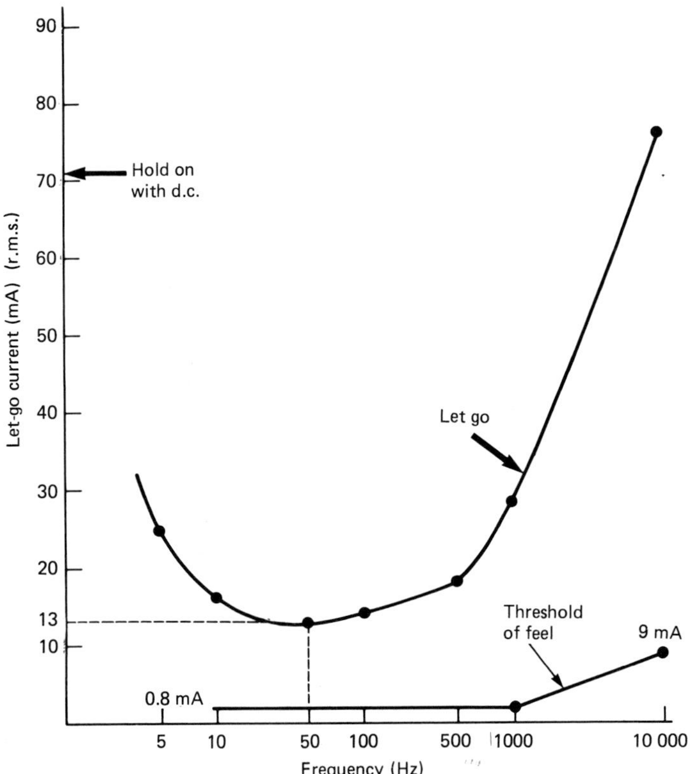

Figure 9.1 Variation with frequency of let-go current and threshold of feel.

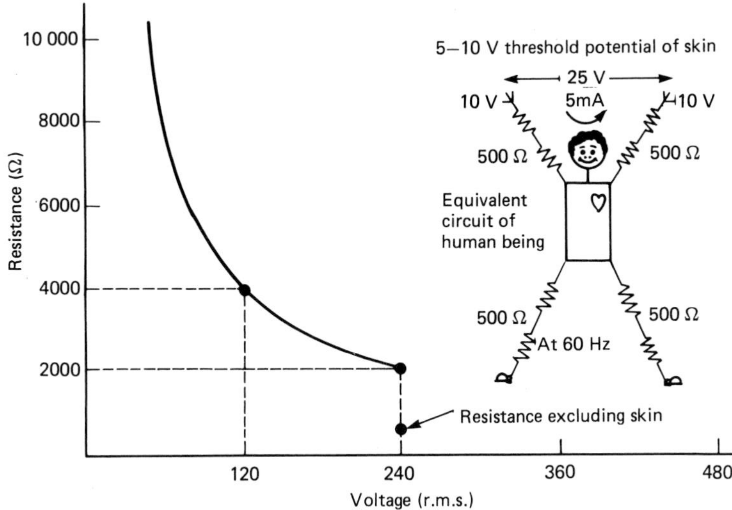

Figure 9.2 (a) Apparent increase of body resistance (hand to hand—dry) with reduction of voltage; (b) equivalent circuit of human being.

right muscles of the heart would stop it functioning. Just how to persuade this current to flow in the practical problem of hand-to-hand electrocution is widely discussed. Some sources suggest currents of the order of 10 A are necessary and others suggest there is a possibility of 40 mA being enough. The level of current is further complicated because there is a time factor involved in stopping the heart, and some protection techniques rely at least partially on this effect to achieve safety. The change is quite dramatic. For example, one reference suggests that heart fibrillation is possible at 50 mA if applied for 5 s and 1 A if applied for 10 ms. There seems little doubt, however, that the conventional 250 V 50 Hz supply used in the United Kingdom is potentially lethal, and that standing chest deep in a swimming pool with a defective under-water low-voltage lighting system is one very effective way of shortening a human being's life span.

The majority of modern instrumentation systems operate at 30 V or below, which to most people is not even detectable and is generally well below the accepted level of paralysis. There are, however, circumstances where even this voltage might be dangerous. Undersea divers are obviously at risk, but people working in confined hot spaces where sweat and moisture are high also need special care. Once the skin is broken, the danger is increased, and the possibilities of damage caused by electrodes fastened to the skull are so horrendous that only the highest level of expertise in the design of this type of equipment is acceptable. However, for the majority of conventional apparatus a level of 30 V is useable and is generally regarded as adequately safe. The design problem is usually to prevent the mains supply from becoming accessible, either by breaking through to the low-voltage circuitry, making the chassis live, or some other defect developing.

9.2.1 Earthing and bonding

It follows from the previous discussion that if all objects which can conduct electricity are bonded together so that an individual cannot become connected between two points with a potential difference greater than 30 V, then the installation is probably safe. The pattern of earthing and bonding varies slightly with the type of electrical supply available. Figure 9.3 illustrates the situation which arises if UK practice is followed. The supply to the instrument system is derived from the conventional 440 V three-phase neutral earthed distribution system, the live side being fused. A chassis connection to the neutral bond provides an adequate fault path to clear the fuse without undue elevation of the instrument chassis. All the adjacent metalwork, including the handrail, is bonded to the instrument chassis and returned separately (usually by several routes) to the neutral star point. Any personnel involved in the loop as illustrated are safe, because they are in parallel with the low-resistance bond XX′ which has no significant resistance. If the bond XX′ were broken then the potential of the handrail

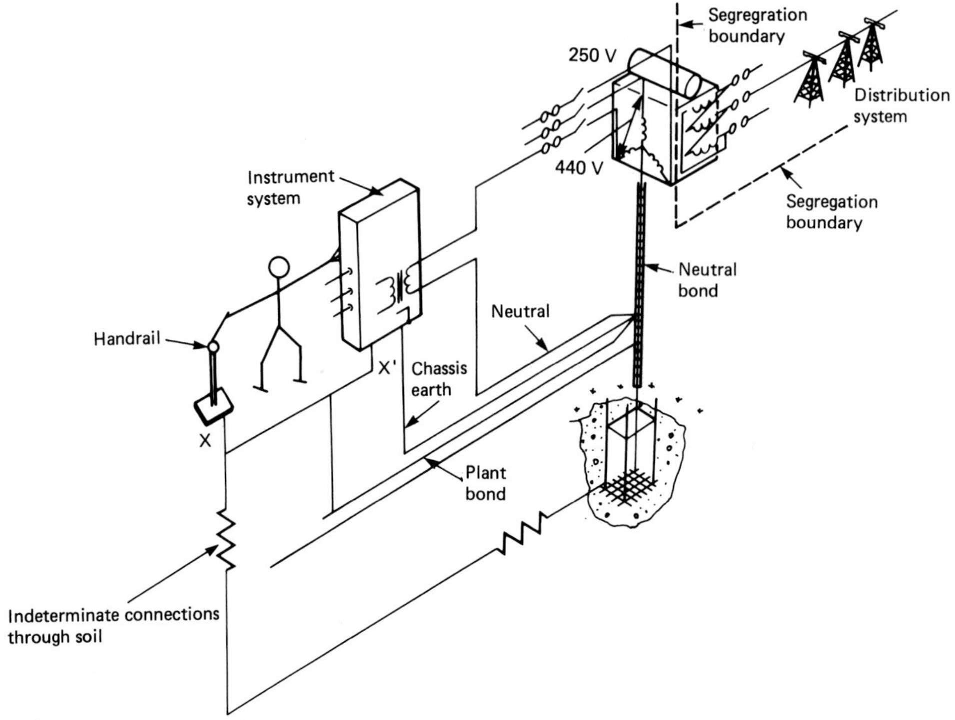

Figure 9.3 Normal UK installation with bonded neutral.

would be determined by the ill-defined resistance of the earth path. The instrument system would be elevated by the effect of the transient fault current in the chassis earth return, and the resultant potential difference across the human being might be uncomfortably high.

The fundamental earthing requirements of a safe system are therefore that there should be an adequate fault return path to operate any protective device which is incorporated, and that all parts of the plant should be bonded together to minimize potential differences.

There are, however, a number of circumstances where earthing is not used as a means of ensuring protection. Large quantities of domestic portable equipment are protected by 'double insulation', in which the primary insulation is reinforced by secondary insulation and there would need to be a coincident breakdown of two separate layers of insulation for danger to arise. Similarly, some areas for work on open equipment are made safe by being constructed entirely of insulating material, and the supplies derived from isolating transformers so as to reduce the risk of electrocution.

Where the environment is harsh or cables are exposed to rough treatment there is always the need to reduce working voltage, and there are many variants on the method of electrical protection, all of which have their particular advantages. Figure 9.4 shows the type of installation which is widely used in wet situations and, provided that the tools and cables are subject to frequent inspection, offers a reasonable level of protection.

The transformer is well designed to reduce the available voltage to 110 V which is then centre tapped to earth, which further reduces the fault voltage to earth to 55 V. Both phases of the supply are fused but a more sensitive detection of fault current is achieved by using an earth leakage circuit breaker (ELCB) which monitors the balance of the phase currents and if they differ by more than 20 mA triggers the circuit breaker. This sensitive fast detection combined with the lower voltage produces a reasonably safe system for most circumstances.

There are therefore many different techniques for reducing electrical shock risk. They all require consideration to be given to the nature of the supply, the design of the equipment, the environment, use, the method of installation and the frequency and effectiveness of inspection. These factors all interact so strongly that any safe installation must consider all these aspects.

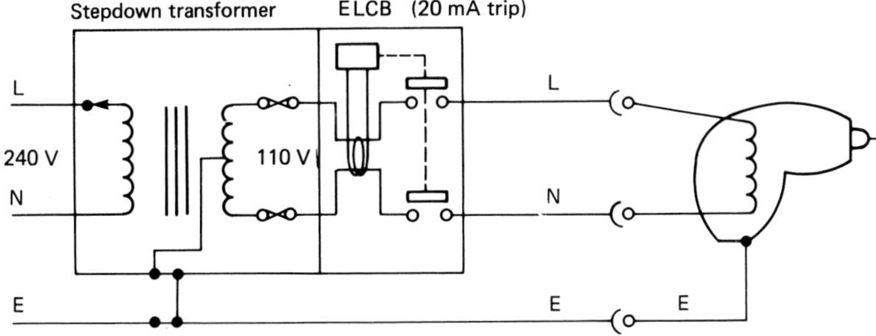

Figure 9.4 Isolating transformer supplying 110 V centre tapped to earth with earth leakage circuit breaker.

9.3 Flammable atmospheres

A large proportion of process control instrumentation is used in the petrochemical industry, where there is a possible risk of explosion if the equipment comes into contact with a flammable atmosphere. In practice, similar risks occur in all petrochemical and gas distribution sites, printing works, paint-spray booths and the numerous small stores of varnish, paint and encapsulating compounds which exist on most manufacturing sites.

The other related risk is that of dust explosions, which tend to attract less interest but are possibly more important. Almost any finely divided material is capable of being burned (most people are familiar with the burning steelwool demonstration) and, in particular, finely divided organic substances such as flour, sugar and animal feedstuffs all readily ignite. Dust explosions tend to be dramatic, since a small explosion normally raises a further dust cloud and the explosion rolls on to consume the available fuel. However, in general dusts need considerably more energy than gas to ignite them (millijoules rather than microjoules) and are usually ignited by temperatures in the region of 200°C. Frequently the instrumentation problem is solved by using T4 (135°C) temperature classified intrinsically safe equipment in a dust-tight enclosure.

The basic mechanism of a gas explosion requires three constituents: the flammable gas, oxygen (usually in the form of air) and a source of ignition (in this context an electrical spark or hot surface). A gas–air mixture must be mixed in certain proportions to be flammable. The boundary conditions are known as the lower and upper flammable limits, or in some documents the lower and upper explosive limits. The subject of explosion prevention concentrates on keeping these three constituents from coming together. The usual approach is to attempt to decide on the probability of the gas–air mixture being present and then to choose equipment which is protected adequately for its environment.

The study of the probability of gas–air mixture being present within the flammable limits is called 'area classification', and is without doubt the most difficult aspect of this subject. Expertise on all aspects of the plant and the behaviour of the gases present is required to carry out area classification well, and hence it is usually done by a committee on which the instrument engineer is only one member. Present practice is to divide the hazardous area according to the IEC Standard 79-10, as follows:

Zone 0: in which an explosive gas–air mixture is continuously present or present for long periods.
(*Note*: The vapour space of a closed process vessel or storage tank is an example of this zone.)

Zone 1: in which an explosive gas–air mixture is likely to occur in normal operation.

Zone 2: in which an explosive gas–air mixture is not likely to occur, and if it occurs it will only exist for a short term.

By inference, any location which is not a hazardous area is a safe area. Many authorities prefer the use of 'non-hazardous area', for semantic and legalistic reasons. The use of 'safe' is preferred

Table 9.1 Temperature classification

Class	*Maximum surface temperature (°C)*
T1	450
T2	300
T3	200
T4	135
T5	100
T6	85

in this document since it is a shorter, more distinctive, word than 'non-hazardous'.

American practice is still to divide hazardous areas into two divisions. Division 1 is the more hazardous of the two divisions and embraces both Zone 0 and Zone 1. Zone 2 and Division 2 are roughly synonymous.

The toxicity of many industrial gases means that an analysis of a plant from this aspect must be carried out. The two problems are frequently considered at the same time.

Having decided the risk of the gas being present then the nature of the gas from a spark ignition or flame propagation viewpoint is considered.

One of the better things that has happened in recent years is the almost universal use of the IEC system of grouping apparatus in a way which indicates that it can safely be used with certain gases. Pedantically, it is the apparatus that is grouped, but the distinction between grouping gases or equipment is an academic point which does not affect safety. The international gas grouping allocates the Roman numeral I to the underground mining activity where the predominant risk is methane, usually called firedamp, and coal dust. Historically, the mining industry was the initial reason for all the work on equipment for flammable atmospheres, and it retains a position of considerable influence. All surface industry equipment is marked with Roman numeral II and the gas groups are subdivided into IIA (propane), IIB (ethylene) and IIC (hydrogen). The IIC group requires the smallest amount of energy to ignite it, the relative sensitivities being approximately 1:3:8. The representative gas which is shown in parentheses is frequently used to describe the gas group.

This gas classification has the merit of using the same classification for all the methods of protection used. The boundaries of the gas groupings have been slightly modified to make this possible.

Unfortunately, the USA and Canada has opted to maintain their present gas and dust classification. The classifications and subdivisions are:

CLASS I:	Gases and vapours
	Group A (acetylene)
	Group B (hydrogen)
	Group C (ethylene)
	Group D (methane)
CLASS II:	Dusts
	Group E (metal dust)
	Group F (coal dust)
	Group G (grain dust)
CLASS III:	Fibres
	(No subgroups)

Gas–air mixtures can be ignited by contact with hot surfaces, and consequently all electrical equipment used in hazardous atmospheres must be classified according to its maximum surface temperature. BS 4683: Part 1 is the relevant standard in the United Kingdom, and this is almost identical to IEC 79-8. The use of temperature classification was introduced in the United Kingdom quite recently (late 1960s), and one of the problems of using equipment which was certified prior to this (e.g. equipment certified to BS 1259) is that somehow a temperature classification has to be derived.

For intrinsically safe circuits the maximum surface temperature is calculated or measured, including the possibility of faults occurring, in just the same way as the electrical spark energy requirements are derived. The possibility that flameproof equipment could become white hot under similar fault conditions is guarded against by generalizations about the adequate protective devices. All temperature classifications, unless otherwise specified, are assessed with reference to a maximum ambient temperature of 40°C. If equipment is used in a temperature higher than this, then its temperature classification should be reassessed. In the majority of circumstances regarding the temperature classification as a temperature-rise assessment will give adequate results. Particular care should be exercised when the 'ambient' temperature of a piece of apparatus can be raised by the process temperature (e.g. a pilot solenoid valve thermally connected to a hot process pipe). Frequently, equipment has a specified maximum working temperature at which it can safely be used, determined by insulating material, rating of components, etc. This should not be confused with the temperature classification and both requirements must be met.

When the probability of gas being present and the nature of gas has been established then the next step is to match the risk to the equipment used. Table 9.2 shows the alternative methods of protection which are described in the CENELEC standards and the areas of use permitted in the United Kingdom.

In light current engineering the predominant technique is intrinsic safety, but flameproof and increased safety are also used. The flameproof technique permits the explosion to occur within the enclosure but makes the box strong enough and controls any apertures well enough to prevent the explosion propagating to the outside atmosphere. Increased safety uses superior construction techniques and large derating factors to reduce the probability of sparking or hot spots occurring to an acceptable level. The other technique which is used to solve particular problems is pressurization and purging. This achieves safety by interposing a layer of air or inert gas between the source of ignition and the hazardous gas.

Table 9.2 Status of standards for methods of protection (as at January 84)

Technique	*IEC symbol Ex*	*Standard*			*UK code of practice part of BS5345*	*Permitted zone of use in UK*
		IEC 79–	*CENELEC EN 50*	*BRITISH BS 5501 Part*		
General requirement		Draft	014	1	1	
Oil immersion	o	6	015	2	None	2
Pressurization	p	2	016	3	5	1 or 2
Powder filling	q	5	017	4	None	2
Flameproof enclosure	d	1	018	5	3	1
Increased safety	e	7	019	6	6	1 or 2
Intrinsic safety	ia	3 Test apparatus	020 apparatus	7	4	0 ia
	or ib	11 Construction	039 system	9		1 ib
Non-incendive	n(N)	Voting draft	021 (Awaits IEC)	BS 4683 Pt3	7	2
Encapsulation	m	None	028 (Voting draft)	None	None	1
Special	s	None	None	SFA 3009	8	1

Where it can be used, intrinsic safety is normally regarded as the technique which is relevant to instrumentation. Intrinsic safety is a technique for ensuring that the electrical energy available in a circuit is too low to ignite the most easily ignitable mixture of gas and air. The design of the circuit and equipment is intended to ensure safety both in normal use and in all probable fault conditions.

There is no official definition of intrinsic safety. EN 50 020, the relevant CENELEC apparatus standard, defines an intrinsically safe circuit as:

> A circuit in which no spark or any thermal effect produced in the test conditions prescribed in this standard (which include normal operation and specified fault conditions) is capable of causing ignition of a given explosive atmosphere.

There are now two levels of intrinsic safety: 'ia' being the higher standard where safety is maintained with up to two fault and 'ib', where safety is maintained with up to one fault. Equipment certified to 'ib' standards is generally acceptable in all zones except Zone 0, and 'ia' equipment is suitable for use in all zones.

Intrinsic safety is, for all practical purposes, the only acceptable safety technique in Zone 0 (continuously hazardous) and the preferred technique in Zone 1 (hazardous in normal operation).

This technique is frequently used in Zone 2 (rarely hazardous) locations to ease the problems of live maintenance, documentation and personnel training. Intrinsic safety is essentially a low-power technique, and hence is particularly suited to industrial instrumentation. Its principal advantages are low cost, more flexible installations and the possibility of live maintenance and adjustment. Its disadvantages are low available power and its undeserved reputation of being difficult to understand. In general, if the electrical requirement is less than 30 V and 50 mA, then intrinsic safety is the preferred technique. If the power required is in excess of 3 W or the voltage greater than 50 V, or the current greater than 250 mA, the probability is that some other technique would be required. The upper limit is a rash generalization, because, with ingenuity, intrinsically safe systems can safely exceed these limits. Between these two sets of values intrinsically safe systems can frequently be devised.

When there is interconnection between more than one intrinsically safe apparatus, an analysis of the interactions and their combined effect on safety reveals that intrinsic safety is essentially a system concept. It can be argued that the other techniques rely on correct interconnection and the choice of the method of electrical protection. For example, a flameproof motor depends for its safety on having correctly rated switchgear for starting overload and fault protection, adequate provision for earthing and a satisfactory means of isolation, all of which constitute a system. However, the danger resulting from the failure of unsatisfactory safe-area equipment in an intrinsically safe system is more immediate and obvious, and hence there is a requirement for a more detailed consideration of all safety aspects which results in a system certificate and documentation. Where a system comprises intrinsically safe apparatus in the hazardous area and a certified source of power and receiving apparatus in the safe area, then the combination can be assessed against the CENELEC system standard EN 50 039. The agreed term for equipment intended for mounting in the safe area which is certified as having terminals which may be connected to the hazardous area is 'associated electrical apparatus'. This inelegant and quite forgettable expression is

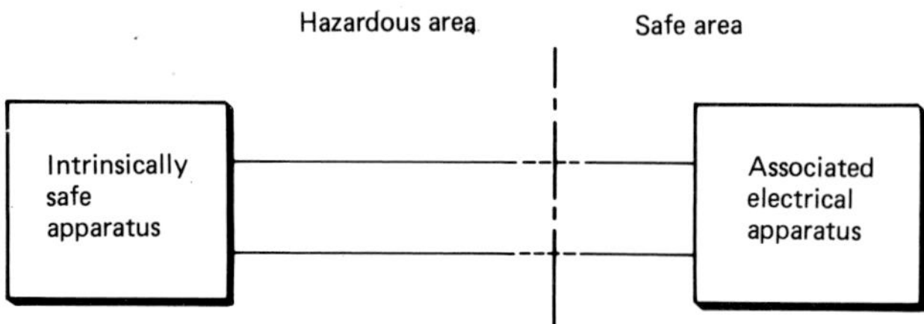

Figure 9.5 System with certified safe area equipment (associated apparatus).

very rarely used by anyone other than writers of standards, but it does distinguish certified safe-area equipment from equipment which can be mounted in the hazardous area.

Where an instrument loop is relatively simple, self contained and comprises the same equipment in the majority of applications, then it is usual for both the hazardous-area and safe-area equipment to be certified, and a system certificate for the specific combination to exist as illustrated in Figure 9.5.

In practice, there are only a few completely self-contained circuits, since the signal to or from the hazardous area is usually fed into or supplied from complex equipment. In these circumstances there is no real possibility of certifying the safe-area apparatus since it is complex, and there is a need to maintain flexibility in its choice and use. The solution in these circumstances is to introduce into the circuit an intrinsically safe interface which cannot transmit a dangerous level of energy to the hazardous area (see Figure 9.6). The majority of interfaces are designed to be safe with 250 V with respect to earth applied to them (i.e. the 440 three-phase neutral earth system commonly used in the United Kingdom).

Whatever the cause of the possible danger and the technique used to minimize it, the need to assess the risk, and to document the risk analysis and the precautions taken, is very important. There is a legal requirement to produce the documentation. There is little doubt that if the risks are recognized and documentary proof that they have been minimized is established, then the discipline involved in producing that proof will result in an installation which is unlikely to be dangerous and is infinitely easier to maintain in a safe condition.

9.4 Other safety aspects

The level of integrity of any interlock or instrument system depends upon the importance of the measurement and the consequences of a failure. It is not surprising that some of the most careful work in this area has been related to the control of atomic piles and similar sources of potential catastrophic failure. The majority of systems are less dramatic, and in the United Kingdom an excellent Code of Practice, BS 5304: 1975 discusses the techniques generally used for safeguarding machinery in non-hazardous circumstances. The general principles to be applied can be summarized as:

(1) The failure of any single component (including power supplies) of the system should not create a dangerous situation.

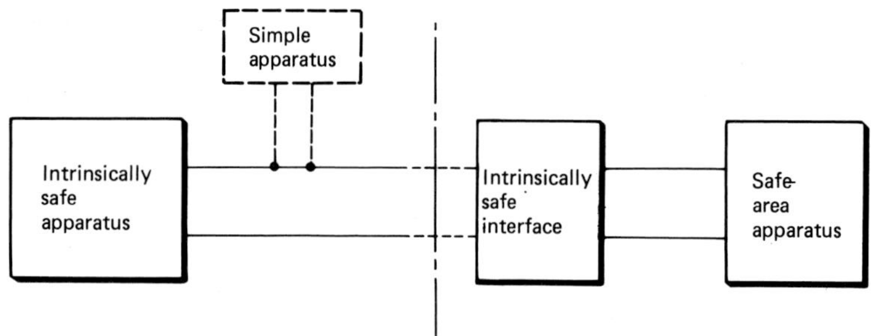

Figure 9.6 System with certified intrinsically safe interface.

(2) The failure of cabling to open or short circuit or short circuiting to ground of wiring should not create a dangerous situation. Pneumatic or electro-optic systems have different modes of failure but may have particular advantages in some circumstances.
(3) The system should be easily checked and readily understood. The virtue of simplicity in enhancing the reliability and serviceability of a system cannot be overstressed.
(4) The operational reliability of the system must be as high as possible. Foreseeable modes of failure can usually be arranged to produce a 'fail-safe' situation, but if the system fails and produces spurious shutdowns too frequently the temptation to override interlocks can become overwhelming. An interlock system to remain credible must therefore be operationally reliable and, if possible, some indication as to whether the alarm is real or a system fault may also be desirable.

These basic requirements, following up a fundamental analysis of the level of integrity to be achieved, form a framework upon which to build an adequate system.

9.5 Conclusion

It is difficult to adequately summarize the design requirements of a safe system. The desire to avoid accidents and in particular avoiding injuring and killing people is instinctive in the majority of engineers and hence does not need to be emphasized. Accident avoidance is a discipline to be cultivated, careful documentation tends to be a valuable aid and common sense is the aspect which is most frequently missing.

The majority of engineers cannot experience or have detailed knowledge of all aspects of engineering, and safety is not different from any other factor in this respect. The secret of success must therefore be the need to recognize the danger so as to know when to seek advice. This chapter has attempted to provide the background for recognizing the need to seek expert advice; it is not comprehensive enough to ensure a safe design.

9.6 References

BASS, H.G. *Intrinsic Safety*, Quartermaine House, Gravesend, Kent (1984)

COOPER, W. F. *Electrical Safety Engineering*, Butterworths, London (1978)

Electrical Safety in Hazardous Environments, Conferences, Institution of Electrical Engineers (1971), (1975) and (1982)

GARSIDE, R. H. *Intrinsically Safe Instrumentation: A Guide*, Safety Technology (1982). Predominantly applications, strong on UK and US technology and standards

HALL, J. *Intrinsic Safety*, Institution of Mining Electrical and Mining Mechanical Engineers (1985). A comprehensive treatise on mining applications of the art

ICI Engineering Codes and Regulations, ROSPA PUBLICATION No. IS 91. Now unfortunately out of print. Slightly dated but the most useful publication in this area. Beg, borrow or steal the first copy you find. Essential

MAGISON, E. C. *Electrical Instruments in Hazardous Locations*, 3rd edn. Instrument Society of America (1978). Comprehensive book portraying American viewpoint.

OLENIK, H. *et al. Explosion Protection Manual*, 2nd edn, Brown Boveri & Cie (1984). An excellent book on West German practice

REDDING, R. J. *Intrinsic Safety*, McGraw-Hill, New York (1971). Slightly dated but still relevant

ROBENS, LORD (chairman). *Safety and Health at Work*, Report of the Committee HMSO Cmnd. 5034 (1972)

Safety in Universities—Notes for Guidance, Association of Commonwealth Universities (1978)

Substances Hazardous to Health, Croner Publications, New Malden, Surrey (1986 with updates)

TOWLE, L. C. *Intrinsically Safe Installations on Ships and Offshore Structures*, Institute of Marine Engineers TP 1074 (1985)

Many British Standards have to do with safety. The following are the most relevant.

Electrical Apparatus for Potentially Explosive Atmospheres, Part 1: General Requirements BS 5501: Part 1: 1977 EN 50 014, British Standards Institution. Largely excluded by EN 50 020 but essential for completeness.

Part 3: Pressurized Apparatus 'p', BS 5501: Part 3: 1977 EN 50 016, British Standards Institution. Interlocks, etc. sets intrinsic safety problems. Useful.

Part 6: Increased Safety 'e', BS 5501: Part 6: 1977 EN 50 019, British Standards Institution. Useful information on terminals creepage and clearance

Part 7: Intrinsic safety 'i', BS 5501: Part 7: 1977 EN 50 020, British Standards Institution. Sets requirements for apparatus. Interpretations should also be read. Essential

Part 9: Specification for Intrinsically Safe Electrical Systems 'i', BS 5501: Part 9: 1982 EN 50 039, British Standards Institution. Sets requirements for combinations of apparatus. Second edition will follow soon to meet Group I political requirements. Essential

Selection, installation and maintenance of electrical apparatus for use in potentially explosive atmospheres (other than mining applications or explosive processing and manufacture).

Part 1: Basic Requirements for all Parts of the Code, BS 5345: Part 1: 1976, British Standards Institution. Includes essential definitions choice of equipment, etc. Table of gas characteristics. Essential

Part 2: Classification of Hazardous Areas, BS 5345: Part 2:

1983, British Standards Institution. Asks all the relevant questions but only gives a very few answers. Not much use but the best available. Useful
Part 4: Installation and Maintenance Requirements for Electrical Apparatus with Type of Protection 'i'. Intrinsically Safe Electrical Apparatus and Systems. BS 5345: Part 4: 1977, British Standards Institution. A bit dated, but the best current advice. Essential
Part 5: Installation and Maintenance Requirements for Electrical Apparatus Protected by Pressurization 'p', Continuous Dilution and Pressurized Rooms. BS 5345: Part 5: 1983, British Standards Institution. A useful technique for solving difficult problems; offers some suggestions
Part 6: Installation and Maintenance Requirements for Electrical Apparatus with Type of Protection 'e'. Increased Safety, BS 5345: Part 6: 1978, British Standards Institution. Not frequently used for instrumentation. The code of practice is very thin. Complementary
Part 11: Specific Industry Applications, BS 5345: Part 11, British Standards Institution. Draft contains many useful references
Code of Practice for Control of Undesirable Static Electricity, Part 1: General Considerations, BS 5958: Part 1: 1980, British Standards Institution. An interesting standard with fascinating sections on dusts, plastics, and human frailties. Essential
Code of Practice for Fire Precautions in Chemical Plant (formerly CP 3013), BS 5908: 1980, British Standards Institution. Standard which ranges widely through all aspects of subject. Appendices give a useful set of references. Controversial link between personnel risk and area classification. Useful
Safeguarding of Machinery (formerly CP 3004), BS 5304: 1975, British Standards Institution. A well-written and beautifully illustrated standard. Illustrates sound basic principles. Useful

Index